CREATION

Accident
or
Design?

Fig. 1.1 COVER: A natural-color photograph of the Earth by Applications Technology Satellite III from an altitude of 22,300 miles above the Pacific Ocean, January 21, 1968. North and South America are clearly visible through the scattered cloud cover.

CREATION

Accident or Design?

Harold G. Coffin, Ph.D.

Research Professor
Geoscience Research Institute

Professor of Paleontology
Andrews University

REVIEW AND HERALD PUBLISHING ASSOCIATION
WASHINGTON, D.C.

Printed in U.S.A.

PREFACE

THE BODY OF INFORMATION referred to as "science" is the fastest growing area of human knowledge. Almost from the beginning men of science have been in conflict with prevailing theological opinion, including that of the Seventh-day Adventist Church. While God evidently does not expect those who acknowledge Him to exercise faith wholly apart from scientific evidence, it would be equally unrealistic to expect such evidence to provide a conclusive refutation of reputedly scientific arguments that question the accuracy of the Holy Scriptures. "Our faith must rest upon evidence, not demonstration" (SC 105).

For many years the need has been felt for a book suitable for college classes in science and religion, or the philosophy of science, that would cover the major aspects of science and Adventist theological belief concerning the physical history of the earth. To this end this volume is now presented, in the hope not only that it will be useful as a text or for supplemental reading in college classes but that it will find a useful place in the libraries of ministers and others who wish to be informed in this area.

Of necessity scientific terms and concepts are used, but these have been kept to a minimum and are either defined in the text or in the glossary at the end of the book. References to the writings of Ellen G. White and *The Seventh-day Adventist Bible Commentary* are abbreviated as follows:

AH—*The Adventist Home*
1BC, etc.—*The Seventh-day Adventist Bible Commentary*, vol. 1, etc.
CD—*Counsels on Diet and Foods*
CT—*Counsels to Parents, Teachers, and Students*
DA—*The Desire of Ages*

5

Ed—*Education*
EW—*Early Writings*
FE—*Fundamentals of Christian Education*
GC—*The Great Controversy*
LS—*Life Sketches of Ellen G. White*
MH—*The Ministry of Healing*
MS—Manuscript
PP—*Patriarchs and Prophets*
SC—*Steps to Christ*
1SG, etc.—*Spiritual Gifts,* vol. 1, etc.
1SM, etc.—*Selected Messages,* book 1, etc.
1T, etc.—*Testimonies,* vol. 1, etc.
TM—*Testimonies to Ministers*

The following persons, whose contributions add greatly to the breadth of coverage in this volume, have contributed chapters in the areas of their special competence: Ernest S. Booth, Escondido, California; R. H. Brown, Walla Walla College; Harold W. Clark, Pacific Union College; Ariel A. Roth, Geoscience Research Institute; E. E. White, Wahroonga, New South Wales, Australia. Many others have contributed through oral or unpublished communications, and their help is sincerely acknowledged. Many have read and criticized the manuscript. I take full responsibility for errors that may be found, but heartily thank all who have had part in making this an accurate and useful volume.

The sources listed in the references for each chapter include both cited materials and other significant literature. These works have been included because of their usefulness, but the authors of this volume do not necessarily concur with all the theories and conclusions expressed by these writers. Each is to be judged on the basis of its own merit.

This book is dedicated to the task of helping God's remnant people to preserve an intelligent faith amid the turmoil and confusion of these momentous days.

CONTENTS

SECTION 6—ORIGINS AND TIME

SECTION 7—THE FORMATION OF NEW SPECIES

SECTION 8—SCIENCE AND GOD

SECTION 9—THE THEORY OF EVOLUTION

APPENDICES

ILLUSTRATIONS

Except as otherwise noted, photographs are by the author. Cover design, drawings, and diagrams by Harry Baerg.

9

LIST OF ILLUSTRATIONS

11

SECTION 1

A PERFECT WORLD

"For in six days the Lord made heaven and earth, the sea, and all that in them is, and rested the seventh day."

Exodus 20:11

Fig. 1.2 Mt. Sinai, where Moses received the Decalogue.

CHAPTER ONE

Creation Week

The First Three Days

IN A WILD SETTING quite in keeping with the inspiring events that were taking place the people waited tensely. They had been awed by an electrical display from the heavy black cloud that enveloped the mountain. The thunder still echoed in their minds. But at this moment there was a strange, unnatural stillness—the calm before the storm, perhaps? If worse was to come, they felt they could not bear it. They trembled in expectancy, and even their leader—usually calm and reassuring—was visibly shaken.

Suddenly, from out of the stillness, the voice of Omnipotence spoke. The crowd quailed and sank to its knees as the words rolled along the flanks of the mountain and down the valley as the great God of Abraham, Isaac, and Jacob declared the ten precepts of the Decalogue that were to be their standard of life.

In the center of this law God placed a command that was to be a special sign, that by observing it a person would acknowledge Him as God above all other gods, Creator of the heavens and the earth. "Remember the sabbath day, to keep it holy. . . . For in six days the Lord made heaven and earth, the sea, and all that in them is, and rested the seventh day: wherefore the Lord blessed the sabbath day, and hallowed it" (Ex. 20:8-11).

For many years the Hebrew people had been exposed to idolatry. They had nearly forgotten their Creator. In large measure they had forgotten the Sabbath during the time of bondage and slavery in Egypt. Now, God would bring them again to a knowledge of Himself. The keeping of the Sabbath week by week would remind them that He is a God above all gods, for no other god claimed to be creator of the heavens and the earth. "Thou, even thou, art Lord alone; thou hast made heaven, the heaven of heavens, with all their host, the earth, and all things that are therein, the seas, and all that is therein, and thou preservest them all; and the host of heaven worshippeth thee" (Neh. 9:6).

Literal Days

As an integral part of this fourth command, God set forth the reason for it. The other articles of the moral law were more obvious, but this one needed explanation. God's people were to rest on the seventh day because God had accomplished His creative work in six days and rested on the seventh. "This reason appears beautiful and forcible when we understand the days of creation to be literal. The first six days of each week are given to man for labor, because God employed the same period of the first week in the work of creation. On the seventh day man is to refrain from labor, in commemoration of the Creator's rest" (PP 111).

During recent weeks the people had been reminded vividly of the Sabbath day. No manna could be collected on the seventh day, as some doubting souls had discovered. Furthermore, the manna became putrid and wormy when kept overnight—except on the night following the sixth day. There was nothing indefinite about the time; the seventh day came regularly at the end of every weekly cycle of seven days. God told them that He had made the world in six days, and that He had then rested on the seventh day and blessed it. There could be no question in the minds of the assembled multitude what He meant when He spoke of "the seventh day." Six literal days had been employed in creation, and the seventh literal day—designated as the day of rest—was to commemorate the activities of the previous six days.

For various reasons, including a supposed better harmonization of the geologic record with Scripture, some have entertained the thought that the days of creation were long, indefinite periods of time. Seventh-day Adventists affirm that the days of creation week were each twenty-four hours in length. Some of the reasons for this position are as follows: Plants were created on the third day, and the first animals on the fifth day. Because of the mutual interdependence of plants and animals (insects for pollination by way of example), there could not have been a long age between the third and fifth days of creation. The origin of the weekly cycle would be obscure if each day of creation week were not a twenty-four-hour period, and the seventh-day Sabbath would have little meaning. Those who observe Sunday, or Friday, or any other day than the seventh, would have difficulty accounting for the origin of such a rest day in relation to creation week.

Inspired writers after Moses certainly looked upon the first portion of Genesis as inspired, and kept the Sabbath for the same reason—as a memorial of the six days of creation. David repeatedly refers to God as the Creator, and indicates the instantaneous nature of the work (Ps. 33:6-9). Psalm 104 follows the days of creation in order. Note especially verses 2, 3 (first and second days), 6-8 (first part of third day), 14, 16 (second part of third day), 19 (fourth day), 25-30 (fifth and sixth days). In the New Testament each of the Gospel authors includes among Jesus' words and instructions, references to creation, the Flood, and earth's early history. This indicates that Jesus accepted the Genesis account (Matt. 11:23, 24; 19:4; 24:37-39; Mark 10:6; 13:19; Luke 11:51; 17:26, 27; John 8:44). The writer of Hebrews links the observance of the Sabbath with God's example of resting on the seventh day of creation week (Heb. 4:3, 4, 10). Peter refers to a total destruction of the antediluvian world by a great Flood (2 Peter 2:4, 5; 3:3-7).

If Jesus had stated positively that creation took place in six literal days, and this statement appeared in the New Testament, all readers would be impressed. Yet God, in the majesty of His glory, affirmed this fact from the top of Mount Sinai in the hear-

2

ing of thousands of people, and recorded this declaration on stone and in Holy Scripture. "Remember the sabbath day, to keep it holy. . . . For in six days the Lord made heaven and earth, the sea, and all that in them is, and rested the seventh day" (Ex. 20:8-11).

Because the seventh-day Sabbath reminds those who observe it of the Creator, Satan has had a special hatred of this rest day and has devoted special efforts to destroy its sanctity and significance. Eventually he succeeded in shifting the rest day to Sunday, and more recently he has destroyed belief in the Creator by the theory of evolution.

The first angel's message of Revelation 14:6, 7 calls attention once more to God as Creator—"and worship him that made heaven, and earth, and the sea, and the fountains of waters." This angel speaks with a loud voice. We understand this to mean that God's message must be proclaimed clearly and emphatically. The seventh-day Sabbath is an important aspect of this task only if it commemorates a literal creation week.

Is the creation story written in poetry? Has the author used poetic license in recording this account? Various features are used to identify Hebrew poetry—each line starting with a new letter of the alphabet, similar thoughts repeated in different words, meter, poetic vocabulary, et cetera. Prose lacks these elements and makes frequent use of conjunctions to link sentences together. It is not difficult to determine that the first two chapters of Genesis are prose, not poetry.

Of greater import is the question, "Is the Genesis story of creation a myth?" Here linguistic and scientific proofs of such a hypothesis are lacking. The study of the Bible and the writings of Ellen G. White help us to solve this problem. By faith we accept this story as a true and literal record that God has given us.

It would be well for all to read again the chapter in *Patriarchs and Prophets* entitled "The Literal Week." The arguments there marshaled and the clarity of expression can hardly be surpassed.

"God Himself measured off the first week as a sample for successive weeks to the close of time. Like every other, it consisted of seven literal days. . . . But the assumption that the events of the first week required thousands upon thousands of years, strikes directly at the foundation of the fourth commandment. . . . It makes indefinite and obscure that which He has made very plain" (PP 111).

"The weekly cycle of seven literal days, six for labor, and the seventh for rest, which has been preserved and brought down through Bible history, originated in the great facts of the first seven days" (3SG 90).

"Human philosophy declares that an indefinite period of time was taken in the creation of the world. Does God state the matter thus? No; He says, 'It is a sign between Me and the children of Israel forever: for in six days [not six indefinite periods of time; for then there would be no possible way for man to observe the day specified in the fourth commandment] the Lord made heaven and earth' " (TM 135).

The First Day

Ever since man first looked up into the night skies he has marveled at their beauty and wondered about the unknown. Modern astronomers have discovered something of the vast size of the universe, which is beyond human comprehension. These stars and galaxies did not come into existence accidentally; they are the objects of God's creative power manifesting itself in the transformation of energy into matter. The first chapter of the book of Genesis describes the creative acts leading to the establishment of one of these heavenly bodies as a home for a new race of beings made in the image of God.

From beginning to end, the first week of earth's history was filled with miracles. God has not seen fit to give many details concerning His acts of creation. The record is brief, but plain and inclusive.

"In the beginning God created the heaven and the earth. And the earth was without form, and void; and darkness was upon the face of the deep. And the Spirit of God moved upon the face of the waters. And God said, Let there be light: and there was light. And God saw the light, that it was good: and God divided the light from the darkness. And God called the light Day, and the darkness he called Night. And the evening and the morning were the first day" (Gen. 1:1-5).

Thus begins the account of creation. How did God perform His creative acts? The Holy Scriptures say that He spoke the world and its living forms into existence, according to the plan that already existed in His mind. Bible writers declare emphatically that God *spoke* as He carried forward the work of creation. "By the word of the Lord were the heavens made; and all the host of them by the breath of his mouth. . . . For he spake, and it was done; he commanded, and it stood fast" (Ps. 33:6-9). "Mine hand also hath laid the foundation of the earth, and my right hand hath spanned the heavens: when I call unto them, they stand up together" (Isa. 48:13). The apostle John declares: "All things were made by him; and without him was not any thing made that was made" (John 1:3).

"In the creation of the earth, God was not indebted to preexisting matter. 'He spake, and it was; . . . He commanded, and it stood fast.' Psalm 33:9. All things, material or spiritual, stood up before the Lord Jehovah at His voice and were created for His own purpose. The heavens and all the host of them, the earth and all things therein, came into existence by the breath of His mouth" (MH 414). For a discussion of when God created inorganic matter see Section VI, chapter 24, "In the Beginning—God."

The phrase "without form, and void" is descriptive of the earth's condition at the time the creative acts began to take place —the molding, fashioning, and organization of the earth's surface into a place habitable by man, and the creation of the myriad life forms upon the earth. This expression describes the chaotic state that was changed by successive creative acts during creation week into one of order and beauty.

Fig. 1.3 "And God said, Let there be a firmament."

The light brought into existence on the first day of creation week evidently came from one point source, and the rotation of the earth resulted in the succession of night and day, a situation no different from today. It is reasonable to think of our solar system—the sun, the planets, and their satellites—being created as a unit.

The Second Day

"And God said, Let there be a firmament in the midst of the waters, and let it divide the waters from the waters. And God made the firmament, and divided the waters which were under the firmament from the waters which were above the firmament: and it was so. And God called the firmament Heaven. And the evening and the morning were the second day" (Gen. 1:6-8).

The second day was occupied in the organization of the atmosphere. Perhaps steam and vapor that may have rested on the surface of the waters were raised above them, and a layer of air was inserted between. The Hebrew word for "firmament" means a great expanse—a good description of the atmosphere. The account of the second day, with its repetition of the concept of the separation of the waters, has suggested to many the possibility of a vapor layer or envelope above the earth. Whether or not this interpretation is warranted, a number of circumstantial evidences tend to support the theory. In brief they are: (1) The repetitive wording in Genesis 1:6-8 regarding a separation of waters seems

21

to emphasize such a situation. (2) The condensation of these vapors through cooling could have been a source of water at the time of the Flood. (3) The water-vapor layer would be a shield from cosmic radiation. The longevity of the antediluvians may have been due in part to an absence of exposure to cosmic radiation. A possible difference in the pre-Flood carbon-12/carbon-14 ratio, as compared with the ratio we know today, could be explained by a vapor shield (see Section VI, chapter 26, "Radiocarbon Dating"). (4) An insulating layer of vapor could have aided in a worldwide mild climate. (5) Ozone layers and warm bands in the stratosphere may have been the repositories of water vapor. Ozone has a strong affinity for water, and increased temperature would permit greater saturation.

On the other hand, it is possible that Moses refers to the clouds when he speaks of the waters above the firmament. "God's glory in the heavens, the innumerable worlds in their orderly revolutions, *'the balancings of the clouds,'* the mysteries of light and sound, of day and night—all were open to the study of our first parents" (PP 51; italics supplied).

The cosmology of the ancients portrayed a solid firmament that could be rolled up like a scroll, with luminaries hanging from the firmament. They thought of themselves as living under a great canopy, or tent, that had solid supports. Windows in this canopy were opened to let in the rain. This concept is reflected in the following texts: Gen. 1:17 (lights set in the firmament); Jer. 10:12; 51:15 (heavens stretched out); Ps. 104:2, Isa. 40:22 (heavens like a curtain, like a tent to dwell in); Job 26:11 (pillars of heaven); Gen. 7:11, 2 Kings 7:2 (windows of heaven opened); Isa. 34:4, Rev. 6:14 (heavens depart and roll up as a scroll); Prov. 8:28, R.S.V. (skies above made firm). In speaking of the heavens of his time (postdiluvian), David used the same expression as did Moses (see Ps. 148:4), yet none argue that a vapor envelope existed after the Flood. It would seem that the theory of a vapor envelope is without much scriptural basis.

Though Moses and the other inspired writers of the Bible at

times make use of the terminology and cosmological concepts of their time, it is not necessary to conclude that they concurred in these popular misconceptions. Literary expressions do not always indicate a writer's personal beliefs. Moses wrote the book of Genesis under the inspiration of the Holy Spirit while he was tending Jethro's sheep in the Sinai desert (see PP 251).

Ecclesiastes 1:6 and 7 reflects an insight into the water cycle in nature and the movement of air masses that is remarkably modern, and not at all in accord with the cosmology of Solomon's day.

The Third Day

"And God said, Let the waters under the heaven be gathered together unto one place, and let the dry land appear: and it was so. And God called the dry land Earth; and the gathering together of the waters called he Seas: and God saw that it was good. And God said, Let the earth bring forth grass, the herb yielding seed, and the fruit tree yielding fruit after his kind, whose seed is in itself, upon the earth: and it was so. And the earth brought forth grass, and herb yielding seed after his kind, and the tree yielding fruit, whose seed was in itself, after his kind: and God saw that it was good. And the evening and the morning were the third day" (Gen. 1:9-13).

Psalm 104:5-9 affords a further picture of creation that adds detail to the brief account in Genesis. Verses seven and eight are especially applicable to the third day. "At thy rebuke they

Fig. 1.4 "Let the waters . . . be gathered together unto one place."

[the waters] fled; at the sound of thy thunder they took to flight. The mountains rose, the valleys sank down to the place which thou didst appoint for them" (R.S.V.). Apparently, great crustal movements occurred which depressed the earth in certain areas and raised mountain ranges and land masses in other areas. The water drained off into the low areas, leaving the higher ground dry. The same description would apply to the later stages of the Flood, but the activity was apparently much slower then than at creation. This draining and drying of the land took place during part of one day, a rate that greatly surpasses the speed of such activities today.

"When God had formed the earth, there were mountains, hills, and plains, and interspersed among them were rivers and bodies of water. . . . The waters were regularly dispersed" (3SG 33).

The latter part of the third day was devoted to the creation of plants. The Genesis account makes it clear that this was more than a sprouting of vegetation. Plants may have been created in all stages of growth, including the fully mature. Adam and Eve did not have to wait until the plants grew up before finding food. Tropical or semitropical climate produced luxuriant vegetation on the whole earth, although the Garden of Eden was especially beautiful.

Coal and other fossil plant remains found in Antarctica and other areas where cold or temperate climates now dominate, indicate the extent of uniform mild weather in the past. Some of the factors that might be responsible for such conditions are a perpendicular axis, a north-south pattern of water distribution, greater solar and lunar radiation, with a shielding vapor and a higher concentration of carbon dioxide in the atmosphere.

"As the earth came forth from the hand of its Maker, it was exceedingly beautiful. Its surface was diversified with mountains, hills, and plains, interspersed with noble rivers and lovely lakes; but the hills and mountains were not abrupt and rugged, abounding in terrific steeps and frightful chasms, as they now do; the sharp, ragged edges of earth's rocky framework were buried beneath the fruitful soil, which everywhere produced a luxuriant growth of verdure. There were no loathsome swamps or barren deserts. Graceful shrubs and delicate flowers greeted the eye at every turn. The heights were crowned with trees more majestic than any that now exist. The air, untainted by foul miasma, was clear and healthful. The entire landscape outvied in beauty the decorated grounds of the proudest palace. The angelic hosts viewed the scene with delight, and rejoiced at the wonderful works of God" (PP 44).

As we attempt to understand the work of God in creation we repeatedly recognize and confess our incompetence and ignorance. "For as the heavens are higher than the earth, so are my ways higher than your ways, and my thoughts than your thoughts" (Isa. 55:9).

REFERENCES

Brown, R. H. 1958. The creation of elementary matter. The Ministry, February.

Gilkey, Langdon. 1959. Maker of heaven and earth. Doubleday and Co., Inc., Garden City, New York. 311 pp.

Hoen, Reu E. 1951. The Creator and his workshop. Pacific Press Pub. Assn., Mountain View, California. 176 pp.

Klotz, John W. 1955. Genes, Genesis, and evolution. Concordia Pub. House, St. Louis, Missouri, pp. 86-119.

Leupold, H. C. 1942. Exposition of Genesis. The Wartburg Press, Columbus, Ohio. 1,220 pp.

Marsh, Frank Lewis. 1941. Evolution, creation, and science. Review and Herald Pub. Assn., Washington, D.C. 304 pp.

————. 1950. Studies in creationism. Review and Herald Pub. Assn., Washington, D.C., pp. 190-278.

————. 1967. Life, man, and time. 2d ed. Outdoor Pictures, Escondido, California, pp. 30-39.

Morris, Henry M. and John C. Whitcomb, Jr. 1961. The Genesis flood. The Presbyterian and Reformed Pub. Co., Philadelphia, Pennsylvania, pp. 212-255.

Ramm, Bernard. 1954. The Christian view of science and religion. Wm. B. Eerdmans Pub. Co., Grand Rapids, Michigan, pp. 173-229.

Seventh-day Adventist Bible commentary, The. 1953. vol. 1. Review and Herald Pub. Assn., Washington, D.C.

Surburg, Raymond F. 1959. In the beginning God created. In Darwin, evolution and creation. Paul A. Zimmerman, ed. Concordia Pub. House, St. Louis, Missouri, pp. 57-64.

White, Ellen G. 1913. Patriarchs and prophets. Pacific Press Pub. Assn., Mountain View, California, pp. 44-51.

————. 1945. Spiritual gifts. vol. 3. Facsimile reproduction. Review and Herald Pub. Assn., Washington, D.C., pp. 33-35.

————. 1903. Education. Pacific Press Pub. Assn., Mountain View, California, pp. 128-134.

CHAPTER TWO

Creation Week

The Next Three Days

The Fourth Day

THE EVENTS of the fourth day are unusually interesting. A casual reading of Genesis 1:14-19 may lead a person to think that God suddenly transferred His creative activity to other parts of the universe. All the other creative acts of creation week, however, took place on the earth and were directly concerned with it. But there is more in this account than may at first appear:

"And God said, Let there be lights in the firmament of the heaven to divide the day from the night; and let them be for signs, and for seasons, and for days, and years: and let them be for lights in the firmament of the heaven to give light upon the earth:

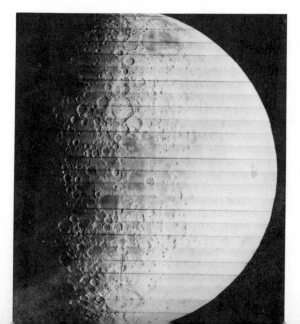

Fig. 2.1 A wide-angle photograph of the moon taken by Lunar Orbiter IV on May 11, 1967, from an altitude of 1,850 miles above the lunar surface. North is at the top. The picture is centered on the moon's eastern limb about halfway between the equator and the South Pole.

and it was so. And God made two great lights; the greater light to rule the day, and the lesser light to rule the night: he made the stars also. And God set them in the firmament of the heaven to give light upon the earth, and to rule over the day and over the night, and to divide the light from the darkness: and God saw that it was good. And the evening and the morning were the fourth day" (Gen. 1:14-19).

The heavenly bodies have always fascinated man. To the one who believes in the God of creation, they illustrate His greatness and power. Isaiah well expressed this conviction: "Lift up your eyes on high, and behold who hath created these things, that bringeth out their host by number: he calleth them all by names by the greatness of his might, for that he is strong in power; not one faileth" (Isa. 40:26). The ancients who drifted away from a belief in the Creator were likewise impressed by the heavenly bodies, but began to worship them (especially the sun) instead of the One who made them. The current name for the first day of the week, for instance, is a relic of this ancient practice. The same is true of the names of the other six days.

A reading of Genesis 1:14 to 19 conveys the distinct impression that God created the sun, moon, and stars on the fourth day. However, we can hardly include the stars, for this would imply the creation of at least the visible universe at that time. This is a geocentric view, similar to the former belief that the earth was the center of the universe. The twinkling rays of distant stars would not yet have reached us (at the present speed of light) unless they were created long previous to creation week. Incidentally, David did not include the stars in his portrayal of creation (Ps. 104:19, 20).

Since the words *"he made"*—in the statement *"he made* the stars also"—(v. 16) were supplied by the translators and are not in the Hebrew text, the sentence may be a parenthetical expression not intended to convey the meaning that the stars were created on the fourth day. A reading of verse 16, leaving out the words *"he made,"* impresses one with the meaning that the stars were to rule the night, as expressed in Psalm 136:9. Or perhaps Moses wanted to make clear that God created the stars, without necessarily implying that He did so on the fourth day, and thus hastened to add, ". . . the stars also."

Some prefer to think that the sun was created on the first day, or at the time the matter composing our solar system was brought into existence. Beginning with day one, the day and night seem to have been no different from the present arrangement consisting of a constant, definitive source of light and a rotating earth.

The events of the previous days had produced dynamic movements of the earth's crust and had established the life-supporting mixture of gases in the space immediately above the earth's surface. These activities were of a nature to produce steam and vapor. Perhaps the sun, moon, and stars were not visible from the earth, as distinct bodies, until the fourth day when the fog was cleared away.

Whether the sun and moon were formed on day four or earlier is relatively unimportant. Certainly each individual is free to hold the opinion he develops from his personal study of this passage.

Astronomers are currently uncertain as to whether the moon was at one time a self-luminous body. The lunar craters are thought by some to be of igneous origin, while others regard them as scars left by the impact of giant meteors. The answer may be found by the first astronauts who reach the moon. That men can reach the moon and return—given sufficient time and money —is well within the realm of possibility. The next step, that of reaching a planet, is a far more complicated matter. Whatever the possibilities of interplanetary travel, however, will God allow the contamination of unfallen, populated worlds by sin? The great controversy will be closed and the terrible experiment of sin demonstrated clearly to all the universe, we believe, before any inhabitants of this earth will be permitted to visit other occupied worlds.

Fig. 2.2 "The waters brought forth abundantly."

The Fifth Day

On the fifth and sixth days the work of God in the creation of this world approached completion. Although the creation of inorganic matter, the establishment of an organized world out of formless void, and the creation of plants were all manifestations of great power and intelligence, the formation of animate, active, responsible creatures provided the spectacular climax to the creation process.

"And God said, Let the waters bring forth abundantly the moving creature that hath life, and fowl that may fly above the earth in the open firmament of heaven. And God created great whales, and every living creature that moveth, which the waters brought forth abundantly, after their kind, and every winged fowl after his kind: and God saw that it was good. And God blessed them, saying, Be fruitful, and multiply, and fill the waters in the seas, and let fowl multiply in the earth. And the evening and the morning were the fifth day" (Gen. 1:20-23).

Moses' descriptions of the different kinds of plants and sea and land animals were not intended to provide us with scientific classifications. The Bible was written for all men in all ages, and few would have scientific training. To attempt to make these

29

simple lists all inclusive and fit into the modern system of classification is doing injustice to the intent and purpose of Holy Scripture. Nevertheless, it is worthy of note that the categories of plants and animals Moses mentions do cover adequately the plant and animal kingdoms in a simple way all readers can understand, though in some instances the translators seem to have given too limited meanings to some words or phrases in the original account.

For instance, "The translation 'whales' is too limited in scope. The word has different meanings, like 'serpent' (Ex. 7:9, 10, 12) and 'dragon' (Isa. 51:9; Eze. 29:3), but must mean 'sea monster' in this passage and in Ps. 148:7. . . .

"The verb 'to move,' *ramaś,* is especially descriptive of creeping animals (Gen. 9:2), either on land (Gen. 7:14) or in the water (Ps. 69:34), though here [Gen. 1:21] it clearly signifies aquatic creatures" (1BC 214).

It would appear from a reading of the King James translation that the fowl were created from the waters, as were the sea creatures. The Revised Standard Version reflects the Hebrew more correctly: " 'Let the waters bring forth swarms of living creatures, and let birds fly above the earth across the firmament of the heavens' " (Gen. 1:20). It is probably immaterial whether the waters brought forth the fowl or whether God chose some other source of raw materials. Sea water and land (soil) have basically the same chemical elements, because the sea has obtained most of its salts and elements from the land. Dust of the earth or dust of the sea—they are one and the same thing. The translation in the R.S.V. does undermine the argument used by some Bible critics that Genesis 1:20 and 2:19 are contradictory because one refers to waters bringing forth fowl and the other says "out of the ground the Lord God formed . . . every fowl of the air."

"The word 'fowl,' literally 'winged beings,' should rather read 'birds.' Both domestic and wild birds are included" (1BC 214). It may be possible to interpret this word even more broadly to include flying mammals, insects, and reptiles.

The types of animals created on day five were extremely varied. Mammals, insects, fishes, worms, clams, and birds were represented. A casual glance at this list along with the realization that the next day also produced worms, mammals, insects, et cetera, precludes any evolutionary sequence. The most complex and the most simple forms of life were created on both days.

The expression "after his kind" used in the descriptions of the creative acts of the third, fifth, and sixth days will be discussed in detail in the next chapter.

The Sixth Day

"And God said, Let the earth bring forth the living creature after his kind, cattle, and creeping thing, and beast of the earth after his kind: and it was so. And God made the beast of the earth after his kind, and cattle after their kind, and everything that creepeth upon the earth after his kind: and God saw that it was good" (Gen. 1:24, 25).

The sixth day completes the work of creating animals. The categories given by Moses again cannot be taken as comparable to any modern classification. Cattle, creeping things, and beasts of the earth would correspond to domesticated animals, a miscellaneous assemblage of simpler forms of life, and wild animals (mammals mainly). This includes nearly every form of land life.

REFERENCES

See chapter 1.

Fig. 2.3 A caribou. "Let the earth bring forth the living creature."

CHAPTER THREE

"After His Kind"

ONE OF THE NOTEWORTHY FEATURES in the narrative of the third, fifth, and sixth days of creation is the repetitive use of the expression "after his kind."

"And the earth brought forth grass, and herb yielding seed *after his kind,* and the tree yielding fruit, whose seed was in itself, *after his kind:* and God saw that it was good" (Gen. 1:12).

"And God created great whales, and every living creature that moveth, which the waters brought forth abundantly, *after their kind,* and every winged fowl *after his kind:* and God saw that it was good" (verse 21).

"And God made the beast of the earth *after his kind,* and cattle *after their kind,* and every thing that creepeth upon the earth *after his kind:* and God saw that it was good" (verse 25).

Is the repeated use of this expression significant and intended to convey some special meaning? The phrase has been interpreted in at least two ways: as a command regulating the future reproductive behavior of plants and animals, and as a way of saying that God created various categories of plants, birds, sea creatures, et cetera, of which those mentioned are intended to be representative.

The expression "after his kind" is used 30 times in the books of Moses, particularly in Genesis 6 and 7, Leviticus 11, and Deuteronomy 14. For instance:

"And these are they which ye shall have in abomination among the fowls; they shall not be eaten, they are an abomination: the eagle, and the ossifrage, and the ospray, and the vulture, and the kite after his kind; every raven after his kind; . . . and the stork, the heron after her kind, and the lapwing, and the bat. . . . Even these of them ye may eat: the locust after his kind, and the bald locust after his kind, and the beetle after his kind, and the grasshopper after his kind" (Lev. 11:13-22).

"And of every living thing of all flesh, two of every sort shalt thou bring into the ark, to keep them alive with thee; they shall be male and female. Of fowls after their kind, and of cattle after their kind, of every creeping thing of the earth after his kind, two of every sort shall come unto thee, to keep them alive" (Gen. 6:19, 20).

It becomes obvious that reproductive behavior is not intended in these passages, and that the author uses the expression "after his kind" simply to indicate all animals of the same class as those named. The phrase "kinds of" would render the meaning more accurately—kinds of fowl, kinds of cattle, and kinds of creeping things. This is the way the Goodspeed translation renders Genesis 7:14, 15: "Together with all the various kinds of wild beasts, all the various kinds of domestic animals, all the various kinds of land reptiles, and all the various kinds of birds, everything with feathers and wings; of all creatures in which there was the breath of life, a pair of each joined Noah in the ark." *

Returning to Genesis 1, it becomes evident that the same meaning is appropriate there. Moses here evidently refers to the kinds of animals and plants God created on the third, fifth, and sixth days, not to reproductive behavior. At the same time, plants and animals do, of course, reproduce according to kind. Moses did not write that they would reproduce after their kinds, but observations reveal that he might correctly have done so.

According to the theory of evolution all living things can be traced back to common ancestors. If this were true there should be a continuous gradation from the simple to the complex for all the major types of plants and animals. However, these "miss-

---

* Smith and Goodspeed, *The Complete Bible: An American Translation.* Used by permission of University of Chicago Press.

ing links" are still missing. This fact, along with the readily observable reproductive behavior of present-day organisms, leads to the supposition that God built into the fauna and flora the characteristic that prevents indiscriminate crossing or hybridization. The account of Genesis clearly reveals that "kinds" of animals and plants—in this sense—were set up from the beginning. The currently existing biota indicate that these "kinds" have been largely maintained since then.

At the time Darwin wrote his *Origin of Species,* religionists strongly maintained the fixity of species on the basis that such was the intent of the phrase "after his kind" in Genesis 1. Darwin, for instance, wrote to a friend that when he first began to realize that species did change, it was like confessing to having committed a murder. Today we realize that their concept of the fixity of the species was not based on a correct interpretation of Scripture.

Although nature does indicate that major categories such as families, orders, and larger taxa have been fixed to a great extent,

Fig. 3.1 Young bears will grow up to be like their parents—a principle that holds true for most animals.

the Bible does not say that there can be no crossing between these larger groups. May it be possible that such behavior has actually been a part of the history of life in the past? We can safely say that if it has, the extent has been limited, otherwise there would have been a breakdown of the distinct taxonomic groups until we would have a continuum with no distinct breaks between kinds. But this is not the case. A discontinuity occurs between major kinds, and this always has existed. But could a small amount of broad hybridization have taken place? This is a distinct possibility, and there is support for this view in both the Bible and the Spirit of Prophecy writings, as well as in nature.

The preface to the story of the Flood gives the reason for this dreadful visitation: "I will destroy . . . both man and beast, and the creeping thing, and the fowls of the air; for it repenteth me that I have made them." Why did God "repent" because He had made the beasts, creeping things, and fowls? Had they sinned? Creatures that don't know right from wrong cannot be accused of sinning. Were they corrupted, and if so, how? The only kind of corruption they could experience would be physical corruption.

According to Genesis 6:12, "God looked upon the earth, and, behold, it was corrupt; for all flesh had corrupted his way upon the earth." That the expression "all flesh" may include more than man is evident from Genesis 6:17: "All flesh, wherein is the breath of life"; verse 19, "every living thing of all flesh"; and chap. 7:16, "they that went in, went in male and female of all flesh."

"Every species of animal which God had created were preserved in the ark. The confused species which God did not create, which were the result of amalgamation, were destroyed by the flood" (3SG 75). We read also that "relics found in the earth do give evidence of conditions differing in many respects from the present, but the time when these conditions existed can be learned only from the Inspired Record" (PP 112).

If conditions were different before the Flood, would not the fossils indicate it? It is a well-known fact that most Paleozoic fossils are very dissimilar to modern species and genera. Many families, orders, and even some classes are unknown today.

In modern times, animals of different species generally do not cross, but natural mixing of species is not rare and no doubt many more could cross, even though they do not do so under normal circumstances. It is much less common for animals of different genera to hybridize, but again quite a large number are known to have done so. The broadest crosses have occurred between families, but these are extremely rare. The situation with respect to plants is about the same.

It is attractive to think that the now extinct bird called the *Archaeopteryx,* with its socketed teeth, clawed wings, and long tail of many vertebrae; or the Permian amphibians with fishlike limb-support bones and scales on the tail; or the bizarre and confused assemblage of dinosaurs; or the so-called ape-men with what appear to be human and ape characteristics, were crosses between bird and reptile, fish and amphibian, different orders of reptiles, and man and ape respectively, but such suggestions are at present mere speculation. Perhaps information may become available in the future that will warrant further investigation into such possibilities, but until then the idea cannot be given serious attention.

Hybridization and progressive evolution are two very different things. Broad crossing could produce what might look like connecting links, but it would not lead to increasing complexity of animal types. Evolution as commonly understood signifies a process that leads from simple to complex through many small transitional steps, until the great variety of living forms, simple and complex, would have been formed. Hybridization of a type suggested here must start with already created major kinds of animals. The virility of plants and animals was greater at creation than now, a fact that may have broadened their capacity for hybridization.

It is not the intention of this discussion to make a strong case for hybridization of major kinds in ancient times, but to point

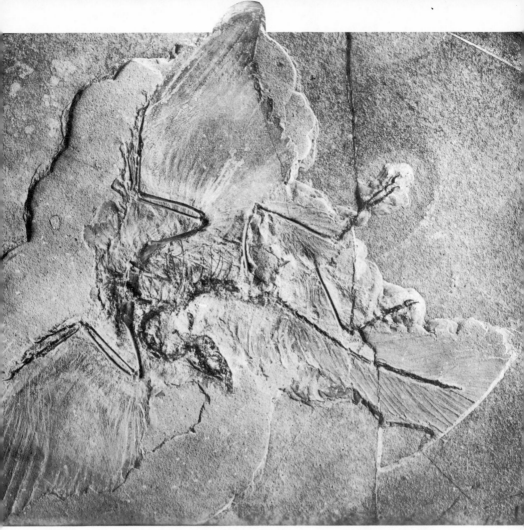

Fig. 3.2 *Archaeopteryx,* **an unusual bird with claws on the front angle of the wings, socketed teeth, and feathers arranged pinnately along the tail.**

out the importance of not reading into the Bible record what is not there. Errors resulting from a careless study of the Bible are as grievous as those that result from interpretations not based on the Bible at all; in fact, they may eventually be—when they are disproved—even more damaging to the faith.

Since Genesis 1 does not declare that animals of diverse kinds cannot cross, we ought to keep our eyes and minds open to the possibility that in the pre-Flood world crossing between more diverse kinds may have occurred on a greater scale than today. To deny emphatically that it could have happened in the past because it does not happen now is to stand on the principle of uniformity—a position creationists should view with suspicion.

The fallen angel who once stood next to God shrewdly incorporates into errors a great deal of truth. Geological theory is often a subtle blend of truth and error that can be difficult to separate. Too often in the past, churchmen have rejected truth along with error as a result of misunderstanding Scripture. When that which had been rejected was shown to be undeniably correct, the damage done to the position of the church has been irreparable. This is especially tragic when it could have been avoided.

Knowledge of the Bible has increased in modern times along with scientific knowledge. It is understandable that the churches must re-evaluate some of their interpretations from time to time. We must not be critical of those who erred; nevertheless, the lesson is there for us. In every situation the Bible must be studied prayerfully to find out exactly what it says and what it does not say. The most diligent study will not lead to the truth, however, unless the Holy Spirit is present to direct the mind. His presence is assured when the sincere request of the earnest seeker after truth is prayerfully presented.

REFERENCES

Clark, Harold W. 1940. Genes and Genesis. Pacific Press Pub. Assn., Mountain View, California, pp. 85-106.
Marsh, Frank Lewis. 1944. Evolution, creation, and science. Review and Herald Pub. Assn., Washington, D.C., pp. 89-180.
————. 1950. Studies in creationism. Review and Herald Pub. Assn., Washington, D.C., pp. 236-251.
Nelson, Byron C. 1952. After its kind. Augsburg Pub. House, Minneapolis. 197 pp., 60 figs.
Ritland, Richard M. 1964. After his kind. The Ministry, October.
Running, L. G. 1964. A study of Hebrew words in the creation record. The Ministry, September.
Smith, J. M. Powis and Edgar J. Goodspeed. 1935. The Bible, an American translation. The University of Chicago Press, Chicago.
The Torah, the five books of Moses. 1962. The Jewish Publication Soc. of America, Philadelphia.

CHAPTER FOUR

In God's Image

IN THE CREATION OF MAN, God brought into being a creature whose mind was equipped with the Godlike abilities of reason, judgment, and conscience. This set man apart from the animals.

"And God said, Let us make man in our image, after our likeness: and let them have dominion over the fish of the sea, and over the fowl of the air, and over the cattle, and over all the earth, and over every creeping thing that creepeth upon the earth. So God created man in his own image, in the image of God created he him; male and female created he them. And God blessed them, and God said unto them, Be fruitful, and multiply, and replenish the earth, and subdue it: and have dominion over the fish of the sea, and over the fowl of the air, and over every living thing that moveth upon the earth" (Gen. 1:26-28).

Man came into being as a son of God, the product of His planning and execution. He was a fit creature to inhabit a beautiful and perfect earth. But the clear words of Genesis are in conflict with the prevailing theory of the evolutionary origin of man, and there can never be a satisfactory reconciliation of the two. "God created man in his own image. Here is no mystery. There is no ground for the supposition that man was evolved by slow degrees of development from the lower forms of animal or vegetable life. Such teaching lowers the great work of the Creator to the level of man's narrow, earthly conceptions" (PP 45).

The following quotation from *The Ministry of Healing*, page 415, seems to indicate, at least to some degree, the method God used in the creation of Adam:

"When God had made man in His image, the human form was perfect in all its arrangements, but it was without life. Then a personal, self-existing God breathed into that form the breath of life, and man became a living, intelligent being. All parts of the human organism were set in action. The heart, the arteries, the veins, the tongue, the hands, the feet, the senses, the faculties of the mind, all began their work, and all were placed under law. Man became a living soul. Through Christ the Word, a personal God created man and endowed him with intelligence and power."

It is also obvious from this statement that organization was not enough to initiate life. Man was first made perfect in all his arrangements, but he was not alive. It took the breath of God to impart life to that mass of lifeless protoplasm. Life cannot be defined in any better way than simply "the breath of God."

The Genesis record implies that when God created the varied forms of plant and animal life on successive days of creation week, He made use of material He had already brought into existence. Vegetation came forth from the earth, marine animals from "the waters," birds and animals from "the earth" (Gen. 1:11, 12, 20, 21, 24; 2:19). The fact that "the Lord God formed man of the dust of the ground" (Gen. 2:7) similarly suggests either the use of existing materials or defines the kind of matter man's body is composed of, or both.

Has God made matter without recourse to previously created material since creation week? Was new matter produced when Jesus fed 5,000 persons from five loaves and two fishes? What took place when He healed the man with the withered arm? (See DA 269.) Did God, at that moment, create the fish Peter caught when he cast his net on the other side of the boat? When the lepers were healed, did they receive back their missing fingers, toes, and noses? In these instances it would seem that the power of God in the creation of new matter is indicated. (For a further discussion of the creation of elementary matter, see Brown, 1958.)

No definite figure is given in the writings of Ellen G. White for Adam's height. We read simply that "as Adam came forth from the hand of his Creator, he was of noble height, and of beautiful symmetry. He was more than twice as tall as men now living upon the earth, and was well proportioned. His features were perfect and beautiful. His complexion was neither white, nor sallow, but ruddy, glowing with the rich tint of health" (3SG 34).

If Adam were twelve feet tall or more, he could have weighed nearly a ton. An increase in height of more than two times would increase the weight by more than eight times, because there would be a corresponding increase in girth, as well as height, in order to maintain the same proportions. Adam was a giant in another aspect: "If Adam, at his creation, had not been endowed with twenty times as much vital force as men now have, the race, with their present habits of living in violation of natural law, would have become extinct" (3T 138, 139). In the creation of man, God's work reached its grand climax. The Creator lavished His greatest thought and care upon this last creative act. If any should doubt this statement, he needs but remember the lengths to which God went to make it possible for fallen man to be restored eventually to his original created perfection.

At the final deliverance of God's people, when the righteous will be raised from their graves and all will gather on the sea of glass before entering the heavenly city, the marked differences in size between Adam and men of later generations will be most noticeable. Adam will tower well above them, and will nearly equal the Son of God, at whose feet he falls in joyful worship (see GC 644).

The procedure God used in the creation of Eve is significant. It was not necessary for God to use a rib from Adam for the creation of Eve. By this act Adam and all men after him were to know that if they mistreated the one joined with them in marriage, they would be afflicting their own bodies. By this act Eve and all women after her were to know that, though they should expect treatment as equals with man, he was to be head of the home.

Genesis 2:21, 22 graphically portrays the creation of Eve. God put Adam to sleep, performed an operation, took out a rib, and "sewed" up the incision. It records the introduction of Eve to Adam in what must have been an appropriate marriage ceremony. This occurred after Adam had had opportunity to examine the birds and mammals and feel his need for companionship on his own level.

As soon as Adam was placed in the Garden, he was also given work to do. It is clear from this example that God's plan for man does not embrace idleness. Not only physical health but mental and spiritual development are also involved in the active use of hands and brain in beneficial employment. "To Adam was given the work of caring for the garden. The Creator knew that Adam could not be happy without employment" (AH 27).

The Sabbath

The work of creation was now complete. Everything that God had planned to make was finished. It was all good—worthy of the hand of the Ruler of the universe. He was satisfied. The rest that He now took was not necessary because of weariness resulting from labor. God knew the needs of the creature that He had created, and He rested on the seventh day, blessed it, and gave it to man as a memorial of creation. "The sabbath was made for man" (Mark 2:27). Man cannot labor continuously without rest or change. For physical, mental, and spiritual health he must have periodic rest. This fact is well understood in the world today.

It is especially fitting to "remember the sabbath day" by study and appreciation of the things God has made. The lessons of the natural world are appropriate to the needs and abilities of all people, young and old, the uneducated and the learned. The things of nature are simple, and the child running through the meadow yellow with buttercups, or wading in the sparkling brook, is able to appreciate his Creator. The things of nature are profound, and the scientist bending over his microscope or looking through a telescope is unable to comprehend its depths. He also appreciates his Creator. To both, the Sabbath provides an opportunity to remember the Creator and to worship Him as the one who made heaven and earth.

If man had faithfully observed the Sabbath day and kept it holy down through the ages, it is most unlikely that the theory of evolution would have developed. "The importance of the Sabbath as a memorial of creation is that it keeps ever present the true reason why worship is due to God; for the worship of God is based upon the fact that he is the Creator, and that all other beings were created by him. The Sabbath, therefore, lies at the foundation of divine worship, for it teaches this great truth in the most impressive manner, and no other institution does this." —J. N. ANDREWS, *History of the Sabbath*, 1887 ed., p. 515.

REFERENCES

See Chapter 1.

CHAPTER FIVE

Sin and Change

SIN ORIGINATED WITH LUCIFER in the courts of heaven. Since God does not force any of His creatures to obey or love Him, the development of evil in created beings had always been a possibility. The very nature of God, and His ruling of the universe by love, would have made it inconsistent for Him to destroy Lucifer immediately.

"Satan's rebellion was to be a lesson to the universe through all coming ages—a perpetual testimony to the nature of sin and its terrible results. The working out of Satan's rule, its effects upon both men and angels, would show what must be the fruit of setting aside the divine authority. It would testify that with the existence of God's government is bound up the well-being of all the creatures He has made" (PP 42, 43).

The loss of eternal life and Paradise through the sin of our first parents was a great tragedy. All subsequent heartache and misery stem from this first sin. Even the Son of God (and the Father also) was not unaffected by this rebellious act, as the whole Bible so clearly reveals.

We do not know how long Adam and Eve enjoyed Eden. However, the sin that drove them out must not have been long in ripening, because Adam and Eve had no children when they were dismissed from the Garden.

With the entrance of sin many changes, all harmful and undesirable, took place in the natural world. These changes were the natural result of man's alienation from God.

First let us consider changes that occurred in the physical

world. These may have been more far reaching than we might at first think.

The climate became less uniformly mild than it had been, making it necessary for Adam and Eve to protect themselves from the cold. There is no way of knowing how great the extremes in temperature were, but it is not likely that severe cold such as the world experiences today was known then. "The atmosphere, once so mild and uniform in temperature, was now subject to marked changes, and the Lord mercifully provided them with a garment of skins as a protection from the extremes of heat and cold" (PP 61; see also p. 57). Such changes in temperature would have considerable effect on the plants and animals. If temperature fluctuations were seasonal, trees would likely show rings. It must be remembered also that precipitation is more important than temperature in the formation of annual tree rings. The falling of leaves and the fading of flowers, referred to later in this chapter, may have been hastened by these climatic changes.

Certain other possible physical effects of the entrance of sin are mainly speculation. There may have been changes in the intensity of solar radiation. Cosmic rays may have penetrated the atmosphere more than before. There may have been a shift in the axis of the earth in relation to the sun. Perhaps there was a change in the carbon dioxide content of the air. Perhaps some of these factors were involved in the curse upon the soil.

Precisely what was involved in that curse is not clear, but the thorns and thistles were obviously the work of Satan (Gen. 3:17-19). Were there other effects—such as lessened fertility of the soil, erosion, and the development of infertile areas as a result of volcanic activity and drought? There is reason to believe that erosion and volcanic activity were absent or limited before the Flood.

Biological Changes

Next we turn to a consideration of biological changes. Here the results are more definitely known and more clearly to be seen.

There are many interesting questions, nevertheless, to which only speculative answers can be given.

A threefold curse was pronounced when Adam and Eve sinned—on the ground, on the serpent, and on mankind. We have already considered the effect of sin upon the ground; now let us inquire what happened to man.

The curse upon Eve was felt in the pain accompanying child-birth. As for Adam and his male descendants, the support of the family has proved to be a task that requires the "sweat of thy face" and a major portion of their available time. The effects of sin were not immediately total, otherwise man would have died shortly after he sinned. It was nearly one thousand years before the inroads of sin brought about the death of Adam. The other results of sin were no doubt also progressive. (Even the serpent, probably, was not immediately changed.) The pain and difficulty associated with childbirth may have increased in severity as degeneration affected the race.

The modification of leaves and stems into thorns and spines, and the fearful flight or evasive tactics of animals must have amazed and saddened Adam as the years advanced. He recognized the evil that was at work in the world. He knew that "God who guides the planets works in the fruit orchard and in the vegetable garden. He never made a thorn, a thistle, or a tare. These are Satan's work, the result of degeneration, introduced by him among the precious things; but it is through God's immediate agency that every bud bursts into blossom" (6T 186).

It is perhaps no more difficult to produce modifications in plants such as thorns than it is to manipulate the reproduction and development of plants and animals in such a way as to cause them to become adapted to parasitic and carnivorous existences. Was the ability to digest cellulose and to synthesize the essential amino acids from a grass or straw diet lost by the lion and other carnivorous animals? Did the changes in teeth and the anatomical modifications in the digestive system automatically come about with the change in diet? Did the hermit crab, which now requires an empty snail shell as a home, originally get along without one? Did ticks and parasitic insects which now require blood formerly subsist on some other diet? Did the robin first have a vegetarian diet? Questions such as these could be multiplied almost without number. In most cases there are no clear answers. We can always know, however, as we see the use of tooth and claw, and witness the "survival of the fittest," that this is not God's first plan for the earth. We can know that "an enemy hath done this" (Matt. 13:28).

The greatest consequence of sin was death. As the years passed and Adam saw the results of his sin in the lives of his descendants, he was filled with great sorrow. Eventually he came to welcome death as a relief from the heartache of life. But he did not die without hope.

At first, death must have been a frightening prospect to Adam and Eve. "As they witnessed in drooping flower and falling leaf the first signs of decay, Adam and his companion mourned more deeply than men now mourn over their dead. The death of the frail, delicate flowers was indeed a cause of sorrow; but when the goodly trees cast off their leaves, the scene brought vividly to mind the stern fact that death is the portion of every living thing" (PP 62).

Progressive Degeneration

There were three distinct times in the history of the earth when God cursed the earth by removing His blessing. These were following the first sin, at the killing of Abel, and the time of the Flood. Each time the effects of the curse were felt more strongly. The history of man from the time of the first sin until the time of the Flood is not a pleasant one. For instance, "Cain lived only to harden his heart, to encourage rebellion against the divine authority, and to become the head of a line of bold, abandoned sinners" (PP 78).

"The descendants of Seth had separated themselves from the wicked descendants of Cain. They cherished the knowledge of

47

God's will, while the ungodly race of Cain had no respect for God and His sacred commandments" (3SG 60).

"The race of Cain, spreading from the place of their first settlement, dispersed over the plains and valleys where the children of Seth had dwelt; and the latter, in order to escape from their contaminating influence, withdrew to the mountains, and there made their home" (PP 81).

"Those who honored and feared to offend God, at first felt the curse but lightly; while those who turned from God and trampled upon His authority, felt the effects of the curse more heavily, especially in stature and nobleness of form" (3SG 60).

"But in the lapse of time they ventured, little by little, to mingle with the inhabitants of the valleys. This association was productive of the worst results. 'The sons of God saw the daughters of men that they were fair' (Genesis 6:2). . . . Mingling with the depraved, they became like them in spirit and in deeds . . . , 'and they took them wives of all which they chose.' . . . Sin spread abroad in the earth like a deadly leprosy" (PP 81, 82).

REFERENCES

Hoen, Reu E. 1951. The Creator and his workshop. Pacific Press Pub. Assn., Mountain View, California, pp. 103-111.

Marsh, Frank Lewis. 1950. Studies in creationism. Review and Herald Pub. Assn., Washington, D.C., pp. 293-308.

———. 1967. Life, man, and time. 2d ed. Outdoor Pictures, Escondido, California, pp. 97-115.

Seventh-day Adventist Bible commentary, The. 1953. vol. 1. Review and Herald Pub. Assn., Washington, D.C.

White, Ellen G. 1888. The great controversy. Pacific Press Pub. Assn., Mountain View, California, pp. 492-562.

———. 1913. Patriarchs and prophets. Pacific Press Pub. Assn., Mountain View, California, pp. 33-43; 52-62.

———. 1945. Spiritual gifts. vol. 3. Facsimile reproduction. Review and Herald Pub. Assn., Washington, D.C., pp. 36-46.

———. 1947. The story of redemption. Review and Herald Pub. Assn., Washington, D.C., pp. 13-31.

SECTION 2

THE FLOOD

"And, behold, I, even I, do bring a flood of waters upon the earth."

Genesis 6:17

Fig. 6.1 "And the waters prevailed, and were increased greatly upon the earth; and the ark went upon the face of the waters." Genesis 7:18.

CHAPTER SIX

What Caused the Flood?

THE GENESIS ACCOUNT attributes the Flood to the corruption and wickedness that prevailed among men—the breakdown of morals, polygamy, and intermarriage of those who believed in God with those who did not. "The sons of God saw the daughters of men that they were fair; and they took them wives of all which they chose" (Gen. 6:2).

Physical Causes

The immediate physical cause of the destruction was flooding by water. This water, according to the account by Moses, came both from the sky and from "the fountains of the deep." To produce flooding of such an extent as to inundate the globe, one of two things must have happened. Sufficient water came down from heaven and up from the earth to raise the water level above the tops of the highest mountains, or the surface of the earth was evened out by the lowering of the dry land and the raising of the sea bottoms so that the water that already existed (along with what came from the sky and subterranean sources) was sufficient to cover all land.

We do not know how much variation in elevation existed before the Flood. There is some reason to believe that the mountains were not as lofty as the high peaks of today and that the antediluvian seas did not have the extent or depth of present-day oceans. Today the total variation in elevation is about 65,000 feet. It is not necessary to assume that there was sufficient water to cover the top of present-day Mount Everest, for instance. The waters in the current oceans probably represent all, or most, of the water that covered the earth during the Flood. The second possibility mentioned above—that of the surface of the earth being leveled out to allow the existing water to spill out over the land—is supported by both the Bible and the Spirit of Prophecy writings. Note the following:

"The same day were all the fountains of the great deep broken up, and the windows of heaven were opened" (Gen. 7:11). The breaking of the fountains of the great deep has usually been taken as the breaking forth of subterranean waters. This is entirely possible, but the word "deep" even more reasonably can refer to the seas. This statement could mean that the antediluvian seas, which had been confined within their boundaries since the third day of creation, were no longer thus limited. Something dramatic happened to the sea basins. "Thou didst set the earth on its foundations, so that it should never be shaken. Thou didst cover it with the deep as with a garment; the waters stood above the mountains. At thy rebuke they fled; at the sound of thy thunder they took to flight. The mountains rose, the valleys sank down to the place which thou didst appoint for them. Thou didst set a bound which they should not pass, so that they might not again cover the earth" (Ps. 104:5-9, R.S.V.).

This passage seems appropriately to describe divine activity, both at creation and at the Flood. The rising of the mountains and the sinking of the valleys to provide a receptacle for the floodwaters would be the reverse of what happened at the beginning of the Flood, when "water appeared to come from the clouds in mighty cataracts. Rivers broke away from their boundaries, and overflowed the valleys. Jets of water burst from the earth with indescribable force, throwing massive rocks hundreds of feet into the air, and these, in falling, buried themselves deep in the ground" (PP 99). "In many places, hills and mountains had disappeared, leaving no trace where they once stood; and plains had given place to mountain ranges" (p. 108).

Strong earthquakes have been observed to produce geysers

and spouts of water. These are thought to be the result of sudden compaction of water-saturated ground from violent earthquake waves. This, it seems, happened on a gigantic scale at the beginning of the Flood. Earthquakes are the result of crustal movements. If, at the time of the Flood, mountain areas sank down and ocean basins rose, crustal movements would certainly produce earthquakes of unprecedented magnitude.

The paradoxical evidence in many present mountain chains—ocean-bottom deposits lifted up to become the highest areas of the earth—is explained by crustal adjustments of the sort suggested here. Note Ellen G. White's reference to the appearance and disappearance of mountain ranges. Of considerable interest in connection with the vertical movement of the surface of the earth during the Flood, is the apparent recency of the modern ocean basins. To date, no sediments older than late Mesozoic are known from the ocean basins (Shepard, 1959, p. 195). On the basis of this information we might suggest that these basins did not sink down until the latter part of the Flood, because they did not collect Paleozoic sediments. (See chapter 10 for a discussion of the geological time periods.) Sinking of the ocean basins may have continued for quite some time after the Flood. Flat-topped mountains located mostly in the Pacific Ocean, which seem to indicate that their tops were truncated by waves, are now several thousand feet below the surface of the water.

A more basic question is the cause of the breakup of the earth's crust. Several possible explanations have been given, but their merits are difficult to determine, because of a lack of information. Changes in atmospheric conditions must have occurred to initiate the first falling of rain the earth had known. How such changed conditions are related to tectonic (mountain-building) upheavals is not clear.

It is not possible or desirable to attempt to explain all aspects of the Flood by natural laws or observable phenomena. Much of the activity is beyond man's present ability to explain. This is not to say that God does not work by using the laws of nature, but that He used laws and processes about which we presently know little or nothing and with respect to which we have no satisfactory explanation. The crustal movements mentioned above, the saving of the ark and its inhabitants, the preservation of sea creatures in turbid ocean water, the bringing of the animals into the ark and their peaceful existence there, and many other points may never have scientific answers. But we have sufficient evidence that this deluge did occur, and we have faith to believe it occurred in the way the inspired writer describes, even though evidence may in some instances be lacking.

REFERENCES

See chapter 7. The Story of the Flood.

CHAPTER SEVEN

The Story of the Flood

By Ernest S. Booth

PERHAPS NO STORY in the entire Bible is quite so dramatic as that of the Flood recorded in Genesis 6, 7, and 8. Few even of those who peruse the Bible carefully really know the full story even after reading it. But if one will jot down the dates and time periods mentioned, and the specific events and their mutual relationships in chart form, the story will come out more clearly.

The Biblical Account

God told Noah some 120 years before the beginning of the Flood that He would destroy the earth. He gave Noah specific directions for the building of the ark, and instructed him how to prepare for the Flood. Noah followed God's instructions to the letter, and during the 120 years preached to all who would listen.

On the seventeenth day of the second month of Noah's 600th year (Gen. 7:11), the Flood began. The water came from two sources: (1) "the windows of heaven," and (2) "the fountains of the great deep." The first refers to rain; "fountains of the great deep" refers either to underground water or to the oceans. According to Genesis 7:12, rain fell continuously for 40 days and nights. Thereafter the waters continued to rise, and not until 110 days later did they begin to subside. The sequence of events is given as follows:

1. Rain fell for 40 days and 40 nights (Gen. 7:12).
2. Thereafter the water level continued to rise: "The waters

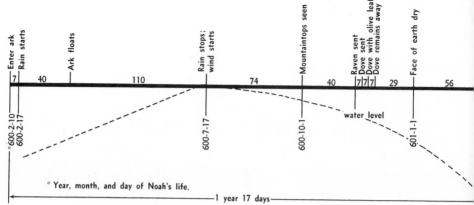

Fig 7.1 Chronology and duration of Flood events.

prevailed, and were increased greatly . . . ; and the ark went upon the face of the waters" (Gen. 7:18).

3. The highest mountains were covered to a depth of at least 15 cubits (Gen. 7:20).

4. All land animals and all people except those within the ark were killed (Gen. 7:21-23).

5. The Flood prevailed for 150 days, reckoned from the time the rain began to fall (Gen. 7:24; cf. chs. 7:11; 8:4).

6. After 150 days a wind began to blow upon the water (Gen. 8:1).

"The entire surface of the earth was changed at the Flood. A third dreadful curse rested upon it in consequence of sin. As the water began to subside, the hills and mountains were surrounded by a vast, turbid sea. Everywhere were strewn the dead bodies of men and beasts. The Lord would not permit these to remain to decompose and pollute the air, therefore He made of the earth a vast burial ground. A violent wind which was caused to blow for the purpose of drying up the waters, moved them with great force, in some instances even carrying away the tops of the mountains and heaping up trees, rocks, and earth above the bodies of the dead" (PP 107).

7. Simultaneously, the fountains of the deep and the windows of heaven were stopped, and the waters began to recede gradually (Gen. 8:2, 3).

56

8. At the same time the ark found a quiet haven among the mountains of Ararat (Gen. 8:4). When the wind began to blow, the ark evidently needed special protection from the strong wind and waves.

"As the waters began to subside, the Lord caused the ark to drift into a spot protected by a group of mountains that had been preserved by His power. These mountains were but a little distance apart, and the ark moved about in this quiet haven, and was no longer driven upon the boundless ocean" (PP 105).

9. "The waters decreased continually until the tenth month," on the first day of which the tops of the mountains—probably the mountains of Ararat—became visible (Gen. 8:5). This would be 74 days after the close of the 150-day period.

10. Forty days after the tops of the mountains became visible —284 days after the rain began to fall—Noah opened the window and released a raven, to learn the state of the earth's surface (Gen. 8:6, 7). Although it found no place to rest it remained outside the ark.

11. Seven days later he released a dove, which, unlike the raven, returned to the ark when it could find no suitable place to rest (Gen. 8:9).

12. Psalm 104:6-9 appears to provide a clue to one important means by which land areas became free of water after the Flood: The mountains rose, the valleys sank down. The dry land was uplifted out of the waters, as on the third day of creation. The drying process mentioned in Genesis 8:13, 14 refers primarily to the land areas drying out, not to the waters of the Flood drying up.

13. When Noah sent the dove out the second time, it returned with a fresh olive leaf (Gen. 8:10, 11). But there had been no land in sight one week before. Where did that fresh leaf come from?

"The beautiful trees and shrubbery bearing flowers were destroyed, yet Noah preserved seed and took it with him in the ark, and God by his miraculous power preserved a few of the different kinds of trees and shrubs alive for future generations.

"Soon after the flood trees and plants seemed to spring out of the very rocks. In God's providence seeds were scattered and driven into the crevices of the rocks and there securely hid for the future use of man" (3SG 76, 77).

Possibly, clusters of trees and shrubs were floating about during the Flood as rafts. Such rafts of vegetation are common in the Amazon River, and have been seen hundreds of miles from shore in the Atlantic Ocean. Such a raft may have floated past the ark on the day the second dove was released.

The olive is a hardy tree. It is a common practice to start new trees by cuttings which may range in size from a limb several inches in diameter and six feet long, to little twigs. New roots develop quickly.

The tops of the mountains had been seen 47 days previously. A tree or limb buried just beneath the mud at a higher elevation could have begun growing even while submerged, and sent up a shoot and produced leaves. There had been ample time for this to take place.

14. It was on Noah's birthday that he removed the cover of the ark and looked out (Gen. 8:13, 14). The ground was still muddy, not fit for man or beast to walk upon. Not until a month and 27 days later "was the earth dried."

The Preservation of Plants and Animals

According to the Genesis record (Gen. 7:21-23) every living creature upon the dry land died during the Flood. No mention is made of plants or of marine animals.

While the Bible is silent about the fate of plants during the Flood, few if any plants could escape destruction so severe as to obliterate animal life. Aquatic plants, however, might well survive. Microscopic algae and many other aquatic forms of plant life must have come through the Flood, for they are with us today though it is doubtful that Noah took them into the ark.

Aquatic animals should have been able to shift for themselves during the Flood, though myriads of them doubtless perished.

Fishes, frogs, salamanders, and other aquatic animals normally live in water, at least for a portion of their lives. Yet the fact that we find abundant fossils of some of these animals is indication that many of them died—probably during the Flood. "As the water began to subside, the hills and mountains were surrounded by a vast, turbid sea" (PP 107, 108; see also 3SG 77).

Most fishes cannot exist in water that contains great quantities of mud. Since much of the earth was covered with muddy water during the Flood, aquatic animals with gills must have died in large numbers. Animals with lungs, on the other hand—whales, porpoises, seals, frogs, for instance—could survive by coming to the surface to breathe. But many of them must have died because of the turbulence of the waters and the great amount of debris.

At least one pair of each original kind of land animal was taken into the ark, thereby ensuring a stock of these animals to repopulate the earth after the Flood. "Every species of animal which God had created were preserved in the ark" (3SG 75). Skeptics argue that the ark was too small to hold two of each kind of land animal. This argument might be true if based on the present concept of species. But the original Genesis "kind" may have been broader than our modern species, and the number of kinds of animals taken into the ark thus much less than the number of species recognized today (see the chapter entitled "After His Kind"). Many of the present species have originated since the Flood.

Besides the animals, Noah had stocks of food to feed them. He also had seeds, and perhaps cuttings of important cultivated plants, as well.

Fig. 7.2   Mt. Ararat.

CREATION—ACCIDENT OR DESIGN?

When the earth came forth from the hand of the Creator it was extremely beautiful. Its surface was diversified. It was not all one vast plain, but there were hills and high mountains, rivers and lakes, and seas. Lush vegetation flourished everywhere, from the polar regions to the equator. There were no rocky areas, for the rocks were all covered with soil and vegetation. Animals existed in all parts of the earth, and in all habitats from the high mountains to the seashore.

The climate was subtropical with an even temperature. There was no rain at any time, but at night (or in the evening) a gentle dew watered the earth. This was the earth as it came from the hand of the Creator. Except for minor changes, it remained in this condition until the time of the Flood. During the Flood the entire surface of the earth was changed so completely that no one who had seen the earth before could possibly recognize it. The great geosynclines (former great depressions in the earth filled in with sediments and later uplifted as mountains) may indicate the locations of the pre-Flood oceans. During the early part of the Flood these may have been well filled with sediments. If so, during the last part of the Flood, or later, the geosynclines uplifted to form mountains and plateaus.

The pre-Flood seas were smaller bodies of water than oceans today. As the first Flood rains began to fall, and the first of the fountains of the deep began to break up, rivulets streamed down the hills and mountains toward the seas, carrying with them the first mud and sediments. These sediments washed out into the narrow seas and deposited on the bottom. Soon rivers began to flow, carrying still greater quantities of mud into the seas. Before long the sea basins were filled with sediments. By this time the land areas were inundated, so that the entire surface of the earth looked like one great ocean. No one would have recognized the original location of the pre-Flood seas, for they were filled with sediments.

We recognize four times in the geological history of the earth when sediments were formed: (1) Primordial soils were formed

60

at creation. (2) Before the Flood, sediments were formed in the pre-Flood oceans by such animals as corals, shelled animals along the beaches, plankton in the waters, and larger animals in the seas. (3) Sediments formed by the Flood itself make up the most extensive of all sedimentary deposits. (4) Sediments formed after the Flood constitute the second largest mass of sediments. It is often difficult to distinguish between 3 and 4.

Today, we must use the same methods used by all geologists in order to distinguish among the sediments formed at these different times. There are no set rules by which we can tell them apart. In each case we must study the fossils they contain and attendant local conditions. Inevitably, the study of the sediments becomes one of the most complicated and difficult of all studies, and allows for a wide variety of interpretations.

What is true of the sediments is also true of the fossils—they were formed at three different times in the earth's history: (1) before the Flood, (2) during the Flood, and (3) after the Flood.

It is difficult to know what fossils were formed before the Flood. One possible example might be deposits of diatomaceous and foraminiferous earths seen in certain areas. These deposits of single-celled plants and animals are many feet thick in some areas, and very pure. Diatoms and foraminiferans leave silicon and calcium shells. During pre-Flood times their shells accumulated on the sea bottom. Modern deposits of this kind are called oozes. Other kinds of marine animals may also have accumulated on the pre-Flood ocean bottoms, to be covered later by sediments of the Flood.

Conditions necessary for the formation of fossils are present in the world today and have been since the Flood. Rivers deposit their sediments, which may contain organic remains. Streams deposit sediments into lakes. Winds pile up sand and soil in water or on land. Landslides, glacial deposits, refuse piles of ancient villages, drippings or cave-ins from the ceilings of caves, and the gradual filling in of a lake by moss or plant remains until it is a marsh or peat bog—these are a few methods

61

of fossil preservation. One of the most successful and most extensive is volcanic activity. Ash blown into the air and settling on plants and animals kills them quickly and also preserves them from decay. Many areas in the western United States show fossil preservation by this method.

The La Brea tar pits in Los Angeles, California, are clearly post-Flood. Tars and other petroleum products are probably Flood remains. When we find an area where petroleum seeps out of the ground, with animals caught in the tars, we can be reasonably sure that the animals found in the tars are of post-Flood origin.

Thus we get a glimpse of the continuing formation of fossils long after the Flood. This makes the study of fossils more complicated than previously thought, and much careful work is needed in dealing with problems encountered.

REFERENCES

Booth, Ernest S. 1950. Biology, the story of life. Pacific Press Pub. Assn., Mountain View, California, pp. 451-507.

Clark, Harold W. 1946. The new diluvialism. Science Publications, Angwin, California. 222 pp.

Hoen, Reu E. 1951. The Creator and his workshop. Pacific Press Pub. Assn., Mountain View, California, pp. 119-139.

Marsh, Frank L. 1950. Studies in creationism. Review and Herald Pub. Assn., Washington, D.C., pp. 309-349.

————. 1967. Life, man, and time. 2d ed. Outdoor Pictures, Escondido, California. 238 pp.

Morris, Henry M. and John C. Whitcomb, Jr. 1961. The Genesis flood. The Presbyterian and Reformed Pub. Co., Philadelphia. 518 pp.

Price, George M. 1923. The new geology. Pacific Press Pub. Assn., Mountain View, California, pp. 679-692.

Rehwinkel, Alfred M. 1951. The flood in the light of the Bible, geology, and archaeology. Concordia Pub. House, St. Louis, Missouri. 372 pp.

Seventh-day Adventist Bible commentary, The. 1953. vol. 1. Review and Herald Pub. Assn., Washington, D.C.

Shepard, Francis P. 1959. The earth beneath the sea. The Johns Hopkins Press, Baltimore. 275 pp., 113 figs.

White, Ellen G. 1913. Patriarchs and prophets. Pacific Press Pub. Assn., Mountain View, California, pp. 90-116.

————. 1945. Spiritual gifts. vol. 3. Facsimile reproduction. Review and Herald Pub. Assn., Washington, D.C., pp. 64-95.

CHAPTER EIGHT

Evidences of the Flood—I

THE GENESIS FLOOD was produced by violent storms that accumulated water to a sufficient depth to inundate completely the pre-Flood land features. Associated with the water were large waves and high winds. Crustal movements broke up the surface, with the result that elevated areas became ocean bottoms and pre-Flood sea basins were uplifted to become mountains. Whole continents may have slid or sunk to lower levels. Volcanic disturbances such as can hardly be visualized rocked the earth. Its axis may have been altered and the speed of rotation may have changed, either of which would cause seismic vibrations of great force. Atmospheric pressures and strength, and the direction of the earth's magnetic field may have been changed.

All in all, the Flood was a catastrophe of dimensions that have not been equalled at any other time in the physical history of this planet. The protection afforded the ark at this time was nothing less than miraculous. Even Satan feared for his life (PP 99). The very magnitude of the event makes it difficult for us to understand the action or to interpret the results. Certainly the surface of the earth was completely changed. Topographical features that existed before the Flood would be expected to vanish under its onslaught. It is virtually certain that present seas do not bear any resemblance to pre-Flood seas, either in geographical position or in extent.

If a great catastrophe such as the Bible describes actually did occur, much evidence of such an event should remain. The earth's geologic structure is complex, and constant changes since the Flood tend, in part, to obscure the evidence. Erosion and deposition by wind and water, the action of glaciers, volcanic eruptions, and post-Flood tectonic movements—all have had their influence on the crust of the earth and the topography of its surface.

Nevertheless, many indications of a major flooding of the world by water remain. Any serious study of geological literature, or personal observations in the field, turns up facts that are difficult to interpret as having been produced by any other means. Some of the more obvious and important evidences are described in some detail in this chapter and in other sections of this book.

It is difficult to say definitely in many instances, "This was caused by the Genesis Flood." There is usually more than one possible interpretation of geological and paleontological phenomena. The evidences given below for extensive and rapid water action tend to support the Genesis account of the Flood.

Great Sedimentary Deposits

Sedimentary rocks constitute about 75 per cent of the rocks exposed on the surface of the earth. Only in recent years has the depth of sedimentation in certain areas been shown by drillings or soundings. In North America some of the most extensive and deep sediments are located in the Midwest plains, the Colorado Plateau, the California coastal plains, the Gulf of Mexico coast, and the northern Rocky Mountains. Other areas of the world have similarly deep and numerous sedimentary deposits, with India presenting what may be the deepest known sedimentary basin—60,000 feet or more.

Many of these deposits are so deep that one of the most difficult problems facing the geologist is that of determining their source. Such processes as gradual submergence and the slow accumulations of sediments by erosion seem inadequate to account for the great quantities of water-and-wind-deposited materials. Adjacent areas do not provide sufficient materials for

Fig. 8.1 The Ramparts, Alberta, Canada. A deposit of Cambrian sediments.

deposition on such a scale. But a flood of sufficient extent to cover all land, and a storm of great violence that stirred "roiled water or soft mud" (3SG 77), is sufficient to account for the transport of a vast amount of sedimentary material over great distances, and the filling in of depressions irrespective of the height or extent of adjacent landscapes.

A picture of violent agitation of all the water over the whole earth at the same time—a series of giant tidal waves moving over the globe—is probably incorrect. This would mix the sediments into a homogenous mess and deposit them somewhat uniformly over the earth. Such is not the actual situation. The layered nature of earth's crust is one of the most evident observations. Beds of rock and sediment lying one above another often consist of entirely different materials—limestone above sandstone, shale overlying conglomerate, for example. Evidences of relatively quiet water and little mixing of sediments are seen above or below beds showing heavy water flow and rapid sedimentation.

These characteristics of the earth's crust lead to the formulation of a Flood model that postulates violent water activity locally and at times; while elsewhere the depth of the water, the sheltered position, or the temporary cessation of wind and storm permitted relatively gentle settling of sands and muds. Later uplift or downwarp of the earth's surfaces would create ideal conditions for mud slides beneath the surface of the receding waters. Deposits originating from the sliding of supersaturated submarine sediments (turbidity currents) have been recognized widely around the world in recent years. A universal flood would create ideal conditions for the formation of many deposits of this nature.

An example of overlapping sedimentation from southern California is significant (Fig. 7.1). The San Joaquin Hills, southeast of Los Angeles, have been shown to be underlaid by the marine Monterey Shale. On the southwest side of the San Joaquin Hills beds of breccia (broken fragments of rocks) containing no fossils lie above the shale. The breccia layers thin out and disappear toward the northeast. Here they overlap and interfinger with beds of sandstone with granitic debris that also overlies the Monterey Shale. The sandstone layers are found in the Santa Ana Mountains to the northeast. It thus appears that sediments were swept from both sides into a basin tending northwest-southeast. From the northeast, sands with granitic debris poured some distance into the basin. From the southwest, breccia rolled down and partially overlapped the sandstone. This occurred several times. The sands became sandstone and the rock fragments hardened into breccia.

Movements necessary to produce this kind of action would be considerable. Both the sandstone and the breccia give evidence of rapid deposition by water or by land or mud slides. "Here we are not dealing merely with a Miocene flooding of the continental margin but with a series of earth movements so complex that some particular spots rose high above sea level and then sank far below—as shown by present day soundings—while other spots not far away were going through the opposite movements" (Gilluly, et al., 1959, p. 355).

From the Appalachian Mountains westward to Lake Erie and Ohio, and from New York to Alabama, great beds of sand are

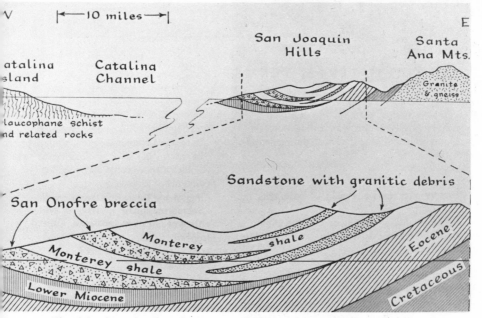

Fig. 8.2 Complex interfingering sediments of southern California.

found below the surface. One called the Tuscarora Sandstone, averaging 500 feet thick over this entire area, is often nearly pure quartz sand without any fossils (Fig. 8.3). Above the Tuscarora Sandstone is the similar Pocono formation, of almost equal dimensions. Great sheets of fresh-water-laid sand that change only slightly in thickness and texture, mile after mile, cannot be observed forming anywhere in the world today. Flowing rivers, meandering streams, and trickling rivulets could not have produced these great deposits of sand. Forces generated during the Genesis Flood, or during more localized adjustments of the shattered crust of the earth, which must have followed for many years after Noah left the ark, were probably responsible.

Examples of thick sediments are seen the world over. The beautiful faultblock and overthrusted mountains of the northern Rockies show exposures of more than 4,000 feet of sedimentary strata, some of which give clear evidence of having been deposited rapidly. The well-preserved ripple marks, the excellent preservation of even delicate fossils, the burial of vast numbers of trilobites and other invertebrates that frequently show no sign of decay or disintegration, are some features that indicate

67

Fig. 8.3 Tuscarora Sandstone, a relatively pure quartz, is widespread in the eastern United States.

that these sediments did not form by a process of gradual accumulation over millions of years.

One interesting sedimentary deposit that covers a wide area, including parts of Colorado, Utah, Wyoming, Montana, New Mexico, and Arizona, contains many remains of prehistoric reptiles. In the Colorado Plateau region, where the Morrison formation, as these sediments are called, is frequently exposed, and its colorful sandstones, clays, and shales are seen, dinosaur remains are found. The museum at Dinosaur National Monument exhibits a profusion of dinosaur bones in an excavated section of the Morrison. This formation is relatively consistent in fossil remains, color, and petrology over most of its range; and the mass burial, the jumbled condition, and the dismembered state of most specimens indicates the mode of deposition. The stratum, which is up to 300 feet thick in places, also contains fish and a few mammals.

These are a few examples of many strata that indicate the

magnitude of sedimentary deposition. Certainly, however, the deposition of all sedimentary strata cannot be assigned to one event, but no cause or event could equal a universal flood of water as an explanation for many of these deposits.

The burial of vast numbers of animals quickly and without noticeable decay has occurred frequently in the past. It constitutes another remarkable evidence of rapid water movement and flooding.

One of the first formations to be described in detail, the Old Red Sandstone (Miller, 1860, p. 221), contains vast quantities of fish. These Devonian rocks, which cover 10,000 square miles or more in England, are filled with a staggering number of fish. The fish themselves bear striking testimony to sudden burial. Miller's remarks on this point are of considerable interest:

"At this period of our history, some terrible catastrophe involved in sudden destruction the fish of an area at least a hundred miles from boundary to boundary, perhaps much more. The same platform in Orkney as at Cromarty is strewed thick with remains, which exhibit unequivocally the marks of violent death. The figures are contorted, contracted, curved; the tail in many instances is bent round to the head; the spines stick out; the fins are spread to the full, as in fish that die in convulsions." The frequent and widespread discovery of fossil fish with open mouths has often been the topic of comment and discussion.

About 7,500 feet above sea level, on a shoulder of Mount Stephen in the Rocky Mountains of British Columbia, countless trilobites lie buried in fine-grained Burgess Shale. The number of specimens that lie exposed is considerable despite the collecting that has been going on for many years. No doubt the majority, a staggering number, remain buried within the mountain. Across Kicking Horse Valley, several miles distant, more trilobites are found on Mount Burgess and other mountains (Fig. 8.4).

Apparently this benthonic (ocean-bottom) marine crustacean was gregarious. Because of its ecological position (ocean bottom), it should have been among the first animals to be overspread with sediments in any flood situation. Trilobites are considered by geologists to be among the oldest organisms to be represented in the fossil record. Burgess Shale is therefore classified as Cambrian. The author has collected at this site several times, and has been impressed each time with the vast numbers and the good state of preservation. Frequently, a thin film of carbonaceous material is seen covering the impression of the animal on a freshly exposed slab. Many other crustaceans and marine invertebrates have been found in Burgess Shale. The fine grain of the shale is ideal for preserving the fine detail (Fig. 8.5). Even soft bodies have left their impressions. Most notable is the delicate impression of a jellyfish. Obviously animals such as this would require sudden covering to prevent disintegration.

Current ocean-bottom sediments are thoroughly reworked by burrowing worms, shells, et cetera. An impression on the sea bottom would be completely obliterated long before sedimentation under present conditions could cover it. Volcanic ash blown out

Fig. 8.4 Countless well-preserved organisms are found in Burgess Shale.

by Tambora volcano east of Java, in 1815, is still found at the surface of the bottom mud, even in areas of fast deposition, because of the constant overturn of the surface layer by marine organisms living in it. Benthonic animals constantly rework the mud in which they live. Under present conditions stratification of sea-bottom muds appears to be limited (Gilluly, *et al.*, 1959, pp. 338-342).

Many other areas of the earth contain deposits with an abundance of fossils. Agate Springs Quarry in Nebraska contains a layer of mammal bones that appears to be thrown together in chaotic profusion. The layer gives evidence of having been much more extensive in the past. The Geiseltal lignites, discussed in more detail below, contain abundant animal remains. A listing of such examples could be extended considerably.

Fig. 8.5   A Burgess Shale trilobite. Mt. Stephen, British Columbia, Canada.

Delicate Preservation

The delicate points and ribs of sea shells, tiny bones of fish, small appendages of crustaceans, textured details of echinoderms, and similar features are so frequently seen among fossils as to preclude any opportunity for abrasion by sand, or any length of time sufficient for decay and disintegration. Francis (1961, p. 18) gives this description of the remarkable Geiseltal lignite deposits in Germany:

"Here also is a complete mixture of plants, insects and animals from all the climatic zones of the earth that are capable of supporting life. In some cases leaves have been deposited and preserved in a fresh condition, the chlorophyll being still green, so that the 'green layer' is used as a marker during excavations. Among the insects present are beautifully colored tropical beetles, with soft parts of the body, including the contents of the intestines, preserved intact. Normally such materials decay or change in color within a few hours of death, so that preservation by inclusion in an aseptic medium must have been sudden and complete."

The veins of the leaves, butterfly wings, caterpillars, and even the hairs and bristles on the caterpillars are all perfectly preserved. In certain areas of these deposits, bones and coprolites, in huge collections, resemble a burial ground.

The beautiful and detailed preservation of fossils is becoming more apparent as techniques are perfected. Wetzel (1953) describes microfossils in Cretaceous flints. A number of taxonomic groups of protozoans are represented, including forms without calcareous or silicious tests. One specimen illustrated in Wetzel's paper still shows the flagellum. It is a member of the class Mastigophora (Flagellata), genus *Ophiobolus*, and is only about thirty microns long. The necessity for speedy preservation of such a specimen is obvious. Other delicate fossil protozoan specimens in astonishing detail are described.

According to Newell (1959, p. 283), G. Arthur Cooper, of the

United States National Museum, has been able to obtain—by working with dilute acids—great numbers of delicately preserved fossils from the Glass Mountains of Texas: "From 30 tons of Permian limestone . . . he [Cooper] has extracted three million individual invertebrate fossils, almost all of which are exquisitely preserved. . . . A single control block of limestone weighing one hundred and eighty-six pounds yielded ten thousand excellent specimens of invertebrates, including Foraminifera, brachiopods, bryozoans, gastropods, and pelecypods."

A good illustration of the rapid burial necessary to preserve delicate structure is furnished from research done recently by Zangerl and Richardson (1963, p. 169). In attempting to evaluate the rate of deposition involved in the burial of fish and other organisms now present as fossils in the Pennsylvanian black shales of Indiana, they placed dead fish in protecting wire cages and dropped them into the black muds at the bottom of several Louisiana lagoons or bayous. These black muds are thought to resemble the sediments from which the dark shales were derived. To the great surprise of the investigators, fish weighing from one-half to three-fourths pound were found to have all the soft parts reduced and all the bones completely disarticulated in six and one-half days! Decomposition to the state of total disarticula-

Fig. 8.6   Fossil fish from Green River Shale, Wyoming.

tion apparently occurs at great speed, perhaps in less time than indicated above, since none were checked before six and one-half days. Delicate fossil fish showing every minute ray and bone in position are common and must represent a burial by oxygen- and bacteria-excluding sediments within hours of death if this experiment is a valid indication.

The most reasonable explanation for the examples from the sedimentary and fossil record listed in this chapter is one based on catastrophism. The Genesis Flood is the most obvious cause of the catastrophe. A literal, universal flood such as that recorded in Genesis is well supported by the rocks and the fossils, and the interpretation of this evidence is not a whit less "scientific" than that to which most geologists point in support of the theory of uniformity. Further evidences of the flooding of the earth are considered in the next chapter.

REFERENCES

Clark, Harold W. 1946. The new diluvialism. Science Publications, Angwin, California. 222 pp.

Francis, Wilfrid. 1961. Coal, its formation and composition. 2d ed. Edward Arnold (Publishers) Ltd., London. 806 pp.

Gilluly, James, A. C. Waters, and A. O. Woodford. 1959. 2d ed. Principles of geology. W. H. Freeman and Co., San Francisco. 534 pp.

Miller, H. 1860. The old red sandstone. Gould and Lincoln, Boston. 403 pp.

Morris, Henry M. and John C. Whitcomb, Jr. 1961. The Genesis flood. The Presbyterian and Reformed Pub. Co., Philadelphia. 518 pp.

Newell, N. D. 1959. The nature of the fossil record. Proc. Amer. Phil. Soc., 103 (2):264-285.

Price, George McCready. 1923. The new geology. Pacific Press Pub. Assn., Mountain View, California. 762 pp.

Rehwinkel, Alfred M. 1951. The flood in the light of the Bible, geology, and archaeology. Concordia Pub. House, St. Louis, Missouri. 372 pp.

Wetzel, Otto. 1953. Resumé of microfossils from upper Cretaceous flints and chalks of Europe. Jour. Paleontology, 27:800-804.

Woodford, A. O., *et al.* 1954. Geology of Southern California, ch. 2. Calif. Div. Mines Bull. 170.

Zangerl, Rainer and Eugene S. Richardson, Jr. 1963. The paleoecological history of two Pennsylvanian black shales. Fieldiana: Geology Memoirs, vol. 4, 352 pp., 50 figs., 55 plates.

CHAPTER NINE

Evidences of the Flood—II

PERHAPS THE MOST CONVINCING EVIDENCE of a universal flood is to be found in the extensive coal reserves of the world. No processes going on today approach in magnitude the action necessary to account for this phenomenon. There are two theories concerning the accumulation of plant remains that turned to coal upon being buried—autochthonous accumulation, or the burial of material *in situ,* that is, in position of growth, and allochthonous accumulation, or burial of material drifted or rafted in from elsewhere. Both of these theories are compatible with the Genesis Flood, and both processes doubtless occurred. However, the rafting in of plant debris for burial in a new location would be more likely in connection with a flood of such dimensions.

Does the evidence support the gradual accumulation of vegetable matter in bogs and marshes as the process that has produced the world's coal? Let us look at some of the features of coal seams and coal-bearing strata.

Characteristics of Coal Deposits

The great majority of the coal deposits, from anthracite to lignite, are composed of woody tissue in various states of preservation. The examples of bogs and moors of today that could be used to illustrate current organic deposition do not apply well, because the organic material accumulating in these bogs is mostly peat (Sphagnum moss) and other marsh plants. Wood of trees is usually only a minor constituent. The condition required to satisfy the picture obtained from the examination of most coal deposits is that of extensive forests and vegetable debris buried suddenly. These conditions are not so well met in the modern peat bog and swamp environment.

The thickness of certain coal beds is well known. Thirty feet is not uncommon, and seams of brown coal in the Latrobe Valley of Victoria, Australia, are reported to exceed five hundred feet in thickness (Herman, 1952, p. 88). In the western United States, seams sixty to ninety feet in thickness are known. Like the vertical extent, the horizontal extent is also tremendous. The Pittsburgh bed covers parts of Pennsylvania, Ohio, and West Virginia, an area of 2,100 square miles, and averages about seven feet thick (Tarr, 1930). The Appalachian coal basin extends over some 70,000 square miles (Stutzer, 1940). The extent of minable coal runs into the thousands of millions of tons. Custer County, Montana, is said to have 1.5 billion tons of minable lignite. The Latrobe Valley in Australia is estimated to be able to yield 70 billion tons (Herman, 1952, p. 88).

The thickness of peat needed to produce one foot of coal depends on a number of factors such as the type of peat, the amount of water in the vegetable matter, and the type of coal. The scientific literature on coal gives figures ranging from a few feet to as many as 20. Let us assume that ten feet would be near an average figure. On this basis, a coal seam 30 feet thick would require the compression of 300 feet of peat. A 400-foot seam of coal would be the result of the compaction of a fantastic 4,000 feet of peat. The 400-foot seam of Australia is composed of lignite, which is soft coal; consequently, less peat would be needed. Even if this 400 figure were cut in half, the depth of peat required is unrealistically large. There are few peat bogs, marshes, or swamps anywhere in the world today that reach 100 feet in depth. Most of them are less than 50 feet. A much more reasonable alternative theory is that the vegetable matter has been concentrated and collected into an area by some force, undoubtedly water. Wood is not so compressible as peat, and would require accumulations of less depth to produce thick coal seams.

The uniform thickness and lateral extent of the beds are remarkable. It is not uncommon for a bed to be traceable over several thousand square miles. The deposit becomes thinner toward the edges of the area, but there is an amazing uniformity in thickness and in the flatness of the floors and roofs over much of the area. The origin of such vast coal beds has been a major concern of geologists. Few, if any, modern marshes or bogs cover such great areas or have such uniform depths, and geologists do not visualize drifted masses of vegetation on so large a scale. As a result, the majority have accepted coastal salt marshes and low-lying bogs as the sources of coal beds, despite the lack of current examples.

The concept of a global deluge that eroded out the forests and plant cover of the pre-Flood world, collected it in great mats of drifting debris, and eventually dropped it on the emerging land or on the sea bottom, is the most reasonable answer to this problem of the great extent and uniform thickness of coal beds.

A feature related to the bedding of the coal seams is the horizontal stratification usually present. Within an inch a bed of coal may show variation from bright, brittle coal to that of a dull appearance, or to coal of yet another structure. The microscope may reveal these bands to be composed mostly of some specific component of plants such as spores, cuticles, or macerated unidentifiable plant pulp. The obvious force in operation to produce this stratification, which is often extremely persistent over wide areas, is water on a large scale.

Another situation associated with coal in Utah and described by Peterson (1924) is remarkable because of the medium and method of preservation. Dinosaurs roaming about on piles of vegetable debris left footprints that protrude into the coal from the mud above. Peterson's description is most interesting:

"The tracks seem to have been made at a time when the peat accumulation was covered with a foot or more of mud. . . . The feet sank through the mud several inches, or even more than a foot at times, into soft, yielding peat underneath. . . . In most places the coal is easily separated from the roof, leaving the track-shaped protuberance extending partly or wholly as a definite appendage from the ceiling. . . . The largest tracks are those which protrude farthest from the roof. The material filling in the track varies slightly, but is for the most part an arenaceous [sandy] shale or an argillaceous [clay] sandstone. . . . The tracks measure 31 inches between the spread of the outer toes and 32 inches from the heel to the front of the middle toe. . . . The tracks . . . have been observed . . . at intervals over an area more than one hundred miles in extent and in different seams of coal, which represent a stratigraphic thickness of more than two hundred feet of sandstone including three or four beds of coal. The coal seams total in thickness approximately thirty-five feet."

It is not reasonable to suppose that successive bogs developed repeatedly in the same location after each previous one was buried suddenly by water-carried sediments, that similar animals played around in each of these marshes, and that these unchanging conditions continued for several millions of years.

On the other hand, it is difficult to visualize clearly how successive levels of tracks were made by these animals under conditions of flooding. However, there is much evidence of the rapid silting over of these vegetable deposits. An event of relatively short duration that deposited vegetable matter and silt alternatively while dinosaurs were wading or swimming around in the muddy water is a better theory.

Boulders consisting of various rock types such as quartzite, granite, and limestone, and ranging in size from several hundred pounds to gravel size or smaller, are frequently found associated

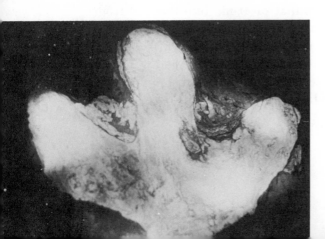

Fig. 9.1 A dinosaur footprint in the roof of a Utah coal mine.

with coal. Considerable discussion of this situation is found in the literature on coal. It is difficult to explain the presence of such materials by any other means than transport of uprooted trees containing boulders in their root systems, or by strong water currents. Gradual subsidence of coastal landforms does not seem to provide a suitable explanation of how these boulders got into the coal. It is of interest to note that the boulders are frequently of a rock type not represented locally. Transportation must have been for a considerable distance.

An Illustration From Nova Scotia

Along the upper end of the Bay of Fundy, which is noted for the world's highest tides, is another phenomenon of great interest that has been known in scientific circles for more than one hundred years. Along a stretch of several miles, upright petrified stumps embedded in the cliffs have been exposed by tidal waters (Fig. 9.2). Minable coal seams are situated along the Bay of Fundy and in other Carboniferous deposits of Nova Scotia. Petrified trees rise from the upper surface of some of the coal seams, or are distributed between coal seams exposed in vertical sequence along the cliffs.

Fig. 9.2 The carboniferous sediments exposed along the Bay of Fundy. A vertical tree is visible in the second coarse-sandstone layer from the top, about one inch from the right margin.

Charles Lyell, perhaps more responsible than anyone else in establishing geology as a definite science, visited the cliffs near Joggins, Nova Scotia, in 1842 (Lyell, 1843, pp. 176-178). A young Canadian scientist, J. William Dawson, accompanied him during a later visit to this area and went on to make the most comprehensive study of the Carboniferous deposits of Nova Scotia ever undertaken. (See references at end of chapter.) Dawson set a pattern of thinking regarding the origin of the petrified trees, the coal seams, and the other phenomena associated with the Carboniferous, that has been rather closely followed to the present time. He considered each level of trees and each coal seam to represent a ground surface or soil level. Eighty-five such horizons were identified and this was felt to be the minimum number of levels revealed along several miles of sea cliffs in this region (Dawson, 1854, pp. 2-10).

The growth of forests and the establishment of soils at many levels would require the repeated rise and fall of the land in order to bury the material growing at each level. The acceptance of this difficult requirement in the uniformitarian hypothesis for the origin and formation of the coal and petrified stumps was considered justified by the evidence. For the land surface in the same locality to be suitable for the exacting requirements of bog formation over the long period of time necessary for many successive emergences from the engulfing waters goes far beyond reasonable probability.

Of the three major evidences for the passage of much time, the vertical position of the stumps is the most obvious. They are almost always at right angels to the plane of the original surface, and the flaring roots can sometimes be traced outward from the base of the trunk for several feet.

The second evidence of *in situ* growth and the necessary time involvement are the *Calamites,* or giant horsetails, sometimes visible in vertical position in the cliffs. Horsetails (sometimes also called scouring rushes, or joint grass) are small plants today, seldom growing over four feet tall and half an inch in diameter. However, the calamite horsetails of the past must have grown several tens of feet tall, as a base diameter of up to a foot would suggest.

Rootlike structures called *Stigmaria,* up to six inches in diameter, are frequently found in the coal measures. They are covered with regularly spaced pits or scars, which are the points of attachment for the rootlets that spread out in all directions into the surrounding rock. These three—upright petrified trees, upright horsetails, and *Stigmaria* rootlet levels—represent the most convincing evidence of a series of ground or soil zones, and consequently the passage of much time. What light has recent research shed on this problem?

Three types of trees are most commonly involved. The upright stumps belong almost exclusively to the genera *Sigillaria* and *Lepidodendron,* two extinct groups represented today by the club mosses. Living club mosses are small, vinelike plants mistaken by most people for overgrown "mosses." *Sigillaria* trees reached a diameter of three feet or over, and *Lepidodendron* was nearly as large. In appearance they were trees. The *Stigmaria* to which the rootlets discussed above attach are roots or rootlike structures of these vertical trees. A unique but not surprising

Fig. 9.3 Vertical and horizontal petrified trees near Joggins, Nova Scotia. The vertical tree is hollow, whereas the prone tree is not.

feature of these two giant club mosses is the hollow or soft pulp interiors. All these vertical trees are filled with sediments, and only the outer wood or bark remains as a thin film of coal (Fig. 9.3). Obviously the trees must have been hollow at the time they were buried by sediments.

Another fossil tree common in the Joggins area is of the genus *Cordaites*, a coniferous tree most closely represented to-day by the Paraná pine of the Southern Hemisphere. None of the petrified *Cordaites* trees were hollow and none of them were found in a vertical orientation. Only the hollow trees in the cliffs were in the growing position. Why did the hollow, more fragile types remain standing amid the inundations that left sediments in and around them, while the solid, more sturdy trees fell to a prone position? (Fig. 9.3).

Of 49 vertical trees examined, 34 (69 per cent) were filled with material not similar to the surrounding matrix. Frequently the hollow center was filled with sandstone while the surrounding sediment (matrix) was shale. Sometimes the internal cast of the tree, like the surrounding matrix, was composed of alternating layers of shale and sandstone, but the shale and sandstone inside and outside the stump did not match (Fig. 9.4). Occasionally the material inside the fossil tree was filled with leaf impressions and other plant remains while the surrounding rock was devoid of fossils, or vice versa. It is difficult to conceive of a hollow stump, standing in a forest, being filled with sand while around it mud was accumulating.

How can one explain stumps floating upright in water and being left in the mud in that position? Yet this would be the only alternative to the *in situ* explanation. Would hollow stumps with their center of gravity in the base of the trunk adjust to a horizontal position as their tissues gradually became saturated with water?

As a matter of fact, trees and logs floating in an upright position are not rare in certain areas. I have seen water-logged timbers in the waters of the Puget Sound in the Northwest, floating upright, with the top barely visible. Loggers from British Columbia and Alaska say that trees or stumps ripped out of the ground by ocean storms or logging operations often float upright. This phenomenon has also been observed in the Bay of Fundy, where the fossil stumps are located. I have noticed and photographed recent stumps sitting upright along the beach or among piles of driftwood, where they were left by high tides or storms.

Others have reported upright drifting trees. Francis (1961, p. 28), in his reference work on coal, writes: "It is natural for short stems attached to the heavy roots of trees to float upright, with the roots downwards, when transported by deep water, particularly if the roots enclose a ball of clay or gravel."

A situation that most closely approaches what one might expect during part of the Genesis Flood is reported in volume one of the famous Challenger Expedition Reports. While sailing along the coast of New Guinea the explorers ran into long lines of driftwood brought down, perhaps, by flooding rivers. "Much of the wood was floating suspended vertically in

Fig. 9.4 Vertical petrified trees with surrounding matrix differing from the sediments filling their hollow centers.

the water, and most curiously, logs and short branch pieces thus floating often occurred in separate groups apart from the horizontally floating timbers. The sunken ends of the wood were not weighted by any attached masses of soil or other load of any kind; possibly the water penetrates certain kinds of wood more easily in one direction with regard to its growth than the other, hence one end becomes water-logged before the other" (Challenger, 1885, p. 459).

Charles Lyell, in his *Principles of Geology* (1867, p. 445), describes upright trees deposited by the Mississippi River. Trees have also been reported floating down the Amazon River, often in upright position.

These reports cause us to examine with care interpretations involving erect fossil trees. It cannot automatically be assumed that such trees are in position of growth.

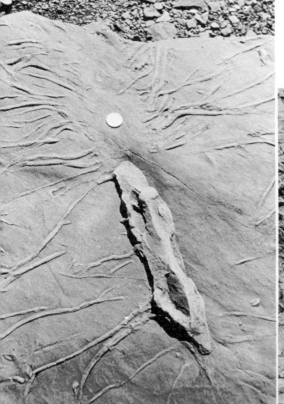

Fig. 9.5 Longitudinal and cross sections of *Stigmaria* roots showing their characteristic radiating rootlets.

The calcareous tubes of *Spirorbis,* a small marine worm, are abundant in some seams of coal, and are often found on and even inside the hollow stumps. The presence of this worm points strongly to the conclusion that these trees floated in salt water long enough for *Spirorbis* to attach to them, or that they were covered by deep, clear sea water.

Hollow stumps standing in a forest would be expected to collect debris falling from branches and limbs overhead. In at least two cases, however, one from my own investigations and the other from a published report (Brown, 1850, p. 127), pieces of *Stigmaria* roots have been found in the sediments inside the stumps. There is no way for such plant parts to have been dropped in from above. They must have been washed in by water.

The evidence points to the conclusion that these trees have been carried into their present positions by water, and are not buried in their positions of growth.

Let us turn now to the problem of *Stigmaria* rootlets, over which paleobotanists have long puzzled. These rootlets spread out into the rocks in "growth" that is parallel. Where one rootlet bends, adjacent rootlets will bend also. They are attached to the *Stigmaria* root in orderly spiral rows.

It is not uncommon to see several feet of *Stigmaria* exposed in the cliff in a longitudinal section. Extending upward and downward from the root are the rootlets, in parallel and regular alignment with one another as if one were seeing a longitudinal section through the middle of a gigantic bottle brush.

Since *Stigmaria* and rootlets are attached to trees whose affinity to the club mosses is not questioned, it follows that some answers to the function of the *Stigmaria* and rootlets might be obtained by examining living sepcimens of club mosses (Fig. 9.6). *Lycopodium* is a vinelike plant that grows along the ground and sends up shoots, on the ends of which are the clublike fruiting bodies. Two features attract attention immediately— the presence of true roots and the creeping stems covered with

Fig. 9.6 *Lycopodium,* a modern living club moss.

stiff scalelike leaves. Although these stiff leaves on the living *Lycopodium* are not as long and slender in relation to the stem from which they arise as the rootlets are to the *Stigmaria,* yet the analogy seems to be obvious. If this is correct, the rootlets of the *Stigmaria* are not rootlets at all, but slender leaflike appendages attached to rhizomes or creeping stems called *Stigmaria.* One obvious characteristic of true rootlets sometimes overlooked is their positively geotropic growth pattern; that is, they grow downward toward the pull of gravity. Occasionally rootlets may grow upward a short distance, but eventually they always turn to the side or downward. The *Stigmaria* rootlets, on the other hand, extend out in all directions. Frequently, the upward-extending rootlets reach a length of three or four feet, and often appear to exceed in length those reaching downward. This is not in agreement with the laws of growth that apply to true rootlets—another reason for doubting that *Stigmaria* rootlets are true rootlets. It is still possible, however, that these "rootlets" did have a water-absorbing capacity and that they served the function of rootlets even though they were attached to a creeping stem in a manner quite unlike rootlets, and have a morphology not characteristic of rootlets with which we are presently familiar.

Exposed along one cliff is a 60-foot length of *Stigmaria* with a diameter of four by two and a half inches at one end and exactly the same dimensions at the other end 60 feet distant! The *Stigmaria* are usually filled with sediments different from those that surround them. These gigantic rhizomes may have extended from one tree to another. As yet no example of the extending of *Stigmaria* from one petrified tree to another has been found, but this lack would appear to be an argument against *in situ* growth. Trees still attached together by rhizomes could hardly have been eroded out and washed about in water unless the action were most gentle and of short duration. This concept of the *Stigmaria* and rootlets is not new. Most paleobotanists have referred to this possibility.

It seems probable to me that if paleobotanists would examine the fossil record and the sediments with a mind open to the possibility that the underclays are not true soils and that plant fossils and coal deposits could have allochthonous origins, real progress would be made in interpretation, and the problem to which they have given rise would vanish. "Modern research has thrown little additional light on the *Stigmaria* problem and the remains are generally ignored by present-day paleobotanists" (Arnold, 1947, p. 124).

If the rhizome, or creeping-stem character, of *Stigmaria* is established, the question of their *in situ* growth is still a question. A discovery that was alluded to earlier bears directly on this subject. Mention was made of short pieces of *Stigmaria* "roots," with "rootlets" attached, found inside hollow stumps. Not only does this strongly argue for water deposition of the material inside the stumps, but the fact that these sections of "roots" had "rootlets" extending out from them also lessens the strength of the argument that "rootlets" grew after deposition.

There is the possibility that the prostrate, or underground, stems would have the ability to send out "rootlets" into the ground even after being buried, even as a piece of potato will grow if dropped into the ground and if the piece contains at least one "eye." This point may be checked by examining thin cross sections through the *Stigmaria* "rootlets" under the microscope, to see whether there is any compaction of the sand and silt grains around the "rootlet." Growing structures that force their way through sediments cause compaction of the grains directly around the structure. If compaction cannot occur, growth cannot continue in that direction. Sometimes rocks are split and cement slabs of sidewalks are lifted by the action of growing roots. Thus a study of thin sections through *Stigmaria* "rootlets" should help to settle whether the *Stigmaria* have grown their "rootlets" before or after being deposited in the muds and sands of ancient Nova Scotia. Although this research angle is being investigated, the examination of a small number of slides shows no compaction of surrounding sedimentary grains.

The situation with the vertical *Calamites* was a little more difficult to explain than that of the trees, because it seemed unlikely that these tall, slender stems could float upright. To my surprise, flotation experiments with living horsetails reveal that a cluster of stems joined together at the base will float upright when thrown into a tank of water. The roots, solid rootstocks, and associated soil that cannot be dislodged readily, cause the lower end to be heavier and to sink down until displacement of the water is equal to the weight of the plants.

Although flotation experiments are continuing with living horsetails, it has already been well observed that individual stems of horsetails that initially floated horizontally on the water's surface have, after some days, swung into an upright position suspended from the surface of the water. As saturation increased, they sank and rested on the bottom in a vertical position. Eventually, some days later, they fell over, to lie horizontally on the bottom of the tank. If sediments were building up around the stems while they were upright, they would not have had opportunity to fall over. Living horsetail stems that have been soaked for a time lose the partitions between joints and become completely hollow, like the fossil *Calamites*.

One evidence of very rapid accumulation of sediments is the banking, or settling, of sediments against the outside and inside the hollow stumps. The gradual accumulation of sediments over a period of time would allow the soil to be smoothed level. Sagging or settling when sediments dried out would be eliminated. Occasionally one finds trees diagonally positioned in the cliffs, with the roots seen to flare out at right angles to the trunks, this indicating that the trees must have stood upright when in growth, but do not now represent a position of growth.

Are the Nova Scotia Carboniferous deposits terrestrial or marine? Dawson was so positive on this point that he made almost no provision for the possibility of marine deposition. Subsequent investigators have followed rather closely this concept, and apparently overlook the rather clear evidences of marine influence in the laying down of the clastic beds. These may be summarized as follows:

1. Limestone beds are not infrequent in these sediments. Limestone can hardly have been deposited in non-marine waters.

2. The calcareous tubeworm, *Spirorbis* (already mentioned), is abundant in many of the beds and among the plant remains and coal. The present-day counterpart (same genus) of *Spirorbis* is strictly an inhabitant of the marine environ-

Fig. 9.7 *Spirorbis*, a marine worm found attached to Carboniferous plant fossils.

89

ment. There is good reason to suppose that the Carboniferous *Spirorbis* was marine also.

3. Several species of a mussel, *Naiadites,* are found in the Joggins area especially. Their shells, often crushed and flattened, lie upon each other in a profusion of uncounted millions. Mussels are generally considered to be marine organisms.

4. Fish scales and teeth are sometimes seen. A variety of genera are found in the Nova Scotia Carboniferous, including a few teeth of sharklike creatures. The failure of past geologists to consider the possibility of a marine mode of deposition reflects the influence of a uniformitarian hypothesis on the interpretation of facts.

Summary and Reconstruction

For more than 100 years the fossil forests of Nova Scotia have been interpreted as trees in growth position, in sequence one above another, and the coal beds and *Stigmaria* rootlet levels have been considered to be additional soil zones and further proof of the gradual accumulation of sediments over hundreds of thousands of years.

However, certain features of the fossils and the enclosing rock raise grave doubts concerning the validity of this view. Vertical hollow stumps and stems with the root systems intact cannot be assumed automatically to represent growth position, especially when their internal contents differ from that of the surrounding matrix, and the sediments banked against the stumps contain ripple marks and show other features of deposition by marine water as determined by the animal fossils associated with the plants. *Stigmaria* and rootlets certainly do not represent soil levels, but are root- or leaf-bearing creeping stems, buried in underclay, coal, shale, and showing up in most unusual sites including the internal casts of stumps.

It will be helpful to attempt to reconstruct a rough model of the Nova Scotia Carboniferous on the basis of a catastrophic Flood hypothesis. A preliminary model will aid in thinking through the problem, one that can be modified as new information becomes available and hypotheses are adjusted.

Plants of probably lowland forests were ripped up by the erosion of an invading and rising sea. As the tree stumps floated in the water they became saturated and slowly swung into an upright position. Eventually they sank down into the muds or sands at the bottom, or were stranded on a mud flat or sand beach when the tide retreated. Continuing fallout of sediments from the water above or tidal rise and fall and wave action caused sediments to accumulate around and in the stumps.

Clusters of horsetails were also washed out into the sea and floated vertically until they became saturated and sank. The giant creeping stems from which the *Sigillaria* and *Lepidodendron* trees arose were broken from their attachments to the trees and scattered about in the sediments. Continued high waters and tidal rise and fall resulted in intermittent deposition of alternating shale and sandstone sediments, with occasional accumulations of organic matter and upright trees.

While plant flotsam was floating in the sea, *Spirorbis*, the calcareous tube worm, attached to much of it; *Naiadites*, the mussel, also may have fastened itself to the floating debris, and fish swam among the material.

Sometime following the deposition, warping of the whole area occurred, causing a tilting of up to 20° in some parts of the basin. Later still, glaciers scoured over the tilted surface and left erratic boulders, glacial till, and other clear evidences of glacial activity. With the rising of the ocean when continental ice melted, the Bay of Fundy and the Atlantic Ocean cut back the cliffs and exposed the interesting fossils and coal seams of Nova Scotia.

Although there is yet much research to do, it is clear that an allochthonous source for the Nova Scotia coal and trees is as scientifically acceptable as the dominant opinion based on the concept of uniformity. The study of this area has made much more understandable the statement, "The waters prevailed, and were increased greatly upon the earth" (Gen. 7:18).

REFERENCES

Ager, Derek V. 1963. Principles of paleoecology. McGraw-Hill Book Co., Inc., New York. 371 pp.

Arnold, Chester A. 1947. An introduction to paleobotany. McGraw-Hill Book Co., Inc., New York. 433 pp.

Brown, Richard. 1848. Description of an upright *Lepidodendron* with *Stigmaria* roots, in the roof of the Sidney main coal, in the island of Cape Breton. Quart. J. Geol. Soc. London 4:46-50.

————. 1850. Section of the lower coal-measures of the Sidney coalfield, in the island of Cape Breton. Quart. J. Geol. Soc. London 6:115-133.

Challenger Expedition. 1885. Report on the scientific results of the voyage of the H.M.S. "Challenger" during the years 1873-76 under the command of Captain Nares and Captain Thompson. Narrative vol. 1. H. M. Stationery Office, London.

Dawson, J. W. 1854. On the coal-measures of the South Joggins, Nova Scotia. Quart. J. Geol. Soc. London 10 (1):1-51.

————. 1866. On the conditions of the deposition of coal more especially as illustrated by the coal-formation of Nova Scotia and New Brunswick. Quart. J. Geol. Soc. London 22:95-169.

————. 1890. On burrows and tracks of invertebrate animals in Paleozoic rocks, and other markings. Quart. J. Geol. Soc. London 46:595-618.

————. 1891. Acadian geology. 4th ed. Macmillan and Co., London. 833 pp.

————. 1894. Note on the genus *Naiadites*, as occurring in the coal formations of Nova Scotia. Quart. J. Geol. Soc. London 50:435-442.

Francis, Wilfrid. 1961. Coal, its formation and composition. Edward Arnold (Publishers) Ltd., London. 806 pp.

Herman, H. 1952. Brown coal. The State Electricity Commission of Victoria. 612 pp.

Logan, W. E. 1845. Section of the Nova Scotia coal measures as developed at the Joggins . . . Canadian Geol. Sur. Prog. Rep. 1843, 92-159. Nova Scotia Inst. Sci. Proc. Trans. 11:419-499 (1908).

Lyell, Charles. 1843. On the upright fossil trees found at different levels in the coal strata of Cumberland, Nova Scotia. Proc. Geol. Soc. London 4:176-178.

————. 1867. Principles of geology. 10th ed., vol. 1. D. Appleton and Co., New York. 671 pp.

Peterson, W. 1924. Dinosaur tracks in the roofs of coal mines. Natural History, 24 (3):388.

Seward, A. C. 1898-1919. Fossil plants. Hafner Pub. Co., Inc., New York. Reprint 1963. vol. 1, 452 pp. vol. 2, 624 pp.

Sternberg, C. M. 1933. Carboniferous tracks from Nova Scotia. Geol. Soc. Am. Bull. 44:951-964, Pls. 35-37.

Stevenson, John S. and Louis S. Stevenson. 1966. Fluorine content of microsaur teeth from the Carboniferous rocks of Joggins, Nova Scotia. Science 154 (3756):1548, 1549.

Stutzer, Otto and Adolph C. Noe. 1940. Geology of coal. The Univ. of Chicago Press, Chicago. 461 pp.

Tarr, W. A. 1930. Introduction to economic geology. McGraw-Hill Book Co., New York. 644 pp.

THE STRUCTURE OF THE EARTH

"Where wast thou when I laid the foundations of the earth?"

Job 38:4

Fig. 10.1 THE GEOLOGIC COLUMN AND TIME SCALE

ERA	PERIOD	EPOCH	TIME*	DOMINANT LIFE	
	Quaternary {	Recent	In millions of years	Animal	Plant
		Pleistocene			
CENOZOIC		Pliocene	1 ↑	Mammals	Seed plant
	Tertiary {	Miocene			
		Oligocene			
		Eocene	↓		
		Paleocene	63		
MESOZOIC	Cretaceous		63 ↑	Reptiles	Conifers
	Jurassic				Cycads
	Triassic		↓ 181		Ferns
PALEOZOIC	Permian		181 ↑	Amphibians	Cordaites
	Pennsylvanian } Carboniferous			Insects	Tree ferns
	Mississippian }				Calamites
	Devonian				Psilophytes
	Silurian			Sharks	
				Lungfish	
				Corals	
	Ordovician			Brachiopods	
				Echinoderms	
	Cambrian		↓ 610	Trilobites	
PRECAMBRIAN	Grenville Orogeny		610 ↑	No fossils	Fungi Algae Bacteria
	[Oldest known rocks]		↓ 4600		

(Adapted from Kulp, 1961, and Gilluly, 1959.)

* These ages are those recorded
in geologic literature and do not
represent the thinking of the authors.

CHAPTER TEN

The Surface of the Earth

ON THE BASIS OF the evolutionary theory, new types of plants and animals have arisen slowly through hundreds of millions of years and their remains have been deposited in the sediments that accumulated during these countless years in a sequential order from "primitive" to "advanced," or simple to complex, the former at the bottom or lower position in the sediments and the latter at the top or upper position.

Life is said to have originated during the Precambrian; however, remains of living organisms are extremely rare until the Cambrian period of the Paleozoic era, when most of the phyla are represented by marine examples. (See Fig. 10.1.) The sudden appearance of such a wide variety of life forms has been a puzzle to paleontologists for more than a century.

Interpreting the Facts

William Smith (1769-1839) and Georges Cuvier (1769-1832) were chiefly responsible for developing the system now used for the classification of strata. Smith, an English canal engineer, noticed that the same kinds of fossils were always located in the same kinds of rocks. When canals were dug or cliffs exposed, he saw that these layers of rocks with their different kinds of fossils lay one above another and that they always lay in the same sequence. Eventually he was able to predict what kind of deposit would be found above or below any given stratum.

If you were walking along a trail and noticed certain kinds of fossils in the ground by your feet, if you walked on into a river canyon and saw that these fossils were embedded in a certain layer of rock in the cliff of the canyon and also noticed that other layers lying above and below this zone contained different fossils, if you took hikes into other canyons and saw that the same layers in the same sequence contained the same kinds of fossils, you would no doubt start drawing conclusions similar to those William Smith drew.

Add to this information certain facts that Cuvier first noticed. He pointed out that if a species disappeared from the rocks as one moved from lower levels to higher strata, it was not likely to show up again as the same species. If it did show up again in higher levels it was at least slightly different. Because Cuvier and other pioneers in this area were believers in a great age for life in the earth and some type of evolutionary progress (this was before Darwin formulated his explanation), they came to a conclusion that is now called the law of Faunal Assemblages: Like assemblages of fossil organisms indicate like geologic ages for the rocks that contain them.

If perchance these pioneers had been creationists with beliefs similar to our own, what conclusions would they have come to? Would they have concluded that certain strata contain certain kinds of fossils? Would they have decided that these kinds of fossils are in consistent vertical sequence? Would they have been justified in saying that the fossils in the upper layers were deposited at a later time than those in the lower layers? The answer to these questions is Yes, because the first two points were determined by actual field observations and the third conclusion is justified because in a series of water-laid sediments the upper ones must have been laid down at a later time than the lower ones, unless they have been disturbed.

Now if after careful study they found that fossil species did not reappear in identical form in upper levels after once disappearing from lower levels, would they have formulated the law of Faunal Assemblages as stated above? In this case the answer would be No, because they would not have been influenced by a previous belief in the long ages for life on the earth and an evolutionary progression. How would they have stated the law of Faunal Assemblages? Perhaps it would have been somewhat as follows: Like assemblages of fossil organisms indicate like ecologic or geographic sources for the sediments composing the rocks that contain them.

A classification of this nature brings together into the geologic periods the deposits that have similar animal and plant fossils even though they may be located far from each other, may have been deposited in vastly different modes, or are embedded in entirely different sediments. In general, various formations of similar geologic age would also be grouped together in the creationist's scale. Strata shown to be overlapping or superimposed one above the other would also represent to the creationist a time sequence from older at the bottom to younger at the top, but the time sequence would be greatly shortened in comparison with geologic time.

A proper understanding of geology and paleontology requires familiarity with the geologic time chart, as all geological and paleontological literature uses this system and its terminology. A creationist who does reading in these areas is constantly confronted with the task of re-evaluating and re-interpreting much of the information (Fig. 10.1).

Geologic time is divided into eras, periods, and epochs. The chart reproduced with this chapter has not included the epochs except for the Cenozoic Era. It must be noted, however, that evolutionists place much less time between the epochs of the Cenozoic Era than between the periods of the Mesozoic and Paleozoic eras. Most of the period names have been derived from the names of ancient English tribes, local geographical names where certain deposits are particularly well exposed or were first discovered, or more or less arbitrary terms that may have arisen from previous classifications no longer in use.

In many parts of the world, especially where the crust of the earth has been exposed by erosion or mountain-building activi-

Fig. 10.2 The Vermillion Cliffs of Utah, composed of Mesozoic rocks containing (top to bottom): Navajo, Kayenta-Wingate, Chinle, Shinarump, Moenkopi, and Kaibab (Paleozoic rock covered at bottom).

ties, an individual who spends some time in the field studying the beds of rock will discover for himself the regularity and predictable nature of these beds. He is limited, however, to what he can see and trace in canyons and cliffs. If the strata have been tipped so that they meet the surface at an angle, it may be possible to trace a sequence of beds by walking along a relatively flat surface.

In the Colorado Plateau region of the United States, stratigraphic correlations, comparisons of the bedding of one area with another, can be done with ease, and the similarity of beds from one site to another is so obvious that even a novice will notice it. One interesting bed in this region, the Chinle, is a colorful marker. Its red, purple, and greenish beds can be traced over thousands of square miles. The upper two thirds is composed mainly of sandstones and sandy silts and shales. The lower third consists largely of marls and silts. Mud cracks, ripple marks, thin lenses of sand, gravel, and conglomerate occur. Few fossils have been found, but some reptilian teeth and bone fragments have been collected.

What lies above the Chinle? Another remarkable formation,

the Navajo Sandstone. This massive group of beds consists of several hundred feet of buff-to-red cross-bedded sand that is well sorted but not well cemented (Fig. 10.3). The most striking feature is the cross-bedding that leads to the interpretation that these beds may be wind deposited. Although fossils are unknown, these beds are not difficult to recognize wherever they are found over their broad range. This formation often stands in vertical cliffs and erodes into bizarre shapes and designs.

A short distance above the Navajo Sandstone is the famous Morrison formation, where many dinosaur remains have been quarried from the rocks. Although some reptilian remains have been found in other beds of the Colorado Plateau, the Morrison is by far the most productive (Fig. 10.4). Aside from its diagnostic dinosaurian remains, it is easily identified over much of the plateau region by its colorful sands and shales which have given some individuals occasion to call it the Rainbow formation (Stokes, 1944). The exhibit of dinosaur remains at the quarry in Dinosaur National Monument in Utah is located in the Morrison.

Fig. 10.3 Cross-bedded Jurassic Navajo Sandstone in Arizona.

What bed underlies the Chinle, the formation with which we began our discussion of this example? A thin bed not over 75 feet, and generally less thick than that, called the Shinarump Conglomerate, has exceptionally wide distribution in the Southwest and maintains remarkable sameness of character. It is composed of conglomerate quartzite and chert rocks up to two inches in diameter. These pebbles are firmly cemented, and the Shinarump often stands out as a hogback, or cliff, because the Chinle and the underlying bed are more easily eroded. Petrified trees up to 40 feet long and two feet in diameter are regular inclusions in these sediments. Its color is also red, but becoming yellow to yellow-brown locally.

All four of these formations—the Shinarump, Chinle, Navajo, and Morrison, representing Triassic and Jurassic periods—are nearly always easily recognized and always maintain the same vertical sequence. Other beds, descriptions of which we cannot here take time to give, are associated with these and also maintain the same stratigraphic relations throughout the Colorado Plateau (Fig. 10.2).

The geologic column represented at Dinosaur National Monument, an exceptionally good location for seeing a large section of the earth's crust, contains beds from the Mississippian Madison Limestone to Cretaceous Mancos Shale (Untermann and Untermann, 1954). Three periods—the Devonian, Silurian, and Ordovician—are missing below the Madison Limestone, which rests directly on the Cambrian. Below the Cambrian are the Precambrian nonfossiliferous rocks.

In the region of the Grand Canyon and southwestern Utah,

Fig. 10.4 Dinosaur skull in Morrison formation at Dinosaur National Monument.

diagonally across the State from Dinosaur National Monument, the Shinarump, Chinle, and Navajo formations are still present and in the same sequence, but the Morrison is missing. The section in the southwest ranges from the Cambrian to the Eocene, but again the Ordovician, Silurian, and most of the Devonian are missing. In addition, the Pennsylvanian is absent. The Madison Limestone at the base of the Mississippian is here also, but it is called Redwall and can be seen as a significant part of the wall of the Grand Canyon.

The Grand Canyon is a marvelous exhibit of Paleozoic geology (Figs. 10.5 and 10.6). Cedar Mountain, on the rim of the canyon, is composed of Triassic, with the familiar Shinarump capping the flat top. Hiking down into the canyon, one passes through Permian, Mississippian, Devonian, Cambrian, and enters the Precambrian, which makes up the walls of the inner gorge. Since the Colorado River has cut through this high plateau for

Fig. 10.5 Generalized section of the Grand Canyon of the Colorado. (After Noble, 1924, and Eardley, 1962.)

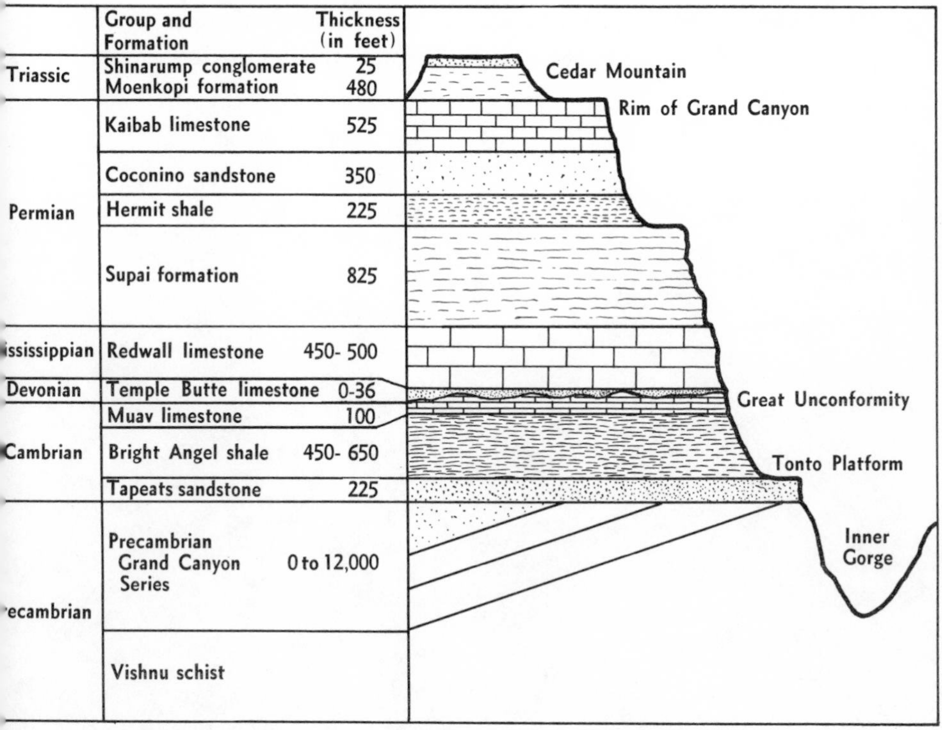

	Group and Formation	Thickness (in feet)	
Triassic	Shinarump conglomerate	25	Cedar Mountain
	Moenkopi formation	480	Rim of Grand Canyon
Permian	Kaibab limestone	525	
	Coconino sandstone	350	
	Hermit shale	225	
	Supai formation	825	
Mississippian	Redwall limestone	450-500	
Devonian	Temple Butte limestone	0-36	Great Unconformity
	Muav limestone	100	
Cambrian	Bright Angel shale	450-650	Tonto Platform
	Tapeats sandstone	225	
Precambrian	Precambrian Grand Canyon Series	0 to 12,000	Inner Gorge
	Vishnu schist		

many miles, one can pass from the east end of Grand Canyon National Park to the west end of Grand Canyon National Monument, a distance of approximately 75 airline miles, and trace the distinct beds horizontally over this distance. Some beds disappear and are replaced by new sediments. Changes in texture and thickness are seen in other beds, but on the whole the orderly, layered nature of the earth's crust is evident.

Beds that have changed can be placed in correct stratigraphic position by examining the fossils contained, the nature of the rock, and the relationship with other strata whose places in the geologic column are already known.

When correlations are made across intervals where no exposures and no well cores are available to help trace the stratigraphy, the work is not as certain as that along a continuous river canyon, but if key beds such as the Madison, Shinarump, Chinle, Navajo, and Morrison are present, the work is made easier. If no easily identifiable beds are visible, the fossils contained within the sediments are compared with fossils in beds of known geologic position. In other words, the law of Faunal Assemblages is brought into play to help identify the new deposits. These assemblages of fossils (guide, or index fossils) were ar-

Fig. 10.6   The Grand Canyon of the Colorado.

ranged by the pioneer geologists of Europe, and have been added to and refined by other scientists in other areas of the globe.

In more recent years the petroleum industry has dug wells in many locations where the bedding of the rocks cannot be observed. Data from oil-well cores have added tremendously to the knowledge of stratigraphy. In turn, this industry has relied heavily on stratigraphy in the exploration and obtaining of oil.

In the southeast Gulf Coast States, the Wilcox sands, considered to be Eocene, are sometimes oil reservoirs. Consequently, new wells dug in this area would plan to penetrate at least to these sands. If no wells have been drilled in the vicinity and stratigraphy of the immediate area is not known, it is important to watch the progress of the digging closely. Since the beds that lie above and below the Wilcox sands are fairly consistent and contain diagnostic fossils likely to be brought up in a dependable sequence as the well bit cuts deeper, it is possible for a paleontologist to tell the crew when they are approaching the Wilcox sands. Sometimes oil and gas are under considerable pressure, and care must be taken to prevent a gusher with its resultant loss of oil and equipment, not to mention the danger of fire and injury to workmen.

The rock chips brought up in the process of oil-well drilling are usually small. Consequently, microfossils are most frequently used as guide fossils when tracing drilling progress. Foraminifera, small single-celled organisms that secreted a small calcareous or siliceous shell, are extremely useful as guide fossils in the petroleum industry. Watching the progress of a wildcat well also prevents waste of money and time by determining when the bottom of the hole has passed the productive zone.

The petroleum industry is a major business, and many geologists are employed by oil companies, mainly to study the stratigraphy. Obviously these men would not be employed unless the basic concepts of stratigraphy with which they work were valid, and of economic value to the oil companies.

Most areas of the earth's surface are covered with only minor portions of the beds necessary to represent all the geologic column, but in many locations a substantial part—indeed, nearly a perfect sequence—can be seen.

Here are the geologic sections of several specific areas in North America. Several of them are quite complete:

Geologic Sections of Specific Areas in North America

Grand Canyon and Southwest Utah	*Wind River Basin Wyoming*	*Rocky Mountains Banff, Alberta, Canada*
Eocene	Pleistocene	Pleistocene
Cretaceous	Miocene	Cretaceous
Jurassic	Oligocene	Jurassic
Triassic	Paleocene	Triassic
Permian	Cretaceous	Permian
Mississippian	Jurassic	Mississippian
Devonian	Triassic	Devonian
Cambrian	Permian	Cambrian
Precambrian	Pennsylvanian	Precambrian
	Mississippian	
	Devonian	
	Ordovician	
	Cambrian	
	Precambrian	

John Day, Oregon	*Southwest Indiana*	*Appalachian Valley Virginia*
Pleistocene	Pennsylvanian	
Pliocene	Mississippian	Mississippian
Miocene	Devonian	Devonian
Oligocene	Silurian	Silurian
Eocene	Ordovician	Ordovician
Cretaceous	Cambrian	Cambrian
	Precambrian	Precambrian

When the series of formations some distance back from the Grand Canyon that are seen to be overlying the same layer that makes up the topmost bed of the canyon rim are added to the Grand Canyon section, a fairly extensive series results. Frequently several beds, each with its own specific name, are classified by geologists within the same period or epoch. They may be of quite different sediments, as was true of the Coconino Sandstone, Hermit Shale, and Supai formation of the Grand Canyon, which are Permian. Often there are no clear breaks between the beds of one period or epoch and those of another.

Although a vertical sequence, or stratigraphic column, has been determined through the years largely by actual observations and field study, the assumption that a great deal of time is represented by the beds composing each era, period, and epoch is *not* based on firm observation and research, but is only one of two or more possible interpretations that might be given to account for the presence of these beds in orderly sequence, and for the index fossils they contain.

Geologic History in Wyoming

The region of Wyoming and Montana incorporating Yellowstone National Park, the Beartooth Mountains, Bighorn Basin, and the Bighorn Mountains is one of remarkable geologic interest. A brief outline of the geology of this country and its probable history brings together a good example of stratigraphy and its relation to crustal movements.

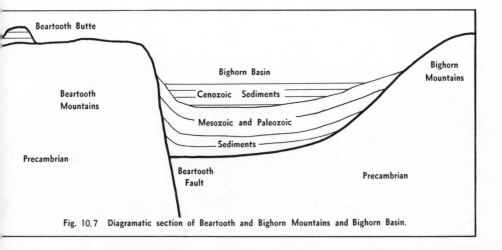

Fig. 10.7   Diagramatic section of Beartooth and Bighorn Mountains and Bighorn Basin.

The Bighorn Mountains represent a simple doming, which has lifted the sediments to over 10,000 feet in elevation. In the higher levels erosion has removed the overlying beds until the crystalline rocks of the Precambrian are exposed. As one drives over these mountains from west to east he passes through the geologic section from bed to bed, until near the summit he encounters Precambrian rocks.

The Beartooth Mountains on the other side of the Bighorn Basin are also uplifted, but instead of a gentle warping into a large anticline, a great block of the earth's crust rose sharply, creating great fault scarps along the south, east, and northern flanks. Here also, sediment cover over the Precambrian has been removed with the exception of several "islands" on the relatively flat Precambrian plateau. The largest of these "islands," called Beartooth Butte, contains an interesting remnant of the blanket of sediments that must originally have covered the Precambrian before it was uplifted (Fig. 10.8).

Beartooth Butte contains Cambrian, Ordovician, and De-

Fig. 10.8   Beartooth Butte, a Paleozoic island on a Precambrian plateau.

vonian in order. Silurian is missing, as also in the Bighorn Mountains. In fact, Beartooth Butte sediments match the lower part of the Paleozoic stratigraphy readily seen on the Bighorn Mountains to the east, in Clark Fork Valley to the south, and where Paleozoic sediments tilt up against the fault scarps of the Beartooth Mountains. Thus it is obvious that Beartooth Butte and the other pockets of sedimentary material scattered over the Beartooth plateau are small remnant beds of the thick sheets that must have covered this area originally and that now overlie the adjacent areas and bend down into Bighorn Basin.

Can we reconstruct the past geologic history of these mountains and the intervening basin? Let us try. A good starting point is the Precambrian rocks, which, incidentally, are rather complex in structure. These are nonfossiliferous sediments and molten matter that formed and consolidated before the Paleozoic sediments were laid down. Many Paleozoic and Mesozoic beds were next deposited on this surface; all this area probably being rather flat. At the close of the Cretaceous, crustal movements raised up the Bighorn and Beartooth mountains and probably dropped down the floor of the Bighorn Basin. This was a major fault; the difference in altitude between the Precambrian surface at the top of the Beartooth Mountains and the Precambrian surface at the bottom of the Bighorn Basin below the deep sedimentary deposits is approximately 20,000 feet.

As the Beartooth Mountains rose the sedimentary beds along their edges were tipped up on edge. Those on top were eroded off and helped to fill the Bighorn Basin. These sediments, which washed into the basin after the uplift of the mountains, are horizontal and truncate along the edges of the basin against the upturned older beds, which were warped by the mountains rising. Thus the time when the movements occurred is clear—the Cretaceous are the uppermost beds that tilt up along the mountain flanks. All beds above these (Paleocene, Eocene, and Oligocene are present in the basin) are flat lying (Fig. 10.7).

A creationist might interpret the activity represented here

somewhat as follows: Perhaps the nonfossiliferous Precambrian basement represents matter originating before or during creation week. The Paleozoic and Mesozoic sediments that were laid down upon the Precambrian may be thought of as sediments that accumulated before and during the Flood. When the mountains were raised up, most of the beds were eroded off the high elevations of the Beartooth and Bighorn mountains and deposited in the Bighorn Basin on top the Cretaceous, which was the last to be laid down before the uplift of the mountains.

In summary of this portion of the discussion: The beds of the earth are arranged like the layers of a gigantic cake. Furthermore, their order generally is consistent and predictable. In some areas a substantial part of the geologic column is present and in correct order. In many other locations much is missing, but those few strata that are present are lying one above another in correct sequence unless the beds have been disturbed by mountain building or faulting.

How are the correct sequences determined? By examining the fossils, the rock types, and the relationships with other beds, and by making comparisons with the standards set up by the early geologists when they began to notice and record the arrangements of the beds of sediments in the earth's crust. Although the fossils in these strata are popularly thought to represent an evolutionary progression from the lower rock horizons to the upper, this concept grew after the basic principles of stratigraphy had been laid down. As Adventists, we may accept an orderly arrangement of the strata and of the fossils they contain, but we do not consider this order to have arisen by gradual accumulations during the course of which evolution was slowly changing the morphology of plants and animals. How, then, can this stratigraphic arrangement be explained? Chapter 16 is devoted to answering this question.

The question that constantly arises in the mind of one who accepts the idea of a literal, universal flood, is the relationship of the geologic column to the Genesis Flood. Where in this column does the Flood fit? Is the Flood responsible for all of it or part of it? And if part of it, what part?

Let us think through the past history of the earth as given by the Bible and as it relates to the formation of fossils. A world void and formless was made to abound with living things in an organized and beautiful environment. The soil formed by God during these days of creation covered the framework of the earth. Before sin brought death to the living organisms there was little possibility of fossils being formed.

The establishment of sin in the world introduced a different situation. Leaves fell from trees, animals died. But since no rain fell and rivers did not flood, there was still little likelihood of fossilization. Organisms must be buried by sediments in order to be preserved; otherwise they decay quickly and soon become unrecognizable. In the lakes and oceans the situation would have been different, however. Planktonic organisms that float in the water would die and their hard tests and shells would settle in a continuous shower on the bottom. Such oozes are abundant on the bottoms of present-day oceans.

Larger swimming organisms would also contribute some bones, teeth, and hard parts to the bottom sediments, although bones would likely be destroyed by scavengers. Corals would build on the calcareous skeletons of their dead ancestors to form reefs. Organisms living along the shores would have had their dead remains mixed with sands and muds and deposited in quiet bays or deeper basins. Thus it would appear that fossils could have been forming in the oceans from the entrance of sin until the time of the Flood.

With the beginning of the Flood, fossil-forming conditions would be optimum. These conditions prevailed until the end of the catastrophe. What happened to the pre-Flood bottom sediments? They either became mixed with Flood-generated sediments and were redeposited, or they were covered by the erosional debris that was being swept into the seas.

After the Flood the saturated ground and nonindurated sediments near the surface would have been eroded and redeposited by heavy rains and high water, which would be expected for a time. This reworking of Flood deposits would tend to erase the line of distinction between Flood deposits and post-Flood sediments. From the termination of the Flood until the present, rampaging rivers have spilled silt-laden waters onto river flats and flood plains, ocean storms have lashed the coasts and torn away soil and rocks, glaciers have scraped the earth bare and washed the soil down their milky streams, and volcanoes have spewed ash and fragments over wide sections of the earth's surface. Conditions for burial and fossilization of organic remains often have been good but not on the scale provided by a global deluge.

Since the geologic column is a product of past geologic conditions, does it support the Biblical outline of past world history? The hypothesis below is only suggestive, and in no sense presented as compulsive evidence (Fig. 10.9). With the knowledge we presently have we are not able to draw definitive conclusions.

Let us make some comparisons between the column as worked out by geologists and the information concerning the Flood given in the Bible and the writings of Ellen G. White. We need a check point from which we can move up and down the column, making comparisons as we do so. Genesis 8:1 speaks of a wind God caused to pass over the earth. *Patriarchs and Prophets,* page 108, describes this fierce wind, which acted on the water to produce great erosional effects on the land. What is there in the geologic column that might match this situation?

There are beds here and there through the sediments from Cambrian to the present that might class as wind-blown deposits or sediments laid down by water greatly agitated by wind, but such materials become abundant in the Mesozoic Era. Sand dunes and wind-borne sediments seem to reach a climax in the Jurassic and Cretaceous, as exemplified by the Navajo Sandstone, which some authorities describe as one of the greatest wind-laid beds in the world.

Fig. 10.9 COMPARATIVE STRATIGRAPHIC INTERPRETATIONS

CATASTROPHIC DESCRIPTION	GEOLOGIC COLUMN	GEOLOGIC DESCRIPTION
	Recent	
	Pleistocene	
	Pliocene	
Climatic change accompanying Flood-post-Flood transition	Miocene / Oligocene / Eocene / Paleocene	Paleoclimatic indicators of rapid temperature change from warm to cool in North America
Animal carcasses covered (PP 107, 108)	Cretaceous	Great reptilian remains in chaotic array in sediments
Tops of mountains eroded off (PP 107, 108)	Jurassic	Guyots
Great winds (Gen. 8:1)		Wind-deposited sediments
Tops of mountains seen (Gen. 8:5)	Triassic	Mountain-building activity
Tides and waves	Permian	Rhythmic deposits (cyclothems)
Forests buried (3 SG 79, 80)	Pennsylvanian	Coal measures
	Mississippian	
	Devonian	
Accumulations of pre-Flood marine organisms or Flood sediments washed into ocean basins	Silurian / Ordovician	Marine fossils only
First burial of animals during pre-Flood times or at commencement of Flood	Cambrian	First appearance of fossils in significant numbers
Pre-Flood sediments and earth's original framework	Precambrian	Mostly crystalline nonfossiliferous basement rocks

111

The effect of the wind is said to be to dry up the waters and to bury the carcasses of animals strewn upon the surface of mountains and hills, then beginning to be exposed (PP 107, 108). Nowhere in the geologic column are remains of large animals (especially reptiles) so abundantly preserved as in the sediments of the Jurassic and Cretaceous periods. Thus the wind-blown materials and the burial of the carcasses of large animals are associated together in the same general segment of this column, which correlates with the catastrophic concept of great winds for the burial of animal flotsam left upon the earth's surface.

Note that the description in *Patriarchs and Prophets* gives one result of these great winds blowing upon the waters. The waves generated and the currents produced were so great that the tops of some of the mountains were eroded away. Do any mountains anywhere on earth qualify as possible examples? Many mountains could qualify, as for instance the Bighorn Mountains of Wyoming. A drive up the west slope of these mountains passes gradually down-section through all the periods from Cretaceous to Cambrian (except Silurian) until finally, near the top, at an elevation of about 10,000 feet, Precambrian rocks are exposed at the surface. In the adjacent basin these same sediments lie in sequence one above another. All the sediments have been eroded off the tops of these mountains and deposited in part in the Bighorn Basin as thick Tertiary sediments.

Marine mountains known as guyots, isolated and in clusters, mainly in the Pacific, are flat topped. Geologists are of the opinion that they have been subjected to wave erosion despite the fact that they are now well below the surface of the water. The oldest fossils taken from the tops of these table mountains are Cretaceous (Menard, 1964). If no older fossils are found, it can be said that the mountains must have been formed at about the same time. It is possible, therefore, that these mountains had their tops removed at approximately the time the wind-blown sediments were being dropped and the great reptiles were being buried. Many coals are also known from the Cretaceous-Eocene

112

portion of the column, as would be expected to result from the activity of great winds and waves.

To provide room for the water that covered the earth, God depressed the ocean basins and raised the continents (Ps. 104:8). According to the Genesis account the waters did not begin to recede before 150 days after the beginning of the Flood. Since the ocean basins have not been shown to contain sediments older than Mesozoic, except along the margins near the continents, one could postulate that the basins were forming and the continents were rising during the later part of the Paleozoic and the first part of the Mesozoic. It is interesting to note that geologists consider this a time of great mountain building and change in the earth. In the sequence of events described in the Flood account in Genesis, the appearance of the tops of the mountains fits well here and is in harmony with mountain-building activity.

As erosion brought on by torrential rains and disturbed seas washed sediments into the ocean basins, the benthonic (bottom-dwelling) creatures would be the first to be covered. Pre-Flood sediments containing accumulations of sea creatures would also be covered or mixed with the new sand and mud and redeposited. The Cambrian, Ordovician, and Silurian periods contain rocks that exhibit exclusively water-dwelling animals, most of which are marine. As waters of the Flood rose higher upon the land, plants and terrestrial organisms were involved. Plants are first seen in the Devonian, and coal outcrops appear in the Mississippian, but reach their climax in the Pennsylvanian. Associated with coal measures are the rhythmic cycles of deposition called cyclothems. These are repeated many times in the Mississippian and Pennsylvanian.

The Flood probably did not terminate abruptly, but continued for a time to ravage portions of the earth, especially the lower elevations. For this reason among others it will be difficult to pinpoint the end of the Flood on the geologic column. Based on the assumptions and comparisons made on this chart, one could say that post-Flood time began somewhere between the

Cretaceous and the Pliocene. The study of fossil plants gives indication of rapid climatic change, especially during the Eocene and Oligocene periods.

This stratigraphic comparison is presented as one model among others that could be drawn. If the facts that become available in the future do not fit this model, it will have to be discarded for another. Even now, many objections and possible contradictions come to mind, but these must be checked thoroughly. Frequently careful examination of a problem opens up other interpretative possibilities not mentioned in the relevant literature. Although they may not always speak in the way we think they should, nature and the Scriptures will not contradict each other.

REFERENCES

Eardley, A. J. 1962. Structural geology of North America. 2d ed. Harper & Row, Publishers, New York. 743 pp.

Gilluly, James, A. C. Waters, and A. O. Woodford. 1959. Principles of geology. 2d ed. W. H. Freeman and Co., San Francisco. 534 pp.

Kay, Marshall and Edwin H. Colbert. 1965. Stratigraphy and life history. John Wiley & Sons, Inc., New York. 736 pp.

Kulp, J. Lawrence. 1961. Geologic time scale. Science 133:1105-1114.

Mather, Kirtley F. and Shirley L. Mason. 1964. A source book in geology. Hafner Publishing Company, New York. 702 pp.

Menard, H. W. 1964. Marine geology of the Pacific. McGraw-Hill Book Company, New York. 271 pp.

Noble, L. F. 1923. A section of the Paleozoic formations of the Grand Canyon at the Bass Trail. U.S. Geol. Sur. Prof. Paper 131, pp. 23-73.

Stokes, W. L. 1944. Morrison formation and related deposits in and adjacent to the Colorado Plateau. Geol. Soc. Am. Bull. 55:951-992.

Untermann, G. E. and B. R. Untermann. 1954. Geology of Dinosaur National Monument and vicinity, Utah-Colorado. Utah Geol. & Min. Sur. Bull. 42. 221 pp.

CHAPTER ELEVEN

The Mountains

MOUNTAINS RISING TO THE SKY draw the eyes upward and appeal to man. They provide the mineral wealth, forest products, and recreational opportunities man needs. Mountains catch the snows that melt to run as rivers to the adjacent plains and prairies. God chose a mountain from which to deliver His law of conduct for man.

Mountain Types

What is a mountain? How did it get there? The first question is easier to answer than the second. Geologists think of four main types of mountain—dome, fault-block, folded, and volcanic. Many ranges exhibit more than one type.

Fig. 11.1   Mt. Rundle, Alberta, Canada, a fault-block mountain.

Dome mountains, such as the Black Hills of South Dakota and the Bighorn Mountains of Wyoming, have been pushed up from below. Often erosion has removed much of the upper deposits, so that crystalline Precambrian rocks may be exposed in the heart or on the top of mountains of this type. It is a paradox that one often goes down geologic section as he drives uphill into a mountainous area.

Fault-block mountains occur when blocks of the earth's crust move up or down along fault lines, thus changing their vertical relationship. Mount Rundle in Banff National Park, Canada, is a classic example (Fig. 11.1). One side slopes up at a constant but easily climbable angle, while the other side breaks off abruptly into precipitous cliffs. This is repeated several times by adjacent mountain ranges, as if they were gigantic frozen ocean waves. Fault-block mountains may also sometimes slide horizontally onto the shoulders of adjacent blocks, thus producing overthrusts.

Folded mountains are well illustrated in the Alps of Europe (Fig. 11.7) and the Himalayas of Asia. The Western Alps are discussed later in this chapter. The complexity of these ranges is often so great that a correct explanation or determination of their structure has been long delayed. Major folding and thrusting have occurred, but a detailed understanding of the sequence of activities and direction and distance of movements has been harder to attain.

Some of the world's greatest mountains are volcanic. South America has several volcanic peaks, which are among the world's highest mountains, and several of them are still active. The accumulation of violently erupted molten and solid materials builds up the bulk of these great mountains (Fig. 11.2).

Theories of Mountain Building

Many theories attempt to explain mountain building, an indication perhaps that no theory yet advanced is satisfactory. The contraction of the crust, with resulting wrinkles as the earth cooled, is an old and persistent theory. However, the distribu-

Fig. 11.2   Mt. Baker, a volcanic peak in Washington.

tion of mountain ranges on the surface of the earth does not fit the shrinkage concept, which should cause equal shrinkage for great lines of equal distance along the surface in any direction.

The drifting of continents has periodically stimulated controversy among geologists. It arises from the fact that the coasts of Western Europe and Africa very nearly fit the coasts of North and South America. Space does not permit a detailed discussion of this theory or of the others. However, the facts marshaled in its support cannot be disregarded, despite some contrary evidences, and it may be necessary to provide room for such a possibility in any Bible-centered history of the earth. Obviously, if movements of this magnitude have occurred, the mountain ranges are but expected minor consequences.

A third theory postulates that heat deep inside the earth causes convection currents within the mantle, and the crust floating on the mantle piles up in areas where currents come together. The mantle is that portion of the earth between the core and the crust. Obviously, rates of movement would be extremely slow and much time would be involved in mountain building by this method.

Folded Mountains*

Although geologists are without an adequate mechanism to explain mountain building, mountains are very much in evidence around the world. The folded mountains, which are the most common and include the greatest mountain ranges, show evidence of having been produced by lateral compressional forces that acted upon the sediments in the geosynclines, shoving them against immovable crystalline blocks, which action caused the weaker sediments to crumple and fold. While it may be impossible to comprehend the magnitude of the movements necessary to accomplish all this, the face of the earth gives plain evidence that such action has taken place.

Many of the ranges of the North American Rockies have undergone complex folding. The Swiss Alps are so complexly folded that geologists have sought for many years to analyze the series of changes necessary to bring about the present situation.

It is much the same with almost all the great mountains of the world. Great complexes of arch and trough folds have been produced by intense compression taking place along narrow belts of great length. Folds are not confined to sedimentary rocks. Precambrian crystalline rocks have also been folded or distorted by compressional forces.

Mountain Arcs

Belts of folded mountains form a regular system. On one side of the earth they radiate from central Asia. Thence they encircle the Pacific Ocean. In North America they are roughly concentric with the Archaean shield of northeastern Canada. In many areas the folding has been so complex that elaborate patterns of faults have been formed. Evidences for these great crustal movements are so strong that Suess, the great Viennese geologist, said:

"Round about the Pacific Ocean, and along the southern

---

* This section and the next, "Mountain Arcs," were written by Harold W. Clark.

Fig. 11.3 Tightly folded limestone strata in Switzerland.

marginal arcs of Asia . . . and in the United States . . . there makes its appearance . . . such an arrangement of the folded ranges that we are led to consider whether . . . we must not admit the action of bodily tides or of rotation . . . as a possible factor in determining the plan of the folded ranges."—1909, p. 626.

Early in geological studies geologists discovered that certain rocks had apparently been forced into a tremendous lateral displacement by terrific compressional forces. The first such area to be reported in detail was in northern Scotland, where by a lateral displacement of about 10 miles certain layers had been thrown over others. Striations were noted parallel to the direction of thrust, and the crystals of gneiss and other crystalline rocks were drawn out and sheared. Metamorphosis had been produced by the action.

Many such areas have been reported from the European Alps. In America a considerable number of such phenomena indicate clearly that terrific tangential movements have taken place. The concept of overthrusting, by which huge masses of rock are supposed to have slid over others for many miles, is so difficult to comprehend that many students of the problem have refused to accept it. But the situation has now been so thoroughly studied, and in so many areas, that it seems impossible to deny that such a process has occurred. To quote from one report:

"The folding, mashing, slicing, and shearing of the rocks in many of the mountains is ample proof of the lateral compressional forces in the earth's crust."—Annual Report, Smithsonian Inst., 1933, p. 293.

It is believed by some authorities that plastic uplift is involved in the overthrusts. A series of breaks in an uplifted mass of stratified rocks may cause a succession of repeated layers.

Central Asia is the vertex of a series of great arcs of tectonic movements that threw up the great mountain ranges of the continent. One such arc sweeps through the islands off the coast of Asia, another runs down into the Malay Peninsula, one forms the Himalayas, and another extends westward to the Mediterranean region. Apparently two "shields" existed in Asia, the Siberian shield to the north and the Sinian shield in China. Compressed between these, the weaker sediments were tremendously distorted and twisted. Another solid block existed in India, and the intensely folded region of southeastern Asia seems to have had its sediments forced westward against the Indian block.

The East Indies comprise one of the most confusing mountain regions of the world. Many of the fundamental problems of tectonics in that region are yet unsolved. The complexity of the problem is well illustrated by Sumatra and Java, which are separated by Sunda Strait. In Sumatra the folds are overturned to the northeast; in Java they are overturned to the southwest. To every appearance, movements have taken place in opposite directions, with Sunda Strait as a hinge line. Buru and Ceram, two other East Indian islands, show a similar phenomenon. They are offset like Sumatra and Java, and are separated by a strait 16,000 feet deep—as if the earth had been torn by a differential movement.

In the South Pacific three great tectonic arcs connect through New Zealand with the Antarctic continent and reappear in the Falklands off the southern tip of South America.

The marginal arcs of northeastern Asia continue in North America in the Alaskan mountains, which are in reality part of the Asian system and not part of the Rocky Mountain system.

The Rocky Mountain region is very complicated. During the

later stages of sedimentary deposition, spoken of in common geological terms as Permian and Cretaceous "times," extensive uplifts occurred. During the Cretaceous much folding took place, with the formation of many local ranges. A belt of intense activity, known as the Cordilleran arc, extends through Montana, western Wyoming, and into Utah, Nevada, and southeastern California. The Wasatch fault, 115 miles long, has displacements of 3,000 to 6,000 feet.

The Great Basin area of Utah and Nevada exhibits a peculiar type of structure known as basin-and-range structure. This area contains more than a hundred isolated ranges, trending mostly north and south. Many of them appear to be tilted blocks. The presence of lava flows that have been broken and tilted subsequent to their formation indicates that the region has undergone a complex series of movements.

Well drilling has revealed geologic features that were previously unknown. In Kansas, the Nemaha "mountains" consist of a granite ridge rising 2,500 feet above the Precambrian surface. They are buried deep beneath sediments, and are revealed only by the records of wells.

The Atlantic Ocean has certain striking tectonic features. The trough south of Cuba is 21,036 feet deep, and the Sierra Maestra, in Cuba, rise to 8,397 feet. Thus there is a difference of 29,400 feet in altitude. This trough is a huge crack 100 miles wide and about 600 miles long.

The Appalachians of America may continue in northern and central Europe as a complex mass of highly folded and overthrust sediments, known as the Armorican "mountains." This "range" traverses parts of France and Germany, but has been worn down and sunk beneath the surface. Its presence is known only from results of well drilling.

In Africa the greatest tectonic feature is the Great Rift Valley. This is part of a series of troughs running from Syria to Lake Tanganyika. The Dead Sea bottom is 5,000 feet below the cliffs on either side. The bottom of the Red Sea, which is part of the trough, lies 7,200 feet below sea level. Lake Tanganyika is nearly 4,700 feet deep, and the bordering cliffs rise 4,000 feet above it.

The total length of the Great African Rift is more than 4,000 miles, and along its course profound displacements have taken place. Geologists declare that it must have had a deep-seated worldwide cause that involved the whole thickness of the crust over a large portion of the earth's surface.

Perhaps no other tectonic phenomenon gives as definite proof for the sudden and cataclysmic nature of great earth movements. To tear the crust of the earth apart along one sixth of its circumference represents tremendous force.

The European Alps

The Alps of Switzerland and adjacent countries and the Himalayan Mountains, perhaps more than any other mountain areas, originated by dynamic and sometimes almost incredible movements. The mountains of Switzerland have been studied for many years, but the geologic riddle represented by the fantastically folded and contorted strata, the lack of relationship of some deposits to any surrounding source, and the scarcity of fossils generally, has been difficult to solve. In more recent times the general features have been worked out and many details filled in. Because these mountains reveal one type of mountain at its best, a type of tectonic activity that of necessity broadens one's concept of the magnitude of past earth movements, a summary of the geology of the Western Alps is here given.

The main topographic features of the Western Alps region, which takes in eastern France, southern Germany, Switzerland, and northern Italy, run in arcs trending from southwest to northeast, with the convex side of the arcs toward the northwest (Fig. 11.4). From northwest to southeast these main features are: the Jura Mountains, the Swiss Plateau, the Prealps, the High Calcareous Alps, the Crystalline Hercynian Massifs, the Pennine Nappes (broad sheets or strata of rocks said to have moved some distance horizontally), the Root Zone, and the Dinarides and

Austrides to the south and east of the area under consideration here.

The Jura Mountains consist mainly of Mesozoic limestones that have been wrinkled into neat anticlines and synclines (Fig. 11.5). The geology of the Juras is generally simple because the folds and bends of the strata are not difficult to trace. The limestones of these mountains rest upon a layer of evaporite (anhydrite in this case; other evaporites are salt and gypsum), which apparently has not been much involved in the contortions of the overlying strata. It is suspected that the limestones became unglued from the anhydrite layer when lateral forces were applied, and slid into the present gigantic wrinkles.

The limestones of the Jura Mountains or equivalent strata underlie the Swiss Plateau, which was filled with sediments draining in from the main Alps, which were rising to the east and south. These sediments are considered to be Tertiary deposits. The topography of the plateau is gently rolling plains.

Along the western flanks of the main Alps, several moun-

Fig 11.4 Generalized map of the mountain arcs of the Western Alps.

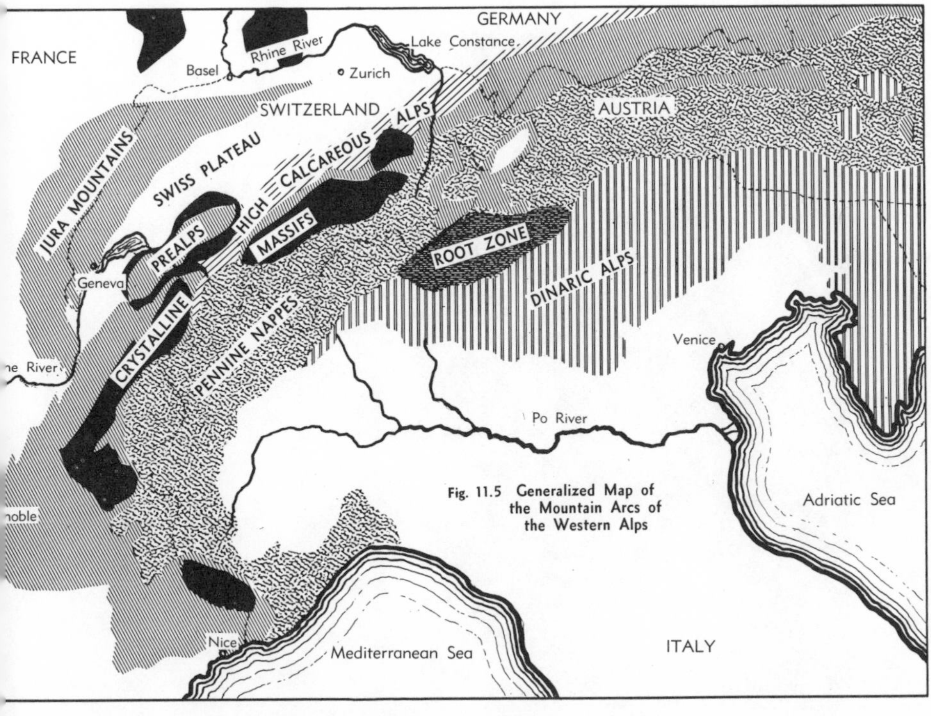

Fig. 11.5 Generalized Map of the Mountain Arcs of the Western Alps

tains or mountain clusters consisting of sediments unrelated to any surrounding area have puzzled geologists for many years. The Prealps exhibit reversed or upside-down strata characteristic of overthrusted mountains. A better understanding of the extent of drawn-out folds and horizontal movements responsible for piling up much of the matter composing the Western Alps has led geologists to the conclusion that the Prealps have been pushed to their present positions from far to the east and south. The intervening portions of the great thrust sheets have since been eroded off and deposited into the Swiss Plateau and other low areas. Sediments filling the Swiss Plateau are more coarse as one approaches the main Alps, thus indicating that this is the probable source of material making up the sediments of the plateau. If this is true—and the evidence strongly supports this hypothesis—the magnitude of transportation of rock masses is stupendous.

The heart of the Western Alps is the series of great wedges of crystalline granite that give rise to the highest peaks of the range, including Mount Blanc (15,781 feet). Squeezed between, and lying around these Crystalline Massifs are tremendous limestone nappes that have been pushed around and over these nearly

Fig. 11.5 Anticlinal fold in the Jura Mountains, Switzerland.

immovable pillars in the earth's crust. In the saddles between these Crystalline Massifs, as many as four thrust sheets have piled up one above another. These were not thrust out simultaneously, because each thrust sheet has folds, warpings, and contortions that bear little relation to the configurations of the strata above or below. In this region of the High Calcareous Alps the greatest progress was made in the beginnings of geologic studies of the Alps, because limestone strata are much more easily traced than the metamorphosed and somewhat crystalline sediments of the Pennine Nappes to the southeast.

The Pennine Nappes do not have the conspicuous stratigraphy of the limestone Alps, but when one uses binoculars or walks the mountains, the complex and thrusted nature of the rocks becomes more obvious. These sheets apparently have been squeezed up out of the ground by lateral forces that compressed a broad basin of sediments into a relatively narrow area. The area where these sediments came up out of the ground, and where the rock layers now rise sharply up from the earth, is the Root Zone.

The earth's crust in this region has obviously been shortened by many miles. One author gives these figures (Gilluly *et al.*, 1959, p. 428): "The arrangement in space—the geometry—of the great thrust masses is such that there must have been tremendous shortening of the outer crust—a shortening that cannot,

Fig. 11.6 The Crystalline Massifs climax the European Alps.

of course, be accurately measured, but which must amount to many scores of miles. A careful estimate by Albert Heim, and an independent one by J. Cadisch, both Swiss geologists, agree that a sedimentary region at least 400 miles wide has been piled together in a mountain range only about 100 miles across!"

What would cause sediments to squeeze up out of the earth like mud between the toes of a barefoot boy? What would cause such a wrinkling and shortening of the crust? Geologists have no good answer. But they are convinced it has happened here, and elsewhere also. The Himalayan Mountains are of the same type as the Western Alps, but on a much larger scale. The Genesis account of the Flood and the writings of Ellen G. White imply that such movements of the earth's crust could definitely have been associated with the Flood. Rapid movements when the sediments may not have been completely hardened appear to be a much better explanation of the sharp folding and overturning than the very slow sliding of the thrust sheets for hundreds of thousands of years, which is the conventional evolutionary interpretation.

On one occasion when Mrs. White passed through these mountains by carriage on her way to the Waldensian valleys of northern Italy, she wrote the following interesting comment in her diary: "Clay, lime, and shells that God had strewn in the bottoms of the seas, were uplifted, thrown hither and thither, and convulsions of fire and flood, earthquakes and volcanoes buried the rich treasures of gold, silver, and precious stone beyond the sight and reach of man" (Ellen G. White, MS 62, 1886). These words, written in 1886 by a person with no training in geology, give a simple but satisfactory description that agrees with the knowledge that has been gained from a study of the Alps in recent times.

If the wealth and talent of the world for the past century and a half had been turned toward the solution of geological problems in the light of the Holy Scriptures, the result would have been a far clearer picture of the physical history of the earth than we now have. This in no way detracts from the practical value of geology, for the basic principles are generally the same whatever theory a

Fig. 11.7 A giant fold in the mountains of Switzerland.

person may hold. There is much to support belief in a catastrophic episode in geologic history.

REFERENCES

Beloussou, V. U. 1962. Basic problems in geotectonics. McGraw-Hill Book Co., Inc., New York. 816 pp.

Billings, Marland P. 1954. Structural geology. Prentice-Hall, Inc., Englewood Cliffs, N.J. 514 pp.

Bucher, Walter H. 1933. The deformation of the earth's crust. Hafner Pub. Co., New York. Reprint 1964. 518 pp., 100 figs.

Collet, L. W. 1927. The structure of the Alps. Edward Arnold and Co., London.

Daly, Reginald Aldworth. 1926. Our mobile earth. Charles Scribner's Sons, New York, pp. 128-291.

Eardley, A. J. 1962. Structural geology of North America. 2d ed. Harper & Row, Pub., New York. 743 pp.

Gilluly, James, A. C. Waters, and A. O. Woodford. 1959. Principles of geology. 2d ed. W. H. Freeman and Co., San Francisco, pp. 415-451.

Goguel, Jean. 1962. Tectonics. W. H. Freeman and Co., San Francisco.

Hills, E. Sherbon. 1963. Elements of structural geology. John Wiley & Sons, Inc., New York, pp. 312-346.

Lombard, A. *et al.* 1962. Guidebook for the international field institute, the Alps, 1962. American Geological Institute. 130 pp.

Milne, Lorus J. and Margery Milne. 1962. The mountains. Time Incorporated, New York. 192 pp.

Putnam, William C. 1964. Geology. Oxford University Press, New York, pp. 409-427.

Suess, Edward. 1904-1924. The face of the earth. Volumes I to V. Trans. Hertha B. C. Sollas. Oxford University Press, London.

Thornbury, William D. 1965. Regional geomorphology of the United States. John Wiley & Sons, Inc., New York. 609 pp.

————. 1954. Principles of geomorphology. John Wiley & Sons, Inc., New York. 618 pp.

Fig. 12.1 Volcanic island of Surtsey in eruption off the coast of Iceland.

CHAPTER TWELVE

Fire in the Earth

AROUND SEVEN O'CLOCK in the morning, November 14, 1963, crew members aboard the fishing vessel *Isleifur* II, working off the southern coast of Iceland, smelled a strange odor, which they could not identify. About fifteen minutes later the cook on the vessel felt an irregular movement of the boat. As he walked around the deck he saw indistinctly in the twilight what appeared to be a rock in the distance. Realizing that no rocks were known to be in this area, he was puzzled. More careful observation revealed that this was black smoke. Thinking that a ship might be on fire and in distress, he awakened the skipper, who called the nearest radio station to determine whether any S O S signals had been received. But there had been none.

Using his binoculars, the skipper was able to see that smoke and eruption columns were rising practically from the water's surface. Immediately he suspected volcanic activity. A new volcano was being born beneath the shallow seas near Iceland. Within a few hours an island had pushed up above the surface of the water. No new volcano has received as careful and continuous observation as has Surtsey, the name given to this new island. For a number of months the permanent existence of this island was uncertain. Heavy seas would quickly erode away the soft sand and ash and eliminate the island, then new eruptions would build it up again. After about four and one-half months lava began to spill out over the crater and form an apron over the island. At the present time much of the island has been covered with lava, and the island is likely to become a permanent feature.

Volcanic activity has always inspired and awed men, because of the magnitude and power displayed. The earth has been profoundly affected by such manifestations, especially in the past. No study of the history of the earth would be complete without a consideration of volcanism.

Other Recent Volcanic Eruptions

A survey of recent volcanic activity could well start with the East Indies, which have long been volcanic and have had a history of violent activity. In 1772 Papandayan collapsed and then erupted with terrific force, reducing the elevation of the mountain from 9,000 feet to 5,000 feet. The volcanoes of Salak, Galoenggoeng, and Keloet, also in Java, changed the entire countryside in their several explosions. Recent active volcanoes are concentrated largely in a great belt encircling the Pacific Ocean, and a shorter belt extending from the Solomon Islands through New Guinea and Indonesia. The greatest concentration of active volcanoes in the world is in Indonesia, where 78 have erupted within historic times and 29 others are still actively giving off gas. Probably the best known of the Indonesian volcanoes is Merapi, the "fire mountain," which has taken thousands of lives.

Eruptions sometimes take a heavy toll of human life because of the concentration of agriculture on the rich volcanic soils. When Tambora in the Indian Ocean east of Java exploded in 1815, it killed an estimated 12,000 people in the surrounding countryside with a combination of gas, wind-blown ash, and tidal waves. Even more destructive was the well-known explosion of Krakatau in 1883. This volcano in the Straits of Sunda near Java had been quiet for some time, but the resurgence of activity resulted in an explosion that blew a large part of the mountain high into the air as dust. An estimated 36,000 people died as a result of a tidal wave about 50 feet high.

Mount Pelee on the island of Martinique in the West Indies erupted in 1902 in a spectacular cloud of superheated gas and ash that descended as an avalanche on the town below, wiping out more than 30,000 people. The force and temperature of this cloud of gas and ash were so great that structures were blown down and ignited by the hot gas, and all vegetation was burned to the ground over a large area. Other mountains that have erupted with a similar rush of superheated gas and ash are Soufrière near Pelee in the West Indies, and Mount Taal in the Philippines.

Mount Vesuvius, perhaps the best-known volcano in the world and the only active volcano on the mainland of Europe, has left a long record of death and destruction going back to A.D. 79, when the two cities, Pompeii and Herculaneum, were buried. In A.D. 472 another great flood of ashes poured over the two buried cities. In 1631 an explosion sent out seven streams of lava that destroyed several villages and took the lives of 18,000 people. It has never been completely quiet since that time. In 1906 the entire top of the cone blew off in an eruption that lasted for 18 days, and more destructive explosions occurred in 1929 and 1944.

Historic volcanoes and their action form an interesting part of geological science. No major geographical region is without some trace of volcanism, and written records of volcanic activity go back to accounts of Mount Etna dated from the seventh or eighth century B.C.

Kinds of Volcanoes and Volcanic Material

Lavas are usually classified on the basis of their silica content and acid or alkaline nature. The most common lavas are basalt and andesite. Basalt, as the name suggests, is basic or alkaline in nature as compared to other lavas such as rhyolite, which are acid. The chemical composition affects the viscosity and influences the way the extruded lava behaves. Volcanoes are of three types: shield volcanoes, composite volcanoes, and cinder cones.

When a dome is formed by viscous lava flowing out of a vent, the mountain formed is broader than it is high and has angles of rise of not over 10 degrees at the summit and two degrees at the base. The volcanoes of Hawaii are shield volcanoes.

A volcano built of a combination of pyroclastic (explosively extruded) materials and lava is characterized by slopes of 30 degrees at the summit and five degrees at the base. Mayon, on the island of Luzon in the Philippines, is an excellent example of a composite cone. The volcanoes of the Cascade Mountains of the Pacific Northwest of the United States are of this type.

Pyroclastic material is used in the building of a cone, usually on the side or in the crater of larger volcanoes. It results in slopes of 30 to 40 degrees at the summit and seldom reaches 1,500 feet in height. Parícutin, in Mexico, is a recent cinder cone.

Another volcanic feature is the crater, or caldera, which often forms at the summit of a volcano. It is usually three or four times as wide as deep, and may be the result of explosion, collapse, or both. Crater Lake in Oregon lies in a crater that is thought to be a collapsed mountaintop. This phenomenon is now recognized in a number of volcanic areas.

The Mid-Atlantic Ridge reaches from the volcanic island of Iceland and the volcanic rim of Greenland southward through the Atlantic, forming a massive range nearly 7,000 miles long.

Fig. 12.2   Crater Lake, Oregon, a water-filled volcanic caldera.

The island mountaintops of this range, such as the Azores, are volcanic. Dredged material and magnetometer records show that much if not all of the hidden ridge is volcanic. Such a mountain range would require massive outpourings of lava, since it is 10,000 feet high in places and as wide as 600 miles (Ewing, 1949).

Volcanic structures are widespread in the western United States—for example, the Cascade Range, the Columbia River Plateau, the Yellowstone region, the various volcanic cones, craters, and flows of the intermountain States, the necks and flows of New Mexico, and the San Francisco Mountains of Arizona. In Maine there are beds of volcanic materials 10,000 feet thick. Formations in South Africa considered to be late Triassic or early Jurassic have been estimated to contain 50,000 to 100,000 cubic miles of igneous rocks. They may be the world's greatest mass of intrusives (Dunbar, 1960, pp. 156, 284). Similar evidences are found around the world, and it may well be inferred that volcanic activity has been tremendous in the past in variety, extent, and effect.

Plateaus formed by layer upon layer of lava exist on nearly every continent. Known plateaus exist in the Argentine, Africa, Iceland, India, and the United States. These plateaus vary considerably in thickness; the Deccan Plateau in south-central India is probably the thickest, with a depth up to 10,000 feet, while the 250,000-square-mile Columbia River Plateau in the northwestern United States is up to 5,000 feet thick. These thick plateaus have been built of lava layers of varying thickness. In the Snake River canyon as many as 26 different flows of basalt (compact lava) have been counted, with a total thickness of up to 2,000 feet.

Fig. 12.3 Basalt cliffs of the Columbia River Plateau in Washington. The mold of a rhinoceros mentioned in chapters 14 and 23 is situated to the left of the top of the highest ridge.

Lava plateaus are thought by many to have erupted from great fissures or feeder cracks in the earth, as indicated by the huge areas covered. A feeder crack that measures up to 600 feet deep has been followed for 18 miles near Eldgja, Iceland. In Hawaii some cracks are uniformly five feet wide from top to bottom, to a depth of up to 4,000 feet. Geologists believe that these great lava flows were not necessarily accompanied by explosions, but merely gushed forth from the earth. One of the most recent known fissure eruptions was in Iceland in 1783.

Yellowstone National Park

One of the most interesting volcanic regions of the world is the Yellowstone area and the adjacent Snake and Columbia River basalt plateaus. It has been estimated that 400 cubic miles of volcanic rhyolite was deposited in the area consisting of Yellowstone Park and the Absaroka Mountains east and south of the park (Boyd, 1961). Although most of the material was deposited as ash, volcanic matter was released from the earth in a variety of forms.

The sequence of flows and ejecta in this region is somewhat as follows: Early acid breccia (angular fragments mixed with ash and mud) was deposited on top of water-laid nonvolcanic sediments called the Madison limestone (Mississippian). Above this breccia deposit are three others, generally breccias also. They are massive formations with a thickness of several thousand feet in some areas. Intermingled with these are a few basalt flows or sheets. These are not usually more than a few miles in extent, and seldom more than 50 feet in thickness. Above these breccias and basalts are three thick sheets of ash that have been cemented into rock. These are referred to as welded tuffs.

A similar situation, on a smaller scale, can be seen in Katmai National Monument in Alaska. An eruption of hot, perhaps almost incandescent, sand or ash spilled into the valley now called the Valley of Ten Thousand Smokes. In places the ash, which may be 500 feet thick, has been welded into hard rock that rises

Fig. 12.4 Rapid erosion of volcanic sand near Mt. Katmai, Alaska.

Fig. 12.5 Yellowstone volcanic breccia.

in high cliffs, where the streams quickly cut deep narrow canyons into it (Fig. 12.4). On the basis of extensive deposits of ash in many other areas of North America and elsewhere, this type of volcanic phenomenon was not rare.

In the John Day region of central Oregon extensive colorful levels of volcanic ash contain unusual fossils of the horse, camel, oreodont, and other mammals. These deposits, unlike those of Yellowstone and Katmai, appear to have been reworked by water after their original deposition. They are not strongly welded, but erode away into typical badland formations.

The three Yellowstone rhyolite ash flows—known, from top to bottom, as the Plateau, Yellowstone, and Jackson-Red Mountain flows (tuffs)—overlap or overlie one another. The last—the Plateau flows—appears to have been contemporaneous with at least the early part of glaciation. The continental ice mass did not reach this far south, but extensive local glaciation did develop in these high mountains.

Most puzzling of these volcanic products are the breccias (Fig. 12.5). These deposits of angular fragments of cooled molten materials are difficult to explain, because no action of a comparable nature and extent is currently taking place in the world. Yet the breccias are so abundant that this must have been a major type of volcanism in prehistoric times. One location northwest of Gardner, Montana, shows exposures of little-stratified breccia equaling 4,000 feet in depth!

Breccias may have originated in several different ways. There is some evidence that fragmented semi-molten magmas erupted as breccias from craters or fissures. This situation is difficult to understand, especially since the material apparently spread out widely even when the angle of flow was slight. Other breccias were produced by the cooling of the surface of a lava flow and the mixing of the cooled, broken crust into the molten material beneath as the flow continued to move along. Still others resulted through molten matter spilling into water, by pyroclastic explosions, and by slides and avalanches of water-soaked ash.

It would seem that during and following the Flood there was much volcanism, and that this activity has lessened gradually to the present low level. How the great quantities of breccias were produced in the past we do not now know. That this did happen is obvious—another example of the impossibility and undesirability of attempting to explain all past events by the so-called law of uniformity. Many phenomena are best explained by catastrophism or by rapid geological processes.

To the west of Yellowstone National Park the Snake River Plains begin. This extensive plain, built up by layer upon layer of overlapping basaltic lavas, almost connects with the Columbia River Plateau, an even greater area of similar origin. The amount of molten materials that gushed from the earth is difficult to comprehend. These two plateaus cover large parts of Washington, Oregon, Idaho, and northern California. (For further information on the Columbia River Plateau see chapter 23, "The Story of a River.")

Fig. 12.6 Left: Air-fall ash from the eruption of Mt. Katmai in 1912. Fig. 12.7 Right: Volcanic ash in central Oregon.

What caused these great flows to rise from the bowels of the earth and push out over the land? Two of the most fundamental questions of volcanology are: What is the source of the heat, or, to put it another way, what causes the materials of the earth to become molten; and what force pushes these products out of the earth onto the surface? If these basic questions could be answered many problems would be quickly solved, but as yet the answers are not known.

Volcanism and the Flood

Another question of great interest concerns the time when this activity happened. Did such major changes in the surface of the earth develop before the Flood, during the Flood, or after the Flood? Let us analyze these questions for a moment.

Volcanic and magmatic materials may have been produced in the creative activities that brought the world's mass into existence before creation week or during the first and third days. Perhaps these are represented by the extensive Precambrian igneous exposures found all over the world. The volcanism described in this chapter does not fit here, however. If volcanic action of such terrifying magnitude happened after creation but before the Flood, at least certain parts of the earth would have been undesirable places for habitation. It is hard to reconcile this state of affairs of the pre-Flood world with such descriptions as those in *Patriarchs and Prophets*. "In the days of Noah a double curse was resting upon the earth in consequence of Adam's transgression and of the murder committed by Cain. Yet this had not greatly changed the face of nature. There were evident tokens of decay, but the earth was still rich and beautiful in the gifts of God's providence" (PP 90).

Could major volcanic activity have occurred during the Flood? Along the Columbia River, in northern Washington, and in Yellowstone Park, levels of upright trees are seen in the volcanic breccia or basalt. These trees perhaps represent forests that were destroyed by eruptions or flows, and the stumps preserved in their original positions of growth. Obviously, time is required for forests to grow, and since the Flood lasted only about one year (it would be more correct to say Noah remained in the ark about one year), all this activity could not have come about during the Flood if the trees are in growth position. Perhaps some of the activity began during the Flood but continued for hundreds, perhaps thousands, of years. The numerous geysers, which give evidence of internal heat, indicate that activity has not yet completely subsided in the Yellowstone region.

This is a critical area for creationists, one in which much more study is needed, especially of the relationships of volcanic activity, petrification of trees, glaciation, and time. Are the current interpretations correct? Are these truly successive land surfaces that supported forests, or could the trees have been transported from elsewhere? Recent research on the petrified trees of Yellowstone National Park leaves open the interpretation of these forests. The trees appear to have grown *in situ,* but further investigation uncovers phenomena that seem to be incompatible with forests in position of growth. There is need for persons trained in geology and related sciences to direct their attention to these problems.

The two fundamental questions concerning the source of magma and the necessary energy for extrusion of the molten material are largely unknown. However, note the following:

"Coal and oil are generally to be found where there are no burning mountains or fiery issues. When fire and water under the surface of the earth meet, the fiery issues cannot give sufficient vent to the heated elements beneath. The earth is convulsed— the ground trembles, heaves, and rises into swells or waves, and there are heavy sounds like thunder underground. The air is heated and suffocating. The earth quickly opens, and I saw villages, cities and burning mountains carried down together into the earth" (3SG 80).

"Coal and oil frequently ignite and burn beneath the surface of the earth. Thus rocks are heated, limestone is burned, and iron ore melted. The action of the water upon the lime adds fury to the intense heat, and causes earthquakes, volcanoes, and fiery issues" (PP 108).

It is of interest to note that steam usually comprises from 75 to 100 per cent of the gases present in ordinary magmas. Second in abundance is carbon dioxide, which is derived principally from the heating of lime in the molten mass ($CaCO_3$ + heat $\rightarrow$ CaO + CO_2). When water reacts with lime large amounts of heat are produced (CaO + H_2O $\rightarrow$ $Ca(OH)_2$ + 16 Kcl/mole). These points accord with Ellen G. White's statements concerning the role of limestone in volcanism.

Burning vegetable materials within the earth may be responsible for volcanic and thermal activities and cause earthquakes, but the statements quoted above do not necessarily imply that this is the only cause of volcanism and earthquakes. Current theory holds that matter deep within the earth, in the region of the contact of the crust and the mantle (the earth is thought to consist of inner core, outer core, mantle, and crust) is in a solid state only because of the great pressure above it. If pressure is released by shifting of the crust, solid rock may become molten magma and ooze up to the surface with a resulting fiery display. Since it appears that volcanism was associated with the Flood before coals and oils were formed, it may be possible that disruption of the crust of the earth by events associated with the violence of the Flood permitted the rise of magma to many areas of the earth's surface. Friction connected with movements of great masses of rock is also thought to generate sufficient heat to melt rock or ignite coal and oil deposits.

During the time Ellen G. White was in Europe she was much impressed by the beauty and grandeur of the Alps. Concerning these mountains she wrote in her diary:

"These mountains to me are significant. Subterranean fires although concealed in them are burning. When the wicked shall have filled their cup of iniquity then the Lord will rise out of His place to punish the inhabitants of the earth. . . . There is a sea of fire beneath our feet. There is a furnace of fire in these old rocky mountains. The mountain belching forth its fires tells us the mighty furnace is kindled, waiting for God's word to wrap the earth in flames" (MS 29, 1885).

REFERENCES

Bauer, Clyde Max. 1962. Yellowstone, its underworld. Univ. New Mex. Press, Albuquerque. 122 pp.

Boyd, Francis R. 1961. Welded tuffs and flows in the rhyolite plateau of Yellowstone Park, Wyoming. Bull. Geol. Soc. Am. 72:387-426.

Bullard, F. M. 1962. Volcanoes: in history, in theory, in eruption. Univ. of Texas Press, Austin. 441 pp.

Chaney, Ralph W. 1956. The ancient forests of Oregon. Univ. of Oregon Press, Eugene. 56 pp.

Dorf, Erling. 1960. Tertiary fossil forests of Yellowstone National Park, Wyoming. Billings Geological Soc., 11th Annual Field Con. Guidebook, pp. 253-259.

Dunbar, Carl O. 1960. Historical geology. 2d ed. John Wiley & Sons, Inc., N.Y.

Ewing, H. Maurice. 1949. New discoveries on the Mid-Atlantic Ridge. Nat. Geog. Mag. 96 (5): 611-640.

Gilluly, James, A. C. Waters, and A. O. Woodford. 1959. Principles of geology. 2d ed. W. H. Freeman & Co., San Francisco, pp. 358-384.

Rittmann, A. 1962. Volcanoes and their activity. John Wiley & Sons, New York. 305 pp.

Ross, C. S. and R. L. Smith. 1961. Ash-flow tuffs: their origin, geologic relations and identification. U.S. Geol. Surv. Prof. Paper 366, pp. 1-77.

Stearns, H. T. 1963. Geology of Craters-of-the-Moon National Monument, Idaho. Craters of the Moon Nat. Hist. Assoc. 34 pp.

Thorarinsson, Sigurdur. 1967. Surtsey, the new island in the North Atlantic. The Viking Press, New York. 47 pp., 54 plates.

Williams, Howel. 1948. The ancient volcanoes of Oregon. Univ. of Oregon Press, Eugene.

Wright, A. E. and D. R. Bowes. 1963. Classification of volcanic breccias: a discussion. Geol. Soc. Am. Bull. 74:79-86.

CHAPTER THIRTEEN

Land Beneath the Sea

THE FLOORS OF THE OCEANS are far from being vast, featureless expanses. In addition to spectacular canyons and troughs, there are narrow ridges, long broad rises, swells that rise to lesser elevations, and seamounts with flat tops far beneath the surface of the sea.

One of the earth's greatest mountain ranges stretches in an apparently unbroken line from Iceland to the latitude of Cape Town in South Africa. This spectacular 7,000-mile-long Mid-Atlantic Ridge sometimes rises to ragged peaks, often 10,000 feet high, and is 600 miles or more wide in some places. Only a few peaks of this range rise above sea level—the Azores, St. Paul's Rocks, Ascension, Tristan da Cunha, and a few others. There are similar ranges in most of the other seas which form a connected, a circumglobal, network of mountains.

The Pacific Ocean does not have a pronounced mid-ocean mountain range, but arcuate island chains with associated deeps on their convex, or oceanward, sides are conspicuous features. This ocean contains the most stupendous heights and depths on earth—the 32,024-foot rise from the ocean floor off the Hawaiian Islands and the 35,770-foot-deep Mariana Trench. Large portions of the oceans are flat, abyssal plains. As a result of geophysical studies over the past few years it has been shown that the structure of the earth in oceanic areas is notably different from that of the continents. Up to several thousand feet of sediments are thought to cover a layer of basalt overlying the mantle. It also appears that the same structure occurs in all oceanic basins, and that continental-type rocks formerly thought to be present under much of the Atlantic do not occur in the submarine plains at all.

Before the International Geophysical Year of 1957-1958 very little was known about the topography of the ocean floors. As the information of that venture becomes published, many interesting facts are coming to light. Mid-ocean mountain ranges have been traced, or new ones found; soundings of both surface and subsurface features have been made; and samples of minerals and rocks have been dredged from deep water.

Early in 1961, in the open Pacific 20 miles off San Diego, California, samples of basalt from below the sedimentary layers were obtained. In the open ocean where the water depth is several miles, the Moho (Mohorovicic discontinuity, where the surface crust lies on the mantle and where seismic waves are bent) is only a few miles beneath the sea bed. The mantle comes nearest to the surface along the perimeter of oceanic islands where the roots of the islands depress the crust. It lies at a depth of ten miles below sea level, only a few miles below the ocean floor. In the near future more information will likely be forthcoming.

The test drilling near San Diego, which took place in water 11,700 feet deep, pierced the 699-foot sedimentary strata to the three-mile-thick layer of basalt. Below that lies the Moho, or break between the crust and the mantle, the 1,800-mile-thick mantle, the 1,400-mile-thick outer core, and the 800-mile-thick inner core.

Ocean Oozes

Through the past millennia, innumerable skeletons of microscopic plants and animals have settled to the bottom of the seas. These sediments, called oozes, consist principally of the outer coverings of one-celled plants and animals known as diatoms and foraminifera. The diatoms use silicon in the manufacture of the external covering. These siliceous diatomaceous oozes are found mainly in a horizontal band across the bottom of the North Pacific Ocean. Foraminifera, on the other hand, have shells composed of calcium. The genus *Globigerina* is predominant, and oozes consisting of this genus are rather widely distributed in all the great ocean basins.

Several other bottom sediment-forming organisms of less import should be mentioned. Another protozoan has a skeletal framework of silicon composed of concentric spheres and radiating spines. These radiolarians, noted for their jewellike beauty, are mostly restricted to the Pacific Ocean. A pelagic (open ocean) mollusk called a pteropod abounds in sufficient numbers to leave a sedimentary deposit of shells on the floor of certain parts of the Atlantic. Calcareous algae produce what are called coccolith oozes. Depth is one of the factors that controls the distribution of the different kinds of marine sediments. In ocean depths of 4,000 meters or over, radiolarian oozes are most generally found, while pteropod oozes are seldom found below 2,000 meters. The *Globigerina* and the diatoms range to depths between these two (Sverdrup, Johnson, and Fleming, 1942, p. 978).

In several places deep layers of ocean-bottom sediments have been found above the sea level. One example of this is the chalk cliffs of Dover. There is little reason to think that the pre-Flood seas did not have microscopic plants and animals such as the diatoms and foraminifera, and that their remains collected on the sea floor. Were these pre-Flood oozes buried by the Flood and then uplifted to the present exposed positions? This is a possibility. But before any conclusion is drawn regarding any specific deposit the stratigraphic position, the associated fauna and flora, and other factors need to be studied.

Attempts to determine how fast these sediments are accumulating have been made by dividing the depth of the sediments by the time assumed in their formation, or by actual measurements of the amount of organic material now being produced in a given area of the sea in a given time. The first method assumes geologic time. The second is difficult, and is based on present conditions in the oceans. In the former, assumptions must be made that there have been no changes in the depth and extent of the oceans, no change in the rate of production of organisms that add their skeletons to the bottom, and no movement or transport of the sediments from one place to another after they accumulate on the bottom.

Submarine Canyons

Another interesting topic in marine geology is the submarine canyons. Just off the beach in Monterey Bay, California, is the head of a gigantic submarine canyon that rivals the Grand Canyon of the Colorado in size. The floors of the oceans are furrowed with many such canyons or valleys, which vary in width, length, and depth. The actual dimensions of only a few are definitely known.

Some of these canyons cut across continental shelves and are actually extensions of large existing valleys on the adjoining land. One of the best-known shelf valleys is the submerged extension of the Hudson River valley off the coast of New York.

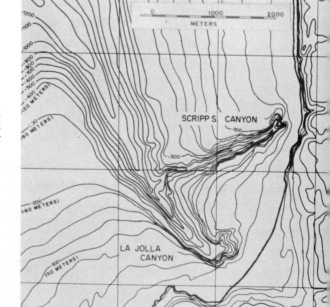

Fig. 13.1 Scripps and La Jolla submarine canyons off the coast of southern California. Contour interval, 100 feet.

This relatively straight valley cuts 200 feet into the continental shelf, and widens from about three miles near the shore line to about 15 miles at its seaward end. This and other valleys at the mouths of rivers are supposed to have been cut by these rivers. Geologists speculate that they were formed during the Pleistocene glaciation, when the sea level was thought to have been about 300 feet lower than it now is (Leet and Judson, 1965, p. 233). The lowering of sea level 300 feet does not explain, however, the canyon that is cut into the outer slopes of the continental shelf to a depth of several thousand feet. Smaller valleys on these continental shelves may be the result of tidal scouring, or the movement of glacial ice.

Theories for the formation of these spectacular submarine canyons are varied. Among them are listed great earth movements—turbidity currents, tidal scour, and the emergence of submarine springs on canyon slopes. It is possible that great currents produced by the lowering of the ocean basins and the raising of the continents during the later stages of the Flood scoured out these unusual canyons. Some of these canyons are cut into Tertiary deposits, and may have developed after the Flood. Geological processes caused by the Flood did not come to an end when Noah and his family left the ark. In some areas of the earth, water could have been receding for hundreds of years afterward.

The formation of submarine canyons is a puzzle to both creationist and evolutionist. The solution to the problem may well answer questions concerning post-Flood earth movements and sea-level fluctuations.

Seamounts

One of the most significant features of the oceans, especially in the Pacific, is the seamount and tablemount. Shepard (1959) defines a seamount as an isolated marine elevation rising 3,000 feet or more above its surroundings. If the elevation is flat-topped, it is called a guyot or tablemount. Seamounts and flat-

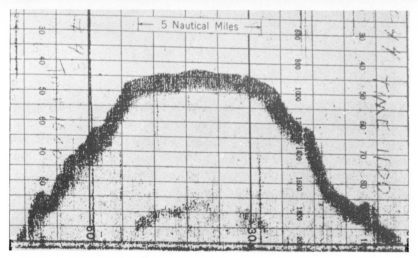

Fig. 13.2 Seismic profile of a North Pacific guyot.

topped mountains do occur in the Atlantic, but they are insignificant in comparison with those found in the Pacific. There, they range in three significant lines, the Emperor Seamounts south of Kamchatka, the Marcus-Necker Rise, west of the Hawaiian Islands, and another in a line from the Marshall Islands to the Marianas. There are ten guyots in close association in the Gulf of Alaska. Many others appear as isolated mountains. The depth from the surface of the water to the top of these mountains varies.

The seamounts and guyots are probably volcanic in origin. It seems likely that these mountaintops were once at or near sea level. "The waves can cut off the summit of a newly erupted volcano in a very short period because so much of the summit of the peak consists of crumbling ash and scoria deposits, which are rapidly attacked by the great mid-ocean waves. The fact that the depth of a guyot summit is slightly greater on the margins suggests wave erosion" (Shepard, 1959, p. 177). In this connection note again the following statement by Ellen G. White: "A violent wind which was caused to blow for the purpose of drying up the waters, moved them with great force, in some instances even carrying away the tops of the mountains" (PP 108).

If these mountaintops were wave-cut by Flood action, the sea bottom must have sunk or the waters must have risen after the tops were planed flat. These mountains may have sunk below

147

the level of the sea as the ocean basins sank to accommodate the great quantities of water on the earth after the Flood.

The origin of atolls has puzzled geologists and biologists for many years. At present, there are two theories to account for these coral formations. Charles Darwin suggests the first hypothesis—that as mountain peaks subsided beneath the seas, coral reefs kept building upward, so that the surface of the coral was never far below the surface of the water. The coral growths would then form a ring of reefs around the sunken peak. If guyots are indeed wave-washed mountains that have sunk below the sea, this explanation by Darwin may well be correct. Borings on atolls have shown the coral to extend down more than 4,000 feet (Schlanger, 1963, p. 991).

Another explanation is based on sea-level fluctuations owing to glaciation. If the sea level were roughly 300 feet lower than now when great quantities of water were locked in the continental glaciers, volcanic peaks and mountains of less-solidly indurated rocks might have been eroded by water to the water line at a depth of 300 feet or more below the present level. As glaciers melted and climatic conditions began to moderate, the seas rose gradually. Coral fringing or barrier reefs, growing on some mountains, built upward, maintaining a level with the surface of the water. It is possible that both processes, sinking of islands and rising of sea level, have been responsible for the formation of atolls. The great depth of the coral accumulations on the tops of some submarine mountains precludes fluctuations of the sea level

Fig. 13.3 Island in the Bahamas composed of Pleistocene coral.

connected with glaciation, as the sole cause of the development of atolls.

Most students of coral reefs have been of the opinion that growth of the reefs is very slow, much too slow to be able to produce 4,000 feet of growth in post-Flood times. This consideration would give rise to a time problem that those who accept the Genesis account of creation and the Flood need to study.

For many years it was not realized that algae, common marine plants, are an important part of a coral reef. In fact, in most cases the algae constitute a greater percentage of the total bulk of the reef than do the corals themselves.

Most corals grow best near the surface of the water, but this position exposes the organisms to breakage and disintegration from violent storm waves. The debris is washed back into the quiet lagoon formed by the atoll or falls down the steep seaward slope of the reef to add to the talus accumulation. Because the organisms are already near the surface, there is not much opportunity for the reef as a whole to grow upward; consequently, growth is chiefly outward, or involves the replacement of damaged or disintegrated parts.

How rapidly can the organisms composing a coral reef grow? Recent research (Goreau, 1963) indicates that a drastic revision in the thinking regarding the growth of corals and algae may be necessary. Using radioactive carbon-14 and calcium-45 as tracers, Goreau measured the growth rate of several species of reef builders. He found that the tip of a growing coral will add to its structure at the phenomenal rate of .3 per cent of its weight per hour. Just back from the tip the rate of growth was still surprisingly rapid—.05 per cent of its weight per hour. The algae were found to have an even more spectacular growth rate. The three species —*Liagora, Galaxaura,* and *Penicillus*—were found to grow at the rate of 9.6 per cent, 14.3 per cent, and 17 per cent of their weight per hour, respectively. This is almost unbelievable. The very slowest-growing alga tested had a growth rate of .2 per cent of its weight per hour.

If following the Flood the ocean basins slowly sank, and later, during the melting of the continental glaciers, the water level slowly rose, the upward growth of corals and algae composing a reef would be ideally possible because of the continuing presence of space between the growing surface of the reef and sea level. Unless the post-Flood sinking of the ocean basins was extremely fast, the figures indicated above for the rate of growth of reef-forming organisms would be fully adequate to maintain the surface of the reef near sea level.

Fossil corals dredged from the surface of North Pacific guyots at a depth of several thousand feet are classified as Jurassic. Apparently the seamounts of the North Pacific sank too rapidly for the coral reefs to maintain their growth at the surface; or, post-Flood cooling of the waters of this region inhibited the continued growth of reef organisms on these guyots.

There is much yet to be learned regarding the oceans and their subsurface features. Submarine canyons, ocean deeps next to arcuate island chains, guyots, seamounts, the shallowness of the earth's crust in the deep portions of the oceans, changes in sea level, atolls, and many other topics call for much study and thought. The facts are beginning to pile up but they need to be interpreted and compared with the Biblical history of the earth.

REFERENCES

Coker, R. E. 1962. This great and wide sea. Harper and Brothers, New York. 325 pp.

Defant, Albert. 1961. Physical oceanography. Pergamon Press, New York, pp. 20-25.

Gaskell, T. F. 1960. Under the deep oceans. W. W. Norton and Co., Inc., New York.

Gilluly, James, A. C. Waters, and A. O. Woodford. 1959. Principles of geology. 2d ed. W. H. Freeman and Co., San Francisco, pp. 293-325.

Goreau, Thomas F. 1963. Calcium carbonate deposition by coralline algae and corals in relation to their roles as reef-builders. Ann. N.Y. Acad. Sci. 109 (1):127-167.

Leet, L. Don and Sheldon Judson. 1965. Physical geology. Prentice-Hall, Inc., Englewood Cliffs, N.J.

Matthews, Samuel W. 1961. Project mohole. Nat. Geo. Mag. 120 (5):686-697.

Schlanger, Seymour O. *et al.* 1963. Subsurface geology of Eniwetok Atoll. U.S. Geol. Sur. Prof. Paper 260-BB., pp. 991-1066, 8 pls., 13 figs., 20 tables.

Shepard, Francis P. 1959. The earth beneath the sea. The Johns Hopkins Press, Baltimore. 275 pp.

Sverdrup, H. U., Martin W. Johnson, and Richard H. Fleming. 1942. The oceans. Prentice-Hall, Inc., Englewood Cliffs, N.J., pp. 972-1037.

SECTION 4

THE FOSSILS

"Speak to the earth, and it shall teach thee."
Job 12:8

Fig. 14.1 (above, left) Two-thousand-year-old man found in peat bog in Denmark.

Fig. 14.2 (above, right) Insect in amber.

Fig. 14.3 (right) Entrance to a lava mold of a rhinoceros body, Blue Lake, Washington.

Fig. 14.4 (below) Animal footprints in sandstone, Monument Valley, Arizona.

CHAPTER FOURTEEN

What Is a Fossil?

THE QUESTION What is a fossil? is not as idle as it may at first seem. Most fossils would be readily recognized as such by almost anyone, but other fossils might be thought worthless and their organic origin not realized. A fossil is sometimes defined as the remains or evidence of prehistoric life. A specimen does not have to be petrified or fossilized in order to be considered a genuine fossil. Some organic remains have been petrified (impregnated with some hard substance) in a relatively few years. At the same time, wood or other plant remains of great age can still be cut or worked with a knife. The line of demarcation between what would interest an archeologist and what would lie in the realm of the paleontologist is not always clear. To put it more bluntly, how can a person be sure he is digging up a fossil and not robbing a grave! The word *prehistoric* used above in the definition of a fossil cannot be held too rigidly, especially by creationists, who contend that the duration of life on the earth has been relatively

Fig. 14.5 Exquisitely preserved fossil bat.

short. No doubt many post-Flood specimens that have become buried and preserved since written records have been kept by man would qualify as fossils.

Although it may be somewhat difficult to define clearly what a fossil is, there are usually no serious problems recognizing them in the field. Occasionally one may pick up an old bone from a farm horse that died a few score years ago, yet not be able to determine this fact without careful study of the bone and the place in which it was found.

Types of Fossils

It has been customary to classify fossils into four main groups, depending on the method of preservation.

Petrification. This is a common type of preservation, perhaps best seen in petrified wood. For many years it was thought that petrified objects were completely devoid of all original organic matter, but this is now known to be untrue in most cases. Original organic material is usually present, and this fact has accounted for the development of a field of science called paleobiochemistry. Impregnating materials, which fill in around the cells and in the hollow spaces, add weight to the specimen and make it hard like

Fig 14.6   Frozen muck in Alaska in which animal and plant remains have been preserved, here being thawed and removed by water.

rock. Some fossils show a complete replacement of the original material by silicon, calcium carbonate, or some other substance. In petrification there may be impregnation, replacement, or a combination of the two.

Carbonization. Coal is the obvious example of carbonization. In such fossils most of the other elements have disappeared, and a concentration of carbon is left behind. The original cellular nature of the matter may still be preserved. With a microscope it is often possible to identify thin sections of coal by the grain of the original wood. Leaves, trilobites, small fishes, and many other organisms are seen as fine brown or black films of carbon on the rock surface. This is a common type of preservation.

Unchanged. For convenience, it is usual to consider this type of fossil under two categories: unchanged hard materials and unchanged soft materials. Unchanged hard fragments or whole specimens of molluscans still have the chalky white appearance, and perhaps even the original mother of pearl sheen. Preserved soft parts are much less common. Woods are sometimes found little changed, but the most spectacular examples are animals frozen in muck or preserved in acid peat or swamp waters. The mammoth, frozen with soft parts relatively intact, is well known. Plants, animals, and even humans have been found in good states of preservation in peat bogs, where oxidation has been held to a minimum (Fig. 14.1).

Molds and Casts. If a dinosaur walked across the mud and left tracks that became permanent when the mud hardened to rock, a fossil would form even though no replaced, impregnated, carbonized, or unchanged remains of the dinosaur were involved. A very definite evidence of life remains, and this qualifies it to be considered a fossil under the definition given above. This type of fossil is a mold. If the track filled with sediments, hardened, and retained the form of the foot after the surrounding material had eroded away, a cast would result. Sediment changed to rock inside a clam is not a cast, however, but an internal mold. It shows the features of the inside of the shells. Trails, burrows, castings, and fecal droppings also point to living things, and provide clues to specific identifications (Fig. 14.4). One fossil that does not seem to fit into any of the above categories, but which is a definite evidence of life, is the gizzard stones or gastroliths said to be associated with certain species of dinosaurs. These pebble-sized stones are thought to have assisted the animal in pulverizing its food, like the gravel in a chicken's gizzard.

Conditions of Preservation

The conditions necessary for preservation and the eventual fossilization of an organism are rather stringent. An animal that dies is likely to be eaten or destroyed by scavengers. But if its features are not destroyed beyond identification, decay will soon finish the task. Wind, water, and frost acting on land, and waves and currents in the oceans, add their damaging effects to the disintegration of a specimen. If it survives these hazards and becomes buried in sediments or other preserving media quickly, it may become fossilized if the pressure of accumulating sediments is not too great, if impregnating substances are available, if oxidation cannot occur, if recrystallization (limestone to dolostone, for example) does not take place, and if erosion of the now-indurated sediments do not obliterate it! Considering all these factors that work against the maintaining of the identity of the specimen long enough to allow its becoming a useful fossil, it is a wonder that the earth gives up so many exquisitely preserved fossils. The concept of catastrophes that provided optimum conditions for burial of organisms is supported by the obvious abundance of fossils.

The most common preserving media are fine-grained sediments, volcanic ash, bog waters, ice, resin (amber), incrusting deposits of caves and hot springs, and tar. Some skeleton, structure, or substance that facilitates fossilization is usually required also. The main preservable materials are calcite in sponges, foraminifera, and some mollusks; aragonite in most mollusks and some foraminifera; silicon in sedges, horsetails, diatoms, sponges, and radiolarians; calcium phosphate in animal bones; chitin in arthropods; and cellulose in herbs, shrubs, and trees.

The fossil fauna and flora may be quite different from the original living assemblage. Animals and plants with hard parts are naturally more likely to be preserved than others. Even those with hard parts have been shown to erode and decompose at vastly different rates (Chave, 1964, pp. 377, 387). The result may be that only a few species of animals and plants that have very hard skeletons and structures show up in the fossil record, resulting in a greatly distorted image of the original life of the area.

In addition to these factors, it is often difficult to determine whether transportation by wind or water has mixed specimens from different ecological zones or habitats before burial occurred. So-called dwarf fauna have been a puzzle to paleontologists for many years. Why were all the specimens of brachiopods, mollusks, et cetera, of a stratum or formation dwarfed or stunted in size? Recent intensive study has suggested that this is the result of differential sorting by water (Tasch, 1953).

For these and other reasons not mentioned here, paleoecology is a difficult subject, and conclusions in this area must be drawn with great care. Yet, this area is one of the most fruitful for the creationist. A study of the association and orientation of specimens, state of preservation, death assemblages, life assemblages (specimens killed in their environmental niches and in their life positions), destructive and transportive forces, comparison with living representatives and conditions, and many other factors make it possible to piece together slowly the jigsaw puzzle of the past and provide pictures (somewhat blurred perhaps) of past conditions that accord with the Bible account of the pre-Flood world and the Flood.

Some Unusual Fossils

Before ending this chapter, let us consider a few of the unusual and unexpected fossils that have been discovered. In 1935, a cavity in the cliffs along the lower Grand Coulee in Washington

State was found to contain miscellaneous fragmental bones and portions of teeth and jaws. These were identified as belonging to an extinct rhinoceros (Fig. 12.3). This would not be unusual, except that the cavity turned out to be the mold of the rhinoceros formed by pliable basalt that had covered it. Basalt hot enough to be semifluid would quickly destroy the body of an animal. The lava in this site was in pillow-shaped masses more or less fused together around the body of the beast now disintegrated to the bones and teeth mentioned. Pillow lava is considered to have been formed when molten basalt flowed into water. This remarkable evidence of prehistoric life came about only because of unique and ideal conditions that are rarely obtained, since no other fossils of this nature have been found in this region (Chappell, Durham & Savage, 1951, p. 907) (Fig. 14.3).

Mummified men, some considered to be as old as 2,000 years, have occasionally been found in peat in Denmark. Peat which is cut and dried for fuel in many countries forms in bogs that are excellent environments for good preservation. One corpse had a rope around his neck, indicating that his entry into the bog was unwilling if not accidental. Tissues of most of the body were beautifully preserved. He had a peaceful expression on his face despite the ominous circumstances leading to his presence in the bog. He had not shaved for a couple of days previous to his death. The over-all appearance of the body was that of a mummy, or a greatly emaciated person (Glob, 1954, p. 419) (Fig. 14.1).

For a number of years gigantic corkscrew formations in Nebraska puzzled paleontologists and others. They spiral down into the ground as far as twelve feet and terminate in a diversion several feet away from the helical column. They were strongly suspected to be of organic origin. Subsequent research and observation turned up petrified bones and vegetable nest materials at the ends of the corkscrews. Evidently, some prehistoric beaver-like animal spiraled down into the ground as he dug his burrow. After the death of the animal and disuse of the burrow, it gradually filled with sediments, which became more resistant to erosion than the surrounding soil. The result is a gigantic cork-screw eroding from the banks. Local residents took to calling them "devil's corkscrews"!

An unusual rock mass was recently found in Utah—an 88-pound rock containing twigs and fragments of trees and plants and occasional bones and teeth. These would be interesting in their own right as fossils, but the fact that the block in which they were embedded lay among bones of a sauropod dinosaur led to the suspicion that this block, which was somewhat flattened and oval, was the fossilized stomach remains of the dinosaur. According to Stokes (1964, p. 576), there is little doubt that this is a correct analysis. On the basis of this interpretation, this slab takes on unusual significance. In a sense these organic fragments are fossils twice over—in their own right, and as evidence of a prehistoric dinosaur. A better understanding of the environment and the food habits of these dinosaurs is now possible.

Perhaps the most exquisite fossils available are the insects and other organisms preserved in pitch (Fig. 14.2). Mysteriously, great quantities of petrified pitch (amber) have been found from a small stretch of the Baltic Coast, and many delicate animals have been preserved in this transparent medium. Although in most cases the tissues have dried to almost nothing, the mold left in the amber has preserved the outline of the creature in the most intricate detail. The finest hairs, bristles, and spines are present, and can be studied at leisure under a microscope. Obviously, identification is not hampered by lack of anatomical details, a problem that is frequently met by the paleontologist.

These are a few examples of the surprises that turn up for the student of fossils. No doubt there will be more in the future, with more exploration and new techniques. Rightly understood, these remains and evidences will help to unravel the history of the past. "God designed that the discovery of these things should establish faith in inspired history" (PP 112).

REFERENCES

Chappell, W. M., J. W. Durham, and D. E. Savage. 1951. Mold of a rhinoceros in basalt, Lower Grand Coulee, Washington. Geol. Soc. Am., Bull. 62:907-918.

Chave, Keith E. 1964. Skeletal durability and preservation. *In* Approaches to paleoecology. John Imbrie and Norman D. Newell, Editors. John Wiley and Sons, Inc., New York, pp. 377-387, 3 figs., 2 tables.

Dunbar, Carl O. 1960. Historical geology. 2d ed. John Wiley and Sons, Inc., New York, pp. 28-49, figs. 14-37.

Glob, P. V. 1954. Lifelike man preserved 2,000 years in peat. Nat. Geog. Mag. 105 (3):419-430, 13 figs.

Matthews, William H., III. 1962. Fossils, an introduction to prehistoric life. Barnes and Noble, Inc., New York, pp. 7-29, figs. 2-15.

Ransom, Jay Ellis. 1964. Fossils in America. Harper & Row, Pub., New York. 402 pp.

Raymond, Percy E. 1958. Prehistoric life. Harvard Univ. Press, Cambridge, pp. 3-11, figs. 1-5.

Simpson, George Gaylord. 1961. Life of the past. Yale Univ. Press, New Haven, pp. 6-19, figs. 2-4.

Stokes, William Lee. 1964. Fossilized stomach contents of a sauropod dinosaur. Science 143 (3606):576.

Tasch, Paul. 1953. Causes and paleoecological significance of dwarfed fossil marine invertebrates. Jour. Paleo. 27 (3):356-444, 6 figs., 1 plate.

CHAPTER FIFTEEN

Life in the Ancient Seas

Approximately three fourths of the surface of the globe is covered with water, which supports swarms of creatures of great variety in a large number of ecological habitats. Living things have invaded them all, and have adapted to their physical, chemical, and biological conditions.

The Salt-Water Environment

In many respects salt water is an ideal environment. The variation in temperature is not so great here as on land or in fresh water. In many oceans the temperature varies only a few degrees from summer to winter. This is quite different from the range of —40° F. (or lower) to more than 100° F. encountered on land. Fresh-water lakes, unless very large, are likely to vary more than the oceans.

Water animals are in no danger of desiccation. Most land animals must have access to water, and many have physiological and morphological adaptations to conserve water. The osmotic pressure of protoplasm is similar to that of sea water; consequently, there is little need for excretory devices to expel from the body water that has been forced in by osmosis, a problem that faces fresh-water animals. Protozoans living in fresh water have one or more contractile vacuoles that pump water out of the body. Similar creatures that live in a salt-water environment have small or no contractile vacuoles, because little water enters the body from the surrounding medium. Food is abundant in most of the ocean, and many creatures are permanently fastened to the

11   161

bottom (sessile) and gather the food as it floats by. Land provides principally a two-dimensional surface for living things, whereas water, and especially that of the oceans, provides a three-dimensional habitat. The density of sea water helps keep floating animals from sinking, and there is seldom a significant change in acidity or alkalinity.

Although the oceans provide many habitats and are generally a good environment for life, they confront organisms with some problems that are not met in other environments. Among these problems are the great pressure (and changes in pressure with vertical movement), and the absence of light in zones below a few hundred feet of the surface. Since few truly abyssal fossil faunas have as yet been discovered (Simpson, 1960, pp. 128, 129), it is speculated that the original seas (pre-Flood) may not have equaled the great depths of modern oceans. The abundant marine organisms, the mud cracks, the ripple or current marks, and the terrestrial or detrital nature of sediments nearly always indicate relatively warm, shallow seas.

Animal life in the seas may be divided roughly into sessile (attached), planktonic (small floating organisms), and nektonic (larger swimming creatures). On the basis of food habits, they are usually classed as planktonic feeders, detrital or debris feeders, and carnivorous animals. Plants, with a very few exceptions, are all algae and do not have true roots, stems, or flowers, but vary in size from microscopic diatoms to kelp several hundred feet long.

The Precambrian Rocks

A study of the fossil-bearing strata of the world reveals that the great majority are marine; that is, they contain the remains of sea animals and plants. Strata containing terrestrial faunas and floras are not rare, but are localized and much less frequently found. In North America they are mostly confined to the western part. Almost no strata below the Devonian are known that contain terrestrial fossils, although some are thought to contain fresh-

Fig. 15.1 The figures of Mt. Rushmore are carved in Precambrian rock.

water fossils. It is with these lower geologic formations that we are especially concerned here.

According to the prevailing concept of the evolutionary development of life, only about one fourth of the total time involved in the progressive evolution of life from a microscopic viruslike structure to the complex and multitudinous forms of today is represented in the geologic column from the Cambrian to the present. Since all the major phyla excepting the chordates are found in Cambrian strata, the evolutionists reason that the evolution of these phyla must have occurred before the Cambrian. With this in mind, many paleontologists have spent much time searching the Precambrian sedimentary strata for the evidences of these ancestral forms that supposedly led to the array of complex crustaceans, brachiopods, segmented worms, et cetera, that filled the Cambrian seas.

Dr. Charles D. Walcott, famous paleontologist of the late 1800's and the early 1900's, published a 156-page paper (Walcott, 1914) entitled "Precambrian Algonkian Algal Flora." Included therein are many descriptions and illustrations of nodular and stratified structures, which he described as calcareous algae from the Belt Series of northern Montana. The Belt Series of sedimentary strata are considered to lie just below the Cambrian.

163

These sediments do not show indications of any extensive metamorphosis, and it has long been felt that if organisms were originally buried in these shales and limestones, they should have remained intact and recognizable. Yet no fossils have been found in the Belt Series, despite a great deal of searching, except for these, which are called calcareous algae (stromatolites), and a few other fragmentary evidences that have since been mostly discredited. Fenton and Fenton (1937), who made a thorough study of the Precambrian sedimentary rocks of northern Montana, came to the conclusion that most of the species named and figured by Walcott are inorganic structures. A few concretions and nodules are still accepted by most paleontologists as valid specimens of calcareous algae. In the Precambrian strata of the Grand Canyon and other areas, worm burrows seem to be obvious. At the present time these, in connection with recent work by Barghoorn and Tyler (1965) on the Gunflint formation of western Ontario showing algal and fungal filaments, are the most authenticated examples of Precambrian fossils.

Precambrian fossils of coelenterates, annelids, and perhaps other forms of life were reported from Australia (Glaessner, 1961). Most of the animals were of the soft-bodied type, and there were fair variety and abundance. There has since developed considerable question concerning the stratigraphic position of these specimens. They are close to the Cambrian-Precambrian contact, and it is difficult to know where to draw the line. They are probably Cambrian rather than Precambrian. As a matter of fact, there is actually some question concerning every reported Precambrian fossil (Cloud, 1965; Schindewolf, 1956). But it may be safe to summarize by saying that, despite a great deal of searching in sediments below the Cambrian, extremely little has been discovered.

The Cambrian Rocks

Immediately above, in the Cambrian strata, fossils make their appearance. Only chordates have not been definitely found in these sediments. The species of marine organisms in the Cambrian are not primitive, simple, poorly developed animals. That they are completely developed, complex organisms showing a complexity of body organization and arrangement of appendages equal to their modern counterparts, is an extremely important point for consideration. Although many Cambrian types are extinct, they do fall naturally into larger classification units. They are definitely worms, crustaceans, or brachiopods, and their complexity is just as great as the worms, crustaceans, or brachiopods of today's oceans. How did they appear so fully developed in the fossil record?

In 1910, Charles Walcott, referred to above in connection with Precambrian calcareous algae, discovered a most unusual fossil site. This quarry, which is located in what is called Middle Cambrian, contains the most complete assemblage of Cambrian organisms known. Especially outstanding is the fact that many of these specimens were soft-bodied animals whose detailed impressions had been left in fine-grained Burgess Shale. An amazing array of segmented worms was discovered, and the impressions retained all the details of spines, bristles, and hairs. The impres-

Fig. 15.2   Well-preserved brachiopods from Ohio.

sions on the dark shale look remarkably like X-ray pictures of modern animals. Even the internal details, such as intestines and stomachs, are sometimes visible. Equally unusual is the collection of crustaceans. Here again, the detail is complete down to the small appendages and mouth parts so characteristic of this class.

Perhaps the most striking representative of the Cambrian is the trilobite. This animal has no modern representative, but the sow bug or pill bug found under stones, flower pots, and boards in many parts of the United States, and which rolls up into a tight ball about the size of a pea upon being disturbed, resembles the trilobite. These fossils were so named because of three longitudinal parts to the body that are not true divisions. The true body divisions are the head, usually called the cephalon, the thorax, and the tail, or pygidium.

The trilobites too could roll up into a ball, and are sometimes found that way in the matrix. Along with insects and crustaceans, they share the phylum Arthropoda. Some of these complex creatures grew to more than a foot in length, but most specimens are less than half that long. They show many different morphological variations of the same basic pattern. Some were eyeless, while others had huge compound eyes. Long spines or processes extended from the corners of the head, thoracic segments, or tail of some species, whereas others had smooth margins all the way around. Most species crawled on the bottom, but a few were burrowing creatures and some may have been good swimmers. Altogether they make up an interesting and unusual segment of the life of the ancient seas.

Among the most unusual specimens found in Burgess Shale were onycophorans (Hutchinson, 1930; Walcott, 1931). *Peripatus*, the current best-known representative of this group, is a caterpillarlike worm with stubby appendages that are not jointed like the legs of insects (Fig. 15.3). A true caterpillar is a transitional step in the cycle of an insect, but this creature maintains this larval appearance throughout its adult life. Its distribution is limited to a few tropical areas where it is found crawling about in the litter of the jungle floor. The significance of *Peripatus* is that it is called an intermediate stage in the evolution from segmented worm to insect. For this reason it has been given study out of proportion to its abundance and economic importance. But if the onycophorans represent a missing link in the development of worms to insects, this "evolutionary step" had already been taken prior to the Cambrian level! Thus the problem of determining the evolutionary steps of the great majority of the marine invertebrates has been shoved back into the Precambrian, where the evolutionists have little hope of solving it.

A Great Mystery for Evolution

The situation is not beyond the recognition of paleontologists, and some are frankly perplexed and have made considerable effort to explain the problem of the sudden appearance of fossil remains in the Cambrian. Even Charles Darwin realized that this was a crucial problem and wrote in his *Origin of Species* after giving the matter some discussion:

"To the question why we do not find rich fossiliferous deposits belonging to these assumed earliest periods prior to the Cambrian system, I can give no satisfactory answer. . . . The case at present must remain inexplicable; and may be truly urged as a valid argument against the views here entertained" (Darwin, 1859, pp. 309, 310).

In Darwin's day the study of paleontology was not old, and it could be argued with considerable validity that the apparent absence of life in the Precambrian and the sudden appearance of many kinds in the Cambrian were merely owing to insufficient

Fig. 15.3 *Peripatus,* a supposed connecting link. Similar fossil forms have been found in the Cambrian rocks.

Fig. 15.4 COMPLEXITY OF CAMBRIAN REPRESENTATIVES OF TWO ANIMAL PHYLA

Type of Animal	Visible Morphological Characteristics	Implications Based on Visible Characteristics
Trilobites (Arthropoda)	1. Chitinous exoskeleton .... 2. Segmented body 3. Jointed legs and appendages ... 4. Compound eyes .... 5. Antennae .... 6. Bristles for swimming and respiration .... 7. Complex mouth parts .... 8. Great variation	Growth by periodic ecdysis (a very complex process of molting) Complex musculature Complex nervous system Blood circulatory system Specialized food requirements
Segmented Marine Worms (Annelida)	1. Segmentation .... 2. Complete digestive system (mouth—anus) 3. Setae and bristles .... 4. Chitinous jaws .... (definitely found in Ordovician and probably also in Cambrian) 5. Eversible proboscis .... 6. Eyes .... 7. Respiratory filaments and gills.. 8. Great variation	Repetition of certain organs in each segment Complex musculature Specialized food habits and requirements; complex musculatu Nervous system similar to living segmented worms Blood circulatory system

collecting and that this situation would undoubtedly change as more people did more searching. Exactly 100 years later, Norman D. Newell (1959), of Columbia University, made the following observations in a paper prepared for the Darwin centennial celebrations. "A century of intensive search for fossils in the pre-Cambrian rocks has thrown very little light on this problem. Early theories that those rocks were dominantly nonmarine or that once-contained fossils have been destroyed by heat and pressure have been abandoned because the pre-Cambrian rocks of many districts physically are very similar to younger rocks in all respects except that they rarely contain any records whatsoever of past life."

A number of theories have been advanced to attempt to explain this situation (Axelrod, 1958). Briefly they are as follows: (1) Precambrian animals had no skeletons because there was no calcium in the seas. (2) Precambrian seas were acid, a condition that prevented the development of calcareous skeletons. (3) The strata are composed of terrestrial deposits which are not ideal for the preservation of fossils. (4) Life originated in fresh water and migrated down rivers to the seas by Cambrian times. (5) Precambrian organisms were not benthonic and consequently did not require hard parts. (6) The adoption of a sessile mode of life made necessary the development of skeletal parts during the Cambrian. (7) Precambrian organisms lived along the coastal margins where erosion was likely to obliterate the organic remains. (8) Gross mutations occurred to living organisms at the beginning of the Cambrian which increased their complexity, variety, and sizes. (9) Precambrian specimens are too small to be readily seen by usual collecting methods. (10) The Cambrian represents a lot of time, and life has not arisen as quickly as it may appear. Axelrod's paper (1958) from which most of the above list was taken gives a good statement of the problem in his introduction:

"One of the major unsolved problems of geology and evolution is the occurrence of diversified, multicellular marine invertebrates in Lower Cambrian rocks on all the continents and their absence in rocks of greater age. These Early Cambrian fossils include porifera, coelenterates, brachiopods, mollusca, echinoids, and arthropods. In the Arthropoda are included the well-known trilobites, which were complexly organized, with well-differentiated head and tail, numerous thoracic parts, jointed legs, and—

like the later crustaceans—a complex respiratory system. . . . Their high degree of organization clearly indicates that a long period of evolution preceded their appearance in the record. However, when we turn to examine the Precambrian rocks for the forerunners of these Early Cambrian fossils, they are nowhere to be found. Many thick (over 5,000 feet) sections of sedimentary rock are now known to lie in unbroken succession below strata containing the earliest Cambrian fossils. These sediments apparently were suitable for the preservation of fossils, because they often are identical with overlying rocks which are fossiliferous, yet no fossils are found in them. Clearly, a significant but unrecorded chapter in the history of life is missing from the rocks of Precambrian time."

The sudden appearance of life is "not only the most puzzling feature of the whole fossil record but also its greatest apparent inadequacy" (Simpson, 1960, p. 144).

Compounding the Mystery

Another problem of nearly equal difficulty is encountered in the study of the fossil remains of the ancient seas. Not only is the complexity of living forms seen for the first time in the Cambrian rocks but the major taxonomic categories, or kinds, of marine invertebrates maintain their differences, with few exceptions, through the geologic column. To put it more plainly, this is the problem of the "missing links." These intermediate steps or missing links are missing all along the so-called evolutionary progression. During the hundred years since Darwin's book was published only a very few fossils have been found that qualify to occupy a position between the basic kinds of animals. Even these are subject to debate. Newell (1959) comments on this problem as follows:

"These isolated discoveries, of course, stimulate hope that more complete records will be found and other gaps closed. These finds are, however, rare; and experience shows that the gaps which separate the highest categories may never be bridged in the fossil record. Many of the discontinuities tend to be more and more emphasized with increased collecting. . . . Several superfamilies [of trilobites] comprising many families appear abruptly near the base of the Lower Cambrian; others are introduced somewhat higher in the Lower Cambrian. Of the ten superfamilies of Lower Cambrian trilobites, not a single ancestor is known. . . . Among the post-Cambrian forms ten of the superfamilies have long and well-documented records in the later Paleozoic. But of these seven cannot be related confidently to any of the known Cambrian groups by means of intermediate fossils. Continued collecting has only emphasized the separation of these groups in the known record."

Simpson (1960, p. 149) expresses similar distress over the problem in different words:

"It is a feature of the known fossil record that most taxa appear abruptly. They are not, as a rule, led up to by a sequence of almost imperceptible changing forerunners such as Darwin believed should be usual in evolution. . . . When a new genus appears in the record it is usually well separated morphologically from the most nearly similar other known genera. This phenomenon becomes more universal and more intense as the hierarchy of categories is ascended. Gaps among known species are sporadic and often small. Gaps among known orders, classes, and phyla are systematic and almost always large."

Both of these problems, the absence of fossils in Precambrian strata and persistent discontinuities between higher categories, are extremely important difficulties to evolutionists. If either or both of these problems cannot be solved (and they have remained unsolved for more than a hundred years), then the theory of progressive evolution must be considered inadequate. One cannot help wondering what Charles Darwin would say if he were aware of the situation today. Would he concede, on the basis of his own statement in *Origin of Species,* that evolution of major groups has not occurred? We can understand why Simpson (1960, p. 149), wrote "These peculiarities of the record pose one of the most important theoretical problems in the whole history of life."

One explanation for the absence of the Cambrian ancestors and intermediate links was not listed in the series of ten explanations given earlier. Faced with the strong evidence, a few brave persons have suggested an explosive type of evolution that quickly populated the ancient seas. This is one step short of saying that a supernatural Being created them and thus quickly caused the seas to be filled with appropriate organisms. This concept is based on the Bible, a source whose accuracy can be scientifically verified in several ways by honest investigation, but unfortunately, it has been unpopular and supposedly unintellectual in scientific circles to make room in one's thinking for an Originator. Yet, both of the fundamental problems we have mentioned are completely solved in the context of such a belief. Is it not time, after these many years, to look the situation squarely in the face and admit that most of the evidence for progressive evolution is lacking, in its most essential features, and turn to an explanation that does fit the evidence satisfactorily?

Let us reconstruct briefly the history of the ancient seas. In the beginning God created the earth and furnished it with water, which contained many suitable habitats for living organisms. He created the life and filled the seas with form and variety. At some later time, perhaps at the start of the Genesis Flood, erosion began to fill these seas, which were warm and shallow. Warping of the earth's crust permitted the continued inpouring of sediments, until several thousands of feet filled these ocean basins. Then pressures within the crust began to squeeze the sediments, breaking, lifting, and overthrusting them above adjacent areas. Erosion by water, by wind, and especially by ice widened and deepened the valleys, gorges, and faulted zones until eventually, since the glaciers melted away, majestic scenery such as that of the Rocky Mountains exhibits no resemblance whatever to the original seas.

As we dig into the rocks and look at the fossils buried in these uplifted sediments we come away convinced that no gradual development from simple to complex has occurred in the history of life on the earth. An intelligent Creator filled the seas with swarms of living creatures of many diverse types. When it became necessary for Him to remove wicked men from the earth by a flood, many of the creatures of the seas were destroyed. They left no traces of their ancestors, because they had none, and in many cases they left no descendants, because none survived the Flood to perpetuate the species.

REFERENCES

Axelrod, D. I. 1958. Early Cambrian marine fauna. Science 128 (3314):7-9.

Barghoorn, Elso and Stanley A. Tyler. 1965. Microorganisms from the Gunflint chert. Science 147 (3658):563-577.

Cloud, Preston E., Jr. 1965. Significance of the Gunflint (Precambrian) microflora. Science 148 (3666):27-35.

Darwin, Charles. 1859. On the origin of species by means of natural selection. The New American Library of World Literature, Inc., New York. Reprint 1958. 479 pp.

Fenton, C. L. and M. A. Fenton. 1937. Belt series of the north: stratigraphy, sedimentation, and paleontology. Geol. Soc. Am. Bull. 48:1873-1969.

Glaessner, Martin F. 1961. Pre-Cambrian animals. Sci. Am. 204 (3):72-78, 12 figs.

Howell, B. F. 1957. Vermes. *In* Treatise on marine ecology and paleontology, vol. 2, H. S. Ladd, ed. Geol. Soc. Am. Mem. 67, pp. 805-816.

Hutchinson, G. E. 1930. Restudy of some Burgess shale fossils. U.S. Nat. Mus. Proc. 78, Art. 11. 24 pp., 5 figs., 1 pl.

Newell, Norman D. 1959. The nature of the fossil record. Proc. Am. Phil. Soc. 103 (2):264-285.

Ross, Clyde P. and Richard Rezak. 1963. The Belt series in Montana. U.S. Geol. Survey Prof. Paper 346. 119 pp.

Schindewolf, O. H. 1956. Über präkambrische fossilien. Geotek. Sym. zu Ehren v. Hans Stille. Münster.

Simpson, George Gaylord. 1960. The history of life. *In* The evolution of life. Sol Tax, ed. The Univ. of Chicago Press, pp. 117-180, 14 tables.

Walcott, Charles D. 1914. Precambrian Algonkian algal flora. Smithsonian Misc. Coll. 64 (2):77-156, pls. 4-23.

————. 1931. Addenda to descriptions of Burgess shale fossils. Smithsonian Misc. Coll. 85 (3):1-46, 11 figs., 23 pls.

CHAPTER SIXTEEN

Fossils and the Flood

By Harold W. Clark

SEVENTH-DAY ADVENTISTS reject the concept that any form of terrestrial life existed prior to creation week. Thus they have always held that the fossils must be interpreted largely in terms of the Deluge described in the seventh and eighth chapters of Genesis. But what should be done with the orderly stratification of rocks and their fossil contents?

An Ecological Sequence

There was a time when many of us regarded the geological column as more or less arbitrary, and assumed that rocks were named from the fossils contained in them and were assigned to certain ages irrespective of their order or position. The fact that Paleozoic rocks were found in the mid-continent, Mesozoic in the Rocky Mountain region, and Tertiary on the Pacific Coast, was explained in terms of ancient faunas or floras, or ecological provinces. Just as we find today that there is a redwood belt, a pine belt, and a spruce belt in our Western forests, none of which coincide, but which are geographically distinct, so the ancient world was conceived to have had biotic provinces. The so-called "sequence" of the fossil zones was assumed to be an imaginary affair invented to bolster up the supposed succession of life through the ages.

In recent years, however, more information has come to light, particularly from oil wells and in some cases from deep mines, and from much more extensive geological mapping than was known half a century ago. This has shown much more regularity to the fossil arrangement than we had commonly believed. In the Midwest, for example, the sequence from Cambrian to Pennsylvanian or Permian is quite uniform and general over the whole area. Farther west, as one approaches the mountains, the Cretaceous and other Mesozoic strata overlap the Paleozoic along the borderline between the two regions. Similarly, as we go still farther west the Paleozoic largely disappears, but the Mesozoic and Tertiary occur in regular order except in those areas where tectonic action can be shown to have upset the original arrangement. This same degree of orderliness can be shown to be quite common in other parts of the world. It seems that we must recognize a certain degree of systematic arrangement of the fossil-bearing strata.

But now the question arises: If we recognize order and system in the arrangement of the fossil zones, how are we to avoid the conclusion that this sequence of the fossils represents ages of deposition? The answer, after all, is quite simple. Just as was at first suggested—that the distribution of the fossils indicates ancient biotic provinces—the order and system, however detailed or however incomplete it may be, represents a remnant, at least, of the original arrangement of these zones.

For instance, the fact that the Cambrio-Ordovician is so prominent in Oklahoma and not well represented in California would indicate that originally certain ecological conditions prevailed in the Oklahoma area that were not found in the California area. Again, in the Wind River mountain area in Wyoming, where all the strata are found in order, we should expect to find a sequential arrangement of the zones from the bottom to the top of the series, which, being buried by the rise of the Flood waters, became spread out in order, later to become upheaved as the mountains were formed, and now to present a view of the whole scale of life existing in that region.

175

Various terms have been used to express this idea, as we have already suggested—fauna and flora, zoological province, biotic area, et cetera. Probably the reason the writer chose to use the term "ecological zonation" was because of his training and experience as a field ecologist. A number of years ago it was my privilege and pleasure to map the distribution, horizontally and vertically, of the biotic zones of a portion of northwestern California. In doing this I had to take into account the distribution of all the fauna and flora of Western America, and to make correlations between my area and others of the West. My study revealed a systematic arrangement of plants and animals similar in pattern to that which we find in the rocks for the life of the past.

To cite a single example: As one goes up through the rising levels of the Sierra Nevada Mountains he encounters in turn the grassland, chaparral, live oak, yellow pine, white fir, red fir, lodgepole pine, and timberline zones, to mention them only briefly. Each of these forest zones contains characteristic plants and animals. Were a rising flood of waters to erode away these mountains today and sweep their life forms out into the Great Valley of California and deposit them one by one, there would be formed a complete sequence of fossils that represented the original life of the forest zones.

Now, if we go to the southern Rocky Mountains, say in New Mexico or southern Colorado, we will find a similar floral and faunal zonation. In most of the zones the species differ from what we found in California, but the ecological types are the same, from the desert to timberline. Chaparral is there, but the species are different from those in California. The pine forest, peculiarly, has the same yellow pine, and in some areas the upper altitudes show the lodgepole forest. The Englemann spruce replaces the Douglas fir, that is, as the geologists would say, is equivalent to it zonally. Thus by means of certain types, some of which are continuous and some equivalent, we can construct ecological tables for the two regions and match them with a considerable degree of accuracy. Of course, we have an advantage over the geologist because we can go into the field and check our arrangement against the climatic conditions as we observe them. Geologically we cannot do this, and this disadvantage results in a degree of uncertainty.

We might now inquire as to how it happens that the rocks of the Appalachian region and as far south as Texas show the same stratigraphic relations as those in England and certain portions of the continent of Europe. Geologists postulate a great trough, which they call a geosyncline. This was supposedly a great waterway, or possibly a lowland with extensive channels or narrow "seas" running through it. It is supposed to have sunk gradually through the ages and to have received the sediments that now constitute the Paleozoic series.

If we concede that such an extensive lowland with its waterways once existed, and that it extended over a considerable distance through what is now North America and Europe, we can readily understand how the early stages of the Flood would wash sediments into it, burying its life and producing what we know as the Paleozoic strata. Geologists tell us that the lower sediments of the Appalachian trough came from the east, but that when the Pennsylvanian "stage" was reached, a reversal began, and the Permian and Mesozoic strata were laid over the earlier deposits, this time from the west. This correlates with the fact, already mentioned, that the Rocky Mountain region is rich in Mesozoic materials.

We have today a very clear illustration of lateral rather than altitudinal zones as we travel from the Gulf of Mexico to Hudson Bay, a distance of about 2,000 miles. On such a journey we would go through all the life zones from the Lower Austral to Boreal. In California we find the same succession of life in an altitudinal difference of 12,000 feet and a horizontal distance of about 100 miles. So it can easily be seen that both altitude and latitude may enter into the distribution of biotic types. Such a situation may have prevailed in the ancient world.

12   177

If we attempt to illustrate the situation in the past, we should notice that a cross section of the country from, let us say, Oklahoma to California would show a succession composed of Paleozoic, Mesozoic, and Tertiary zones, or biotic provinces. Whether these were determined by altitude or by some other ecological factor, we might not be able to say with certainty. But the fact that in certain areas there is a vertical succession would seem to indicate that there was originally an altitudinal difference, leading to a time sequence in order of deposition. To illustrate, the fact that the Cretaceous of the western border of the plains overlies the Paleozoic, and is not simply continuous with it, would suggest that it was washed into place at a later stage than were the Paleozoic sediments. Similarly, California exhibits a succession between Mesozoic and Tertiary deposits. Of course, the time difference between the deposit of a Mesozoic stratum and a Tertiary stratum could possibly be only a matter of weeks or months.

Zonation is seen not only in land types but also in water life, both in fresh and salt water (Fig. 16.1). It is reasonable, there-

Fig. 16.1 Modern benthonic animals.

fore, that we recognize the marine "horizons" of the geologist as truly as we would the zones of land life with their land plants and animals. That such a zoning of marine forms did exist is shown by the methods now used in locating oil strata. Often in drilling wells the presence of a producing formation cannot be detected by the drillers, but is dependent on the identification of certain "indicator" microfossils in the laboratory. Such stratification could be possible on the basis of marine ecology.

What, then, is the ecological zonation theory? It is the suggestion that whatever succession may be found to be valid in the fossil deposits is due, not to successive deposition in long ages of time, but at least in part to successive deposition of materials from the original life, or ecological, zones. Only field studies can determine how much or how little real sequence is to be recognized in any given area, or how much correlation can be made between different regions. We cannot completely ignore the fact that some degree of order and system does exist in the fossils.

Some Problems Considered

As might be expected, there are some problems connected with this theory—as of any theory that might be proposed. A few of these merit consideration here.

To some, the ecological zonation theory may seem like surrendering to evolutionary geology. I do not so regard it, because it is simply recognizing a situation that exists in the field. It is not the facts of field geology with which we disagree, but the interpretation given them by evolutionary geologists. We must accept the facts as they are, and find an interpretation that will be in accord with the Bible record.

The question has been raised as to how any order or system could be possible if the ancient life zones were destroyed by a worldwide flood of violent action and catastrophic proportions. Possibly this question arises from our failure to form a correct picture of the action of the Flood. Many people seem to think of the Flood as one great surge or tidal wave that swept over the whole earth and mixed everything into a heterogeneous mass. According to this concept no order would be possible. But the manner in which we find the deposits completely fails to support such a concept. The very fact that there are certain types in one locality and different ones in others indicates that they were not thoroughly mixed. The wide extension of certain strata over hundreds of thousands of square miles of country, often quite regularly interbedded with others, indicates a systematic manner of burial.

We must keep in mind the Bible record, which says that it was at least 40 days and perhaps 150 days before the tops of the mountains were covered. The fossil beds reflect a rise of water that eroded the land surface gradually. As it advanced higher and higher it swept away the types of life, one after another, until finally everything was overwhelmed. This provides a basis for un-

UPLANDS

LOWLANDS

LAKE

Large mammals, birds, and upland forests

Small mammals,
dinosaurs, amphibians

Fig. 16.2 Diagrammatic presentation of ecological zonation to illustrate how animals could be buried in a roughly predictable order by rising floodwaters.

derstanding the fact that the fossils can be found in order at different levels of stratification.

One point should be made clear. The location where fossils are found does not necessarily represent the site of their original zone. Many of them have evidently been washed for long distances. Others may have been overwhelmed and buried without being transported for any distance, or possibly without being moved at all. But this is not in any way inconsistent with the idea that the arrangement of the fossil zones is in some measure due to original ecological zones, whether they were close to the present site of the fossil bed or far away from it.

It has been asked whether the more mobile forms of life would not escape to the higher lands, and thus destroy the evidence of their original zonal relations. Obviously a certain amount of such movement would take place, but it would be quite limited, and not involve the greater number of creatures. Certainly plants would not be involved, nor small or sluggish animals.

The point has been raised that there is no correlation between the taxonomic system of the animal kingdom and the order in the rocks, and this is true in a general way. But I do not regard it as any obstacle to the ecological zonation theory. Animals today are not arranged in their habitats according to taxonomic plan, but according to ecological relations. Exactly the same is true for the fossils. Protozoans are found in every series of rocks from the Cambrian to the Quaternary, as also are sponges, corals, brachiopods, mollusks, and lobsters. Many others such as

and lowland forests

MARSH

OCEAN

Seashore animals and plants

Swimming sea animals

Bottom 'dwelling sea animals

bryozoans, starfishes, crinoids, nautili, and barnacles are found in nearly all the series. Others are quite restricted, as for example, blastoids and ostracoderms to the lower Paleozoic, amphibians and reptiles from Carboniferous up, and birds and mammals from Jurassic up. When we examine these types in relation to their habitat requirements, we find a natural relationship. Such forms as protozoans, sponges, corals, and mollusks could live in water at almost any elevation. Blastoids and cystoids were evidently more selective in their requirements, for reasons of which we know little. But it is obvious that amphibians and reptiles could not have lived in the same environment as sponges, corals, and mollusks. They could, however, have lived at the same time, along the shores of the waterways occupied by the others. In like manner birds and mammals would come higher up in the ecological scale. We do no violence to any known principle of science when we conceive of these animal forms living in certain habitat relationships, and being buried as ecologic groups (Fig. 16.2).

Some are puzzled by the fact that the stratigraphy of the Southern Hemisphere is almost impossible to correlate with the Northern. Since there are few if any species common to the two hemispheres, how, it is asked, could we know that the classification of the Southern Hemisphere is correct in terms of the Northern? For an answer let us look at the life regions of the earth today. Africa south of the Sahara, for instance, has few if any species of plants and animals known in Europe and North America. Yet it has the same ecological types. The same might be said of South America. The same habitats exist, from low riparian environment through open grassland, brush, hardwood forests, coniferous forest, timberline, et cetera, as in other lands. Although the species are different, the ecologist has no difficulty in recognizing the ecological zones.

The paleontology of Africa and South America reveals that there are types of life similar in nature to those of the Northern Hemisphere, although of different species and genera, and in some cases of higher categories. This should offer no serious problem. To call an African formation Carboniferous would not mean that it has the same species as the Carboniferous of Europe or North America, but rather that it has types of life of the same general character, capable of living under the same conditions under which the others lived, and occurring in the same stratigraphic relationship. Having once established a system of naming the stratigraphic series of the Northern Hemisphere, it is only natural that the same terms should be used for the rocks of the Southern Hemisphere.

It is important to observe that no claim can be made to universal homogeneity for the ecological zones, or whatever we choose to call them. The strata as we now find them cannot represent a perfect order of the ancient world, inasmuch as catastrophic destruction of these ancient land and water zones would result in more or less confusion. All that can be claimed for the ecological zonation theory is that, to the extent we do find order or system at all in paleontology, we should ascribe it at least in part to ancient zonation rather than to ages of time.

Truth is above all the theories of men, but if we pursue it with an open mind we shall find it—accepting all the facts as we observe them, and interpreting these facts in harmony with the revealed truth as we find it in the Word of God.

REFERENCES

Clark, Harold W. 1946. The new diluvialism. Science Publications, Angwin, California. 222 pp.

Morris, Henry M. and John C. Whitcomb, Jr. 1961. The Genesis flood. The Presbyterian and Reformed Pub. Co., Philadelphia. 518 pp.

Price, George McCready. 1923. The new geology. Pacific Press Pub. Assn., Mountain View, California. 726. pp.

————. 1954. The story of the fossils. Pacific Press Pub. Assn., Mountain View, California. Paperback. 73 pp.

Rehwinkel, Alfred Martin. 1951. The flood in the light of the Bible, geology, and archaeology. Concordia Pub. House, St. Louis, Mo. 372 pp.

CHAPTER SEVENTEEN

The Dinosaurs

THERE WAS A TIME when some people did not believe that dinosaurs ever really existed. But those who have collected dinosaur remains in the midwest plains of Canada and the United States, or in the Colorado Plateau region, have no lingering doubt concerning their reality. Thousands of specimens have been found and excavated. Occasional skeletons are nearly complete, and some are in an undisturbed lifelike position. They need only to be removed from the ground and mounted in a museum.

Teeth, armor plates, and, rarely, skin are found, and these give us some concept of external appearance and type of diet. It is quite possible that some of the more detailed features of the flesh and body outline may be wrongly reconstructed, but the general shape and form are correct.

The fossil remains of these reptiles indicate that they were indeed a highly diversified group, ranging in size from that of a rabbit to tremendous beasts 20 feet high, 85 feet long, and weighing up to 50 tons (Romer, 1945, p. 229). It appears that some were relatively light-footed and had bipedal locomotion, while others were quadrupedal and moved about in a slow and cumbersome manner. Some were armored and others armorless. Some had horns, talons, or terrible teeth, while others had no apparent means of defense. Both carnivores and herbivores are represented. Fossil evidence suggests that certain types were well suited to an aquatic habitat, the larger forms being particularly benefited by the support that water offered them.

Because of the unusually large size of fossil reptiles, amateur

Fig. 17.1 Four dinosaur models (clockwise, beginning upper left): *Ankylosaurus,* length 25 feet; *Tyrannosaurus,* 50 feet; *Triceratops,* 20 feet; *Stegosaurus,* 20 feet.

collectors should not attempt to excavate them. Considerable effort with the proper techniques is necessary to bring them out without undue damage. Much expense may also be involved. If an amateur fossil hunter finds what appears to be a valuable specimen, either large or small, it would be well for him to cover the site with soil, mark the spot well, and inform the biology department of the nearest Seventh-day Adventist college or university. If excavation is warranted, arrangements can be made for it.

Classification of Reptiles

All reptiles belong to the class Reptilia. Nine orders are represented by fossils or by present-day living specimens:

1. *Chelonia.*—Turtles are not only abundant today in many parts of the world, but were likewise numerous in the past. One

185

fossil turtle, *Archelon,* grew to a length of 12 feet and weighed almost three tons (Matthews, 1962, p. 260). Both marine and land forms of fossil turtles are known. This order was either able to survive the Flood or was represented in the ark. Many ancient examples of this order are extinct, however.

2. *Ichthyosauria.*—This extinct group of fishlike reptiles was undoubtedly confined to water. Some of the larger fossil specimens reached a length of 30 feet. One of the most interesting fossils ever found is that of a female ichthyosaurus from the fine sediments of Stuttgart, Germany. This reptile had seven young specimens in her body. One or two of the young appeared as though they were being born at the time of the death of the mother—another example of sudden burial (Matthews, 1962, p. 262). It is also obvious that at least some of these ichthyosaurs were ovoviviparous (having eggs but keeping them in the body until they hatch).

3. *Sauropterygia.*—This constituted another group of marine reptiles, but their morphology was quite different from the above type. Perhaps most noticeable were their long slender necks. The appendages were paddlelike flippers obviously modified for swimming.

One of the more unusual features of extinct reptiles is the polished stones known as gastroliths, which are rarely found associated with some forms. Gastroliths may be up to four inches in diameter. It is possible that these animals swallowed these stones to aid in grinding up food. Embryos associated with the skeletons have been found, suggesting that they also were ovoviviparous.

4. *Rhynchocephalia.*—This abundant order of fossil "beak-headed" reptiles is represented today by only one living species, the tuatara (*Sphenodon punctatum*) of New Zealand. For a further discussion of this interesting animal, see chapter 38, "Missing Links and Living Fossils."

5. *Squamata.*—The snakes and lizards of today are included in this order. They are less well represented as fossils except for the mosasaurs, which were large sea-going lizards. The largest

lizards now living are the marine seaweed-eating lizards of the Galápagos Islands and the Komodo lizard of the East Indies, which reach lengths of six to eight feet.

6. *Crocodilia.*—Living crocodilians that reach a length of more than 20 feet are very similar to fossil representatives of this group. They are also closely related to the true dinosaurs, the order Saurischia. One fossil crocodile probably reached a length of 40 feet.

7. *Pterosauria.*—The most unusual of all ancient reptiles were these "winged lizards." The wing span of *Pteranodon* reached up to 25 feet, although the body probably weighed little more than the same number of pounds. They undoubtedly looked more like bats than reptiles because of the membranous wings. The bones were hollow and lightweight. They may take the honor of being the largest animal with flight ability to inhabit the earth. This group, frequently referred to in literature as pterodactyls, ranged in size from that of a sparrow to the *Pteranodon* above.

8. *Saurischia.*—The true dinosaurs belong to this and the following order, and the variation and adaptation that developed in these groups is amazing. Two of the best known of this first order are briefly described below.

Brontosaurus may be described as having a small skull, a long neck, a short back, and a long tail (Fig. 17.2). It was up to 70 feet long and weighed 30 to 40 tons. The feet were short and broad, fitted to support the weight of such a large animal. The teeth indicate that *Brontosaurus* was herbivorous. The bones of the skeleton are so arranged as to suggest that it lived in an aquatic habitat, using the abundant water plants for food, and the water for support of its huge body and for protection from its carnivorous relatives. Until footprints of the animal were found, it was thought that *Brontosaurus* was unable to support its own weight on land.

Remains of *Brontosaurus* are located in the Upper Jurassic Morrison formation, in North America. The majority of the specimens have been found in the Western United States in the States of Utah, Colorado, and Wyoming. This was one of the largest land animals ever to exist.

Tyrannosaurus rex was a huge, vicious reptile with a stride of more than seven feet (Fig. 17.1). This "terrible lizard" is considered the largest carnivorous reptile to have lived on land. It had many huge daggerlike teeth, used for tearing the flesh of other reptiles.

Fossil remains have been found in Mongolia and parts of Western North America. Skeletal portions from the Hell Creek area of Montana and remains and tracks from the Brazos River region of Texas are known. A large skeleton is displayed in the American Museum of Natural History in New York. While walking on the hind legs in its usual bipedal locomotion, it attained a height approaching 20 feet. It is estimated that the creature measured 50 feet long from nose to tail, with a weight of six to eight tons. It had tremendously strong hind legs and reduced clawed forelimbs with which it held its victims. Some of the

Fig. 17.2 Two dinosaur models (left): **Trachodon**, length 30 feet; **Brontosaurus**, 70 feet, one of the largest dinosaurs.

Fig. 17.3 Dinosaur footprints in ripple-marked sandstone.

tracks found in Texas measure 26 inches in length. The skull was about five feet long and primarily composed of bony arches for muscle attachment, but the bony brain case was relatively small.

9. *Ornithischia.*—A second order of dinosaurs with a hip girdle similar to that of birds. The *Trachodon* (Fig 17.2) was a large duck-billed dinosaur, and *Triceratops,* an odd reptile with a bony apron protecting the back of its neck and with three sharp horns on its head (Fig. 17.1). In 1923, in the Gobi Desert in Mongolia, an American Museum of Natural History expedition discovered the first fossil dinosaur eggs, some with unhatched embryo skeletons belonging to a near relative of *Triceratops.*

Stegosaurus, a unique creature with a double row of armor plates down its back and a weight of up to seven tons, had a small brain the size of a walnut (Fig. 17.1). An enlargement of the spinal cord near the pelvic girdle was 20 times larger than the brain, and perhaps served as a second "brain" to control the activities of the posterior portion of the body. Bert L. Taylor, of the Chicago *Tribune,* wrote this comic poem after hearing about *Stegosaurus:*

189

The Dinosaur

Behold the mighty dinosaur,
Famous in prehistoric lore,
Not only for his power and strength
But for his intellectual length.
You will observe by these remains
The creature had two sets of brains—
One in his head (the usual place),
The other at his spinal base.
Thus he could reason *a priori*
As well as *a posteriori*.
No problem bothered him a bit
He made both head and tail of it.
So wise was he, so wise and solemn,
Each thought filled just a spinal column.
If one brain found the pressure strong
It passed a few ideas along.
If something slipped his forward mind
'Twas rescued by the one behind.
And if in error he was caught
He had a saving afterthought.
As he thought twice before he spoke
He had no judgment to revoke.
Thus he could think without congestion
Upon both sides of every question.
Oh, gaze upon this model beast,
Defunct ten million years at least.

Problems of Interpretation

The sudden extinction of the dinosaurs, as shown by the geological record, is a mystery that the evolutionary paleontologists have considerable difficulty in explaining. Fossil reptiles are found first in the Pennsylvanian period. They become more numerous in the Permian and Triassic, and reach their climax in the Jurassic and Cretaceous. But they suddenly disappear toward the end of the Cretaceous. Beerbower (1960, p. 512) makes this interesting statement:

"What happened? Change of temperature? Change in the plants? Blasts of heat from a meteor; mammals eating dinosaur eggs; hyperpituitarism; change in oxygen concentration; over-specialization and senility of the dinosaur stalk; and so on . . . and on . . . and on? Some of these explanations seem absurd, but this illustrates the desperate straits into which paleontologists have been pushed by the mysterious extinction of the dinosaurs."

Three statements in the writings of Ellen G. White cast light on this problem:

"There were a class of very large animals which perished at the flood. God knew that the strength of man would decrease, and these mammoth animals could not be controlled by feeble man" (4SG 121).

"Bones of men and animals are found in the earth, in mountains and in valleys, showing that much larger men and beasts once lived upon the earth. I was shown that very large, powerful animals existed before the flood which do not now exist" (3SG 92).

The following statement presents another aspect of the problem:

"Every species of animal which God had created were preserved in the ark. The confused species which God did not create, which were the result of amalgamation, were destroyed by the flood" (3SG 75).

It would therefore appear that groups of reptiles not now represented among living forms must have been destroyed because they were not examples of God's original created kinds. However, this may be too hasty a conclusion. To say that the extinct subclasses and orders of reptiles were the result of amalgamation (hybridization) would be to say that hybridization occurred between subclasses and orders. This seems somewhat questionable in the light of the laws of reproduction and genetics

191

today. The original created kinds are more likely to be comparable to the smaller classification units. To equate them to orders or higher units, and to allow hybridization and variation to develop between different types of so large a kind is to suggest a great deal of change. It must be remembered, however, that the Bible does not say that animals may cross only within their species, or genus, or even within their created kind. (See chapter 3, "After His Kind.")

Another interpretation would suggest that the giants that resulted from hybridization were destroyed, and the original created representatives of the orders were taken into the ark but have since become extinct. One difficulty with this interpretation is that with the exception of the Chelonia, Rhynchocephalia, Squamata, and Crocodilia, few remains have been found in Cenozoic sediments. From this evidence it seems unlikely that they have existed at all since the Flood. Perhaps one could read "every species" in Ellen G. White's quotation to mean every species excepting the situation cited in her other two paragraphs, that is, every species except the very large animals God did not choose to preserve. To be sure, evolutionists have difficulty explaining the sudden disappearance of the dinosaurs, but Seventh-day Adventists are not without interpretative problems either.

REFERENCES

Beerbower, James R. 1960. Search for the past. Prentice-Hall, Inc., Englewood Cliffs, N.J. 562 pp.

Bird, Roland T. 1954. We captured a live brontosaur. Nat. Geog. Mag. 105: 707-720.

Colbert, Edwin H. 1945. The dinosaur book. Am. Mus. Nat. Hist., New York.

————. 1955. Evolution of the vertebrates; a history of the backboned animals through time. John Wiley & Sons, Inc., New York.

Jepsen, Glenn L. 1964. Riddle of the terrible lizards. Am. Sci. 52:227-246.

Matthews, William H., III. 1962. Fossils, an introduction to prehistoric life. Barnes & Noble, Inc., New York. 337 pp.

Romer, Alfred S. 1945. Vertebrate paleontology. 2d ed. Univ. Chicago Press, Chicago. 687 pp.

Simpson, George Gaylord. 1953. Life of the past. Yale Univ. Press, New Haven. 198 pp.

Swinton, W. E. 1934. The dinosaurs. Thomas Murby & Co., London.

CHAPTER EIGHTEEN

The Horse

THE DEVELOPMENT OF THE HORSE is allegedly one of the most concrete examples of evolution. The changes in size, type of teeth, shape of head, number of toes, et cetera, are frequently illustrated in books and museums as an undeniable evidence of the authenticity of the hypothesis of the development of living things. There is need for a thorough study of this example by a competent vertebrate paleontologist who can examine the problem objectively.

The evolution of the horse is usually shown as follows:

| Name | Geologic Period | Number of Toes | | Other Features |
		Front Foot	Hind Foot	
Hyracotherium (Eohippus)	Eocene	4	3	Dog Size
Mesohippus	Oligocene	3	3	Sheep size
Miohippus	Oligocene	3	3	Larger size
Merychippus	Miocene	3	3	Dew claws
Pliohippus	Pliocene	1	1	Splint bones
Equus	Pleistocene	1	1	Modern type

Hyracotherium was a small beast no larger than a medium-sized dog. It had an arched back, a relatively long tail, a short head with teeth adapted for browsing (eating foliage off bushes and trees), and less noticeable features that were quite different from the modern horse.

Mesohippus, the size of a collie dog, existed in the lower Oligocene. Also in the Oligocene was *Miohippus,* which along with *Mesohippus* had three toes on both front and hind feet. All three toes reached the ground, although the middle one is said to be larger. These two horses were also browsing animals.

13   193

Miocene horses included *Parahippus* and *Merychippus,* the latter being the one most often included in the series. It was a larger horse, the teeth of which appear to be more suited to grazing. This horse also had three toes, but the outer two were considerably smaller and may not have reached the ground. Such toes are frequently referred to as dew claws.

Pliohippus is usually considered a one-toed horse, but there is some confusion concerning the absence or presence of other toes. The feet have rarely been found in the fossil record (Romer, 1945, p. 429). Most of the literature and illustrations show only two splint bones on either side of the first toe bone (cannon bone).

Equus was not much different from *Pliohippus,* except for the foot, which shows no evidence of the side toes. In recent times man has developed a number of varieties of horses, but they all have only one toe.

Interpreting the Horse Series

Offhand, the horse series is impressive and leaves one wondering whether microevolution could account for this much change. There are a number of considerations, however, that make this example a little less conclusive than one is led to believe. The first animal of the series, *Hyracotherium (Eohippus)* is so different from the modern horse and so different from the next one in the series that there is a big question concerning its right to a place in the series. It should probably not be considered a horse at all, for the following reasons: a slender face with the

Fig. 18.1 The supposed evolution of the horse (small to large): *Eohippus,* *Mesohippus, Miohippus, Merychippus, Pliohippus,* and *Equus.*

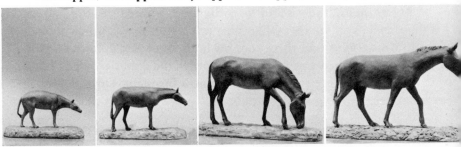

eyes midway along the side, the presence of canine teeth, and not much of a diastema (space between front teeth and back teeth), arched back, and long tail.

Of *Hyracotherium* Simpson (1945, p. 254) says, "Matthew has shown and insisted that *Hyracotherium* (including *Eohippus*) is so primitive that it is not much more definitely equid than tapirid, rhinocerotid, etc., but it is customary to place it at the root of the equid group." Some authorities consider *Hyracotherium* and *Eohippus* to be so similar that they should be included in the same genus if not the same species. This position is used in the discussion here.

There is thus a definite question about the validity of *Hyracotherium* in this series. "In the first place it is not clear that *Hyracotherium* was the ancestral horse" (Kerkut, 1960, p. 149). A search of the literature of fossil horse remains shows that there are quite a large number of genera of horses named from the Oligocene, Miocene, and Pliocene. Some of the fossil remains show the changes given in the table above; others do not. Some show adaptations and modifications in one direction, and others have anatomical changes in another direction. "Horse phylogeny is thus far from being the simple monophyletic, so-called orthogenetic, sequence that appears to be in most texts and popularizations" (Simpson, 1945, p. 254). There may be a certain amount of selecting from the array of species, those that show the best progression.

A problem mentioned in Kerkut's excellent little book *Implications of Evolution* (1960, pp. 145, 146) is the lack of quantitative and factual information on this subject. "In the first place it is difficult to find a critical account of the basic information.

. . . It takes a great deal of reading to find out for any particular genus just how complete the various parts of the body are and how much in the illustrated figures is due to clever reconstruction. The early papers were always careful to indicate by dotted lines or lack of shading the precise limits of the reconstructions, but later authors are not so careful. Secondly it is difficult to find out just how many specimens of a given genus are available for study."

Although the specimens are reported to be taken from consecutive geologic epochs, Eocene through Pleistocene, it is possible that errors have been made in stratigraphy. Since the material for some species is not abundant, and since these fossils are seldom all found in one area, there is room for further study of horse stratigraphy. The amount of time between the deposition of one stratum and the next is also in question. If some of these creatures were contemporaneous, the series as usually shown would be incorrect.

Another consideration is the variation itself. If the first animal of the series is removed because it does not qualify as a horse, the others do not show so wide a variation that micro-

Fig. 18.2 Bones of the hind feet of selected genera of horses. (Left to right): *Hyracotherium* (*Eohippus*, Eocene), *Orohippus* (Eocene), *Mesohippus* (Oligocene), *Merychippus* (Miocene), *Hypohippus* (browsing horse, Miocene), *Hipparion* (Pliocene), *Equus* (Pleistocene), *Equus* (recent).

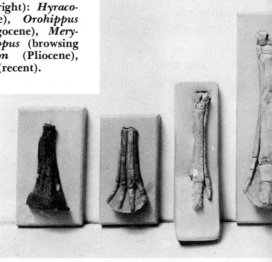

evolution cannot be called in to account for this series of horses. This interpretation would be generally acceptable to creationists, who recognize that considerable change has occurred since the Flood.

REFERENCES

Kerkut, G. A. 1960. Implications of evolution. Pergamon Press, New York. 174 pp.
Romer, Alfred Sherwood. 1945. Vertebrate paleontology. 2d ed. Univ. of Chicago Press. 687 pp.
Simpson, George Gaylord. 1945. The principles of classification and a classification of mammals. Bull. Am. Mus. Nat. Hist. 85:1-350.
————. 1951. Horses. Oxford Univ. Press, New York. 247 pp. 32 pls.

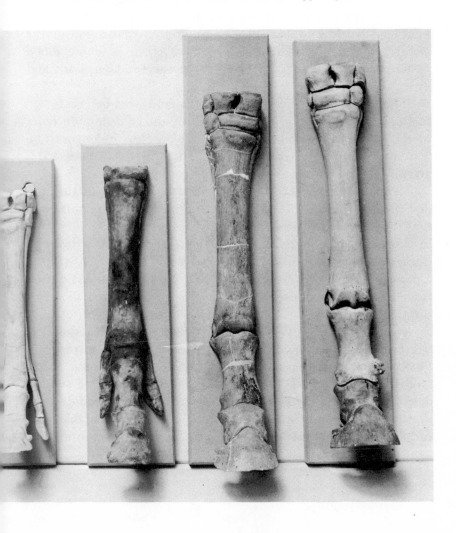

CHAPTER NINETEEN

Frozen Animals

THE RIDDLE OF THE FROZEN MAMMOTHS has puzzled scientists for many years. Did these animals roam the wilderness of the pre-Flood world and become caught in the catastrophe of the Deluge, or did they exist in Siberia and Alaska after the Flood under conditions that could bring about their sudden death and preservation?

The mammoth is referred to a thousand or more years ago in Chinese literature, which mentions the use of mammoth ivory in the manufacture of various articles of use or ornament. The first mammoth ivory was introduced into England about 1611, and since then its use has become increasingly popular.

Various theories have been proposed to account for the sudden preservation of these animals. One of the most popular was that the animals fell into crevasses in glaciers and were preserved in this natural deep freeze. Others thought they mired down in thick mud that later froze. Recently Ivan T. Sanderson (1960), a popular science writer, proposed that volcanic eruptions caused tremendous down drafts of cold air that quickly froze the creatures.

Seventh-day Adventists have generally believed that the Deluge brought about frigid conditions in the Arctic that froze the Flood waters and the mammoths. Consequently, frozen mammoths frequently have been cited as good evidence of sudden destruction by the Flood. Original research and firsthand descriptions of these elephants are few, and it is understandable that such an interpretation has been taken, based on misinformation from secondhand reports. There is ample evidence that the mammoth existed after the Flood.

In France and Spain, drawings and paintings on the walls and ceilings of limestone caves portray a number of extinct animals, sometimes in color. The artistry is remarkably lifelike except for the representations of humans, which in most cases appear to be stylized. The sketches and paintings of mammoths are well executed. It is difficult to come to any other conclusion than that the artists were personally acquainted with the animal. It would have been impossible for lifelike, detailed illustrations to have been drawn from descriptions passed down by word of mouth from survivors of the Flood.

Numerous artifacts have been found associated with mammoth remains. In one case bones of about 600 animals were located, along with many human evidences. It has been suggested that the animals died of natural causes such as blizzard, famine, drought, et cetera, and that the prehistoric people made of it a great occasion of feasting (Ley, 1959). Carvings of mammoths on ivory or bone fragments have also been found.

In North America spectacular cave drawings are not known, but one petroglyph in the Okanogan Valley of Washington State bears a striking resemblance to that of an elephant (Cain, 1950). The mammoths and the mastodons appear to have roamed over most of North America after the Flood. Mammoth bones have been found in Sandia Cave, New Mexico, and in La Brea tar pits in Los Angeles, California, for example. Both of these situations are obviously post-Flood. Mammoth bones were found in a cave on one of the Pribilof Islands. This island, which is in the Bering Strait, is of comparatively recent volcanic origin and has hardly a square foot of soil on it.

A very interesting association of human artifacts with mammoth bones and teeth was found in 1952 in Tepexpan, about 20 miles north of Mexico City. When an irrigation ditch was being dug, bones and tusks of an imperial mammoth were uncovered. Careful excavation of the site unearthed six artifacts associated with the bones. One, a projectile point, was actually lodged between two ribs. Two years later another site, a half mile away, produced further results equally significant. Artifacts were associated with the animal, and there was definite evidence of butchering. Space does not permit mentioning more cases of the association of human artifacts with mammoth remains, but many such sites have now been located (Wormington, 1957).

The discovery of a mastodon reported by Warren (1852) is worthy of note here. Although this chapter is concerned principally with the mammoth, Warren's description of the mastodon is typical of the situation in which both mastodons and mammoths are found. The mastodon is also an elephant not known to exist since the dawn of recorded history. The bones of this mastodon were found in New England, under about three feet of peat and a foot of shell marl. All the bones were present in correct relationship to one another, and in a good state of preservation.

"The anterior extremities were extended under and in front of the head, as if the animal had stretched out its arms in a forward direction to extricate itself from a morass into which it had sunk. The posterior extremities were extended forward under the body" (Warren, 1852). This old reference is but one of the first of many subsequent reports of mammoth remains in North America not far from the surface of the ground, and frequently in bogs or marshes—strongly suggestive of post-Flood situations.

The Beresovka Mammoth

The most classic frozen mammoth carcass known was found in 1901 on the banks of the Beresovka River in Siberia (Fig. 19.1). A scientific expedition reached the location in the fall several months after the discovery of the animal. The mammoth was mostly buried in frozen soil, which had slumped from the high banks behind it. Animals had chewed on the head, trunk, and back. Otherwise the animal was completely intact except for the tusks, which had been removed by the discoverer. The creature was in an upright position, with the front legs stretched forward and the back legs stretched forward also, but under the body. The hair was still attached to the skin on many parts of the body, but usually dropped away when the frozen mud was removed.

Much has been written about the remarkable preservation of frozen mammoths. This is certainly true, but as one reads the original descriptions of this animal he is impressed with the fact that secondary writers have always stressed this point and have failed to note that there was also considerable evidence of decay. In many respects the carcasses appeared to have been partly mummified as well as frozen. The internal organs, upon thawing, gave off most offensive odors and fell apart with the slightest touch (Herz, 1904).

As the excavation of the mammoth continued, it became apparent that the animal was covered with woolly hair one and one-half to two inches long. It also had bristle hairs eighteen inches long protruding beyond the shorter hair. It was obviously well protected against cold. Beneath the hair was a hide three-fourths of an inch thick and fat three and one-half inches thick.

The head was high, and the back sloped down toward the

Fig. 19.1 The Beresovka mammoth, found in Northeastern Siberia in 1901.

hind legs. The short tail had a tuft on the end, and the distended valvules of the anus, for protection against cold, was a feature not previously known by biologists. After many days of vigorous labor, the body was excavated, dismembered, and ready for shipping to St. Petersburg. Since it was now late fall, the parts remained frozen and there was no problem preserving the animal during transportation.

The tissues of the trunk and head were mostly missing on this specimen. Later in 1908, however, reports of another mammoth filtered through, and Pfizenmayer (1939), the taxidermist on the Beresovka mammoth expedition, returned to Siberia. This mammoth, located on the Sanga-Yurakh River near the north coast of Siberia, was not so well represented as the previous one. Fortunately, however, the trunk and other parts that were missing on the first one were found intact on the second. Its position appeared similar to that of the first. It had fallen from the riverbank when the river had eroded away part of the bank and the sun had thawed the soil. Frozen remains of bison, reindeer, rhinoceroses, horses, and ground squirrels have also been located in the frozen soils of Siberia.

Popular literature on mammoths has given the impression that vast numbers of intact frozen elephants have been found in the North. This is far from the truth. Not more than three dozen frozen mammoths have been found, and most of these were fragmentary—at least by the time scientists reached the sites. The most complete specimen of all was the Beresovka mammoth, which was stripped of flesh along the back and head and was without a trunk. Tolmachoff (1929) has taken considerable pains to check and authenticate every report of these animals. No doubt specimens unseen or unreported would increase this number, but it is safe to say that frozen mammoths are rare in Siberia and the arctic areas of North America.

The absence of mammoth remains in glaciated areas is a point that calls for further consideration. Much of northern Siberia and Alaska have not been glaciated, and it is mainly in such areas that these elephant remains are found. It is possible that the development of glaciers in North America cut the North American population of mammoths into two groups—those north of the glaciation belt of Canada and northern United States, and those to the south. Dying as they did north of the permafrost line, their bones and tusks would have been comparatively well preserved. In some instances even the flesh would have been preserved also. The usual absence of mammoth remains in glaciated areas suggests that mammoths and glaciation were at least partly contemporaneous. It is improbable the mammoths would roam about on the great glaciers.

Another aspect of the mammoth problem may be seen on the islands off the coast of Siberia, usually referred to as the New Siberian Islands. The remains of mammoths on these islands and along the extreme northern coast of Siberia are abundant. During the three summers of 1882-1884, Bunge, an early explorer of Siberia, collected 2,500 selected specimens of bones and tusks. This is an average of 14 specimens per day of collecting. Seven animals discovered in one day is certainly remarkable, even if a dozen persons helped him search. However, this is not quite the picture of islands composed of almost nothing but bones that is sometimes conveyed. If one calculates that collecting of ivory has been going on for several hundred years in Siberia, not to mention Alaska, one concludes that many thousands of mammoths must have been required to produce this ivory.

Northern ivory appears in all states of preservation. Some is white, solid, beautifully preserved, and recent in appearance. Other tusks are tarnished, broken, but still usable. Still others are badly decayed, fractured, and completely worthless. Two factors may contribute to the state of preservation of the ivory— the conditions of burial and time. Both factors are probably involved, although the condition of burial is the more important of the two. The mammoths may have lived for many years in these northern regions, and as they died, their bones and especially the tusks, were preserved in the marshy tundra and

203

forest soils. It is highly possible that the severe cold conditions and the establishing of the permafrost did not occur for a considerable time after the Flood.

The Arctic Tundra

To be able to arrive at a conclusion regarding the position of these frozen animals in time it is necessary to examine the environment in which they lived. Much of Siberia and northern Alaska have not been glaciated. These areas are well within the region of sufficiently cold, average annual temperatures, but the lack of precipitation has prevented the development of glaciers. Previous theories of the animals falling into fissures in the ice are based on some fact, however. These flat tundra areas are underlaid by lenses of frozen ice that vary from a few inches to 20 or more feet thick, and that extend up to a mile or more in width. In most cases these frozen lakes were covered with sphagnum moss. Later, soil washed down from adjacent hills or brought in by flooding rivers covered the lakes.

In Alaska, and from the evidence available in Siberia also, the frozen remains were located in the mud, not in the lenses of ice. Herz (1904) and Pfizenmayer (1939) were both of the opinion that the Beresovka mammoth was originally located in the ice, but it must be pointed out that the animal was not in an original position when they excavated it. It could have been either in the few feet of soil and peat above the ice, or in the silt below the ice. It is very improbable that the animal was actually frozen in the ice, since this situation appears similar to others, all of which show the remains in frozen soil, not in ice.

In 1884 Capt. C. L. Hooper, of the U.S. Revenue Steamer *Corwin,* stopped at Elephant Point in Kotzebue Sound, Alaska. He examined an ice layer along a considerable length of wave-cut cliff. At one place he discovered to his amazement a beaver's nest in position on a small island in the ice cliff. Apparently the beavers had selected a shallow place or a small island in a lake on which to build a nest. When the lake froze, the nest was pre-

Fig. 19.2 Lens of ice found below the frost line in Alaska.

served in it. Undercutting by wave action and thawing by the sun had crumbled the ice to form a cliff and expose the nest.

The tundra of Alaska today contains many small, shallow lakes or peat bogs. In the summertime walking over this country is difficult because the ground is saturated. The frozen soil two or three feet below the surface prevents drainage of the water. If a gradual change to colder climate conditions occurred the bogs would remain perpetually frozen, especially if soil were washed down over them. This would bring a return of conditions identical to those which must have existed in the past.

The lenses of ice seen along the banks of the Yukon River, the Porcupine River, the Old Crow River, the Beresovka River, and many others in Canada, Alaska, and Siberia no doubt formed in the following manner. The ancient landscape consisted of low, slightly undulating plains of tundra with many shallow lakes of various sizes. Moss began to grow, and peat moss also established itself. Twigs, leaves, et cetera, as well as moss, accumulated on the bottom of the lake, while peat spread out over the top. In some cases beavers lived in the water, and beaver-gnawed twigs were added to the litter on the bottom (Maddren, 1905). With an advancing cold climate, ice formed on the surface of the lakes in winter. With summer thawing, the water opened in the middle, not yet covered with sphagnum, but near the margins the insulating nature of the moss prevented the complete melting of the ice beneath it. Eventually moss covered the whole lake, preventing winter ice from melting (Russell, 1890). Shallow lakes of this nature would freeze to the bottom and remain frozen until warmer climate returned, or until they were exposed by the eroding action of a river.

On the basis of this reconstruction of past environment it would appear that the mammoth lived in an area of shallow lakes and peat bogs. The food found in the mouth and stomach of the Beresovka mammoth consisted of grasses and herbs of a variety that would be expected in the tundra, or in pine-spruce forests. Some of the genera of plants found in the stomach of this animal were the wild thyme (*Thymus*), a labiate; an alpine poppy (*Papaver*); the bitter crowfoot (*Ranunculus*); a variety of gentian, a lady's slipper (*Thalictrum*); *Atragene* and various other plants still found in Siberia or in the alpine regions of Europe (Pfizenmayer, 1939). From the picture that emerges it appears that the mammoth roamed the northern areas of the world during a time when the climate was very little milder than now.

With this understanding of the environment in which the mammoth lived, let us attempt to reconstruct the situation that brought about the sudden death of these animals. From the food in the mouth and stomach of the Beresovka mammoth and others, it appears that these animals were grazing on the vegetation of a northern meadow or peat bog, probably in the autumn. The heavy beasts unknowingly wandered out onto peat and away from the true edge of the meadow as they grazed. The layer of ice below the peat and vegetation gave the deceptive feeling of a firm foundation. Suddenly, as an elephant had a mouthful of plant food, the ice below the peat moss gave way with a crack, dropping the startled animals into the mucky, freezing water (Fig. 19.3). With two or three feet of peat and several inches of ice on the water, the mammoths could easily have become caught beneath these layers and drowned quickly.

State of Preservation

In other situations the animals may not have actually broken through ice, but may have become mired in the bogs and died of exhaustion or drowning. In several cases, the Beresovka mammoth especially, death must have come suddenly, otherwise, the animals would have swallowed their food.

Peat bogs are noted for the marvelous preservation of plant and animal materials that fall therein. Well-known cases are the 1,000- to 2,000-year-old human bodies discovered in peat bogs in Denmark. In one case a man had apparently been thrown into the bog against his will, as suggested by a length of rope around his neck. The preservation was remarkable; the tissues of the body were well preserved, although in a somewhat mummified condition. The expression of his face, even the hair on his chin, were all clearly discernible (Glob, 1954). The carcasses of the mammoths also give strong suggestion of preservation under similar conditions previous to freezing. Some of the soft parts, such as the trunk and ears, are considerably shrunken. Pfizenmayer (1939) referred to them as mummified.

The position of the Beresovka mammoth and the position of the bones located a few feet below the surface of a peat bog in New England, referred to earlier, were similar. Both appeared to be attempting to rise, or perhaps to swim.

It has been suggested that because the flesh is so well preserved the animals must have been frozen suddenly by exposure to a temperature of -150° F. (Hapgood, 1958). Such a statement does not take into account the preservative qualities of bog water. The preservation of the tissues by burial in peat and cold water for several years before freezing, for instance, could have

Fig. 19.3 Proposed explanation for the death and preservation of some mammoths, by sinking into a peat bog as they grazed.

an effect on the appearance of the tissues. It is conceivable, in some cases, that tissues of mammoths could have frozen and thawed several times and yet been preserved, if the animals were contained in a peat bog. Microscopic study of mammoth tissue must be made to determine whether such sudden freezing occurred. It would be difficult to obtain suitable tissues for such studies.

Animals that died in the fall, and at the time of a major long-term change in the climate toward more severe cold, could be quickly frozen with relatively good preservation of the cellular nature of the tissues, especially those located near the surfaces of the body. Major post-Flood climatic fluctuations are well authenticated by studies of tree rings, pollen analyses from peat bogs, and even historical records.

The Arctic and Antarctic regions are not devoid of fossils that should be considered true Flood remains. Coral reefs, coal measures, and palm fronds are indicative of a climate quite different from that experienced by the mammoths. How could animals with much hair, well insulated with fat, and eating sub-arctic vegetation, be living at the same time and in the same place with tropical fauna and flora? Yet this is what is required if the Flood is the cause of the destruction of both the mammoths and tropical plants and animals.

These considerations lead to the conclusion that the frozen mammoth of the far North was probably an animal of post-Flood times. These reasons may be briefly summarized as follows:

1. The animal was physically fitted for cold weather—long, thick hair, a thick layer of fat, and distended valvules of the anus.

2. The food contained in the animal's stomach was composed of plants from northern or alpine habitats.

3. The remains of the animals are located in peat bogs that are most probably post-Flood.

4. Obviously Flood fossils found in the North indicate a different climate than that experienced by the mammoths.

5. There is reason to believe that the mammoths associated with man were contemporary with those in Siberia and Alaska.

14

REFERENCES

Cain, H. Thomas. 1950. Petroglyphs of central Washington. Univ. Wash. Press, Seattle.

Cantwell, John C. 1887. A narrative account of the exploration of the Kabok River, Alaska, p. 48. *In* Cruise of the revenue steamer Corwin in the Arctic Ocean in the year 1885. Treasury Dept. Document, Washington.

Cowan, McT. I. 1960. Personal communication.

Digby, Bassett. 1926. The mammoth and mammoth hunting in Northeast Siberia. H. F. & G. Witherby, London.

Farrand, W. R. 1961. Frozen mammoths and modern geology. Science 133:729-735.

Glob, P. V. 1954. Lifelike man preserved 2,000 years in peat. Nat. Geo. Mag. 105 (3):419-430.

Hapgood, Charles H. 1958. Earth's shifting crust. Pantheon-Books, New York.

Herz, O. F. 1904. Frozen mammoths in Siberia. Annual Report Smithsonian Inst., pp. 611-625.

Hooper, C. L. 1884. Cruise of the U.S. revenue steamer Corwin in the Arctic Ocean in 1881. Notes and observations. Treasury Dept. Document No. 601, pp. 79-82.

Ley, Willy. 1959. Exotic zoology. Viking Press, New York.

Lippman, H. E. 1962. Science 137:449-452. (Rejoinder on article by Farrand, 1961.)

Maddren, A. G. 1905. Smithsonian exploration in Alaska in 1904, in search of mammoth and other fossil remains. Smithsonian Misc. Coll., vol. 49.

Pfizenmayer, Eugene W. 1939. Siberian man and mammoth. Blackie and Sons, Ltd., London.

Russell, I. C. 1890. Notes on the surface geology of Alaska. Bull. Geol. Soc. Am. 1:99-162.

Sanderson, Ivan T. 1960. Riddle of the frozen giants. The Saturday Evening Post 232 (29):39.

Tolmachoff, I. P. 1929. The carcasses of the mammoth and rhinoceros found in the frozen ground of Siberia. Trans. of the Am. Phil. Soc. 23:11-71.

Warren, John C. 1852. The mastodon giganteus of North America. John Wilson and Sons, 22 School St., Boston.

Wormington, H. M. 1957. Ancient man in North America. 4th ed. The Denver Mus. of Nat. Hist., Popular Series No. 4.

CHAPTER TWENTY

Ancient Man

IT IS DOUBTFUL that any phase of paleontology, indeed any science, has suffered from a lack of careful scientific study and has been plagued with so many heated controversies as has the study of ancient man. The layman who reads only occasional articles in popular journals or books is probably unaware of this situation, except for sensational cases such as that of the Piltdown man. Even elementary geology and paleontology textbooks give the impression of unanimity of opinions and adequacy of fossil material in this area. The research literature portrays a far different picture. Interpretations based on the fragmentary evidences are as numerous as authors. This is somewhat understandable when one considers that all the fossil evidence of prehistoric man, excluding Neanderthal man and Cro-magnon man, could be spread out on a medium-sized table. However, recent discoveries in Africa are increasing this number rapidly.

The paucity of the human fossil record has left no alternative but to attempt interpretations on the fragmentary remains. The tendency to accept preliminary, uncritical statements, to extend early descriptions based on few remains or little knowledge to all later discoveries, and to be blind to obvious errors because of preconceptions, has given the non-anthropologist a poor impression of the caliber of the work done in this field. There is much straining to make the few fossil remains fit the evolutionary theory in the critical area of human evolution.

Australopithicus, Zinjanthropus, and *Homo habilis.*—A number of fossil skull bones and fragments seeming to illustrate quite

Fig. 20.1 Excavation in Olduvai Gorge, East Africa.

a range in morphology have been found in South Africa over the past 40 years, and these have been given a number of generic names. Now the trend is to lump these together with some of the material from Olduvai Gorge in East Africa into the genus *Australopithicus*. Most of these specimens represent a small ape less than half the size of modern man. The morphology of the postcranial bones (rarely found) suggests a bipedal gait. The teeth show some tendency to lie intermediate between those of ape and man—large molars as in apes and no pronounced canine teeth as in humans.

In 1959 Dr. Louis Leakey discovered the skull of a humanlike creature in Olduvai Gorge that he called *Zinjanthropus*. Most notable of its features were the very large molar teeth and the extremely low forehead, which flattened almost immediately above the eyebrows. The fossil was thought to be the remains of an individual about 18 years of age. Potassium-argon dating has given him a supposed age of 1.75 million years.

Since then a number of skull fragments, jaws, and postcranial parts have been found in the same general region. Those working with this material have recently proposed a new scheme of classification, which places some of the remains in the genus *Homo* under the name *Homo habilis,* and the others in the Australopithecine subfamily. *Homo habilis* is based on fragmentary remains of several specimens that are thought to lie intermediate between the man-apes *(Australopithicus)* and the most primitive ape-men (Java man—*Homo erectus).*

Homo erectus.—Java man was first represented by a discovery consisting of a skull cap, femur, pieces of nasal bones, and three teeth. In 1936, 1938, and 1939 three more skulls were found, which helped to fill in the information not obtainable because of the poor condition of the first skull. The specimens indicate a flat nose, protruding teeth and jaws, and a small cranial capacity, 900 cc. as compared to an average of around 1500 cc. in European man, and 1350 cc. for all modern men.

Nine skulls or fragments found in 1931 and 1932 not far from the site of the first remains have characteristics much closer to Neanderthal man than Java man. These have been called Solo man, *Homo soloensis.*

A cave in north central China produced fragments of nearly 45 skulls (Peking man). Few bones other than the skulls were found. Broken hackberry seeds and charcoal indicated that the cave had been occupied by prehistoric man. These remains, along with those from Java, show evidence of more than accidental damage to the skulls, usually at the rear or base. This material was lost during World War II, but F. Weidenreich's monograph (1943) and plaster casts of the originals rather adequately describe the material despite its loss. These remains were quite similar to the Java material, but the cranial capacity averaged somewhat larger.

Homo neanderthalensis.—The remains of Neanderthal or neanderthal-like men are found in Africa, Europe, and Asia. A number of nearly complete skeletons and skulls are known, as well as much fragmentary material. Without doubt it is the best authenticated of the so-called primitive men. The original finds were unearthed in Germany in 1856 (Fig. 20.2). The description in most textbooks, until recently, was of a man with low brow, receding chin, stooped stance, and low-slung head. The description along with the bestial illustrations often associated with Neanderthal man in biology and geology textbooks may have been instrumental in turning many an inquiring mind to the acceptance of the animal origin of man.

Cro-magnon man (*Homo sapiens*).—This prehistoric occupant of Europe was variable in size and skull features, but many specimens had heights of six feet or more, high foreheads, large crania equal to or surpassing that of modern man, and other features that clearly label this man as no connecting link in human evolution. Magnificent artistry and sculpture in caves of France and Spain are attributed to him. He is thought to have replaced Neanderthal man in Europe, not by evolution, but by migration or invasion. This point has been questioned, however (Brace, 1964).

Interpretations

There is little doubt that the Australopithecinae comprise a varied group of apes, but they do show manlike characteristics not seen in modern apes. They may have walked erect, at least in part, and the cranial capacity was somewhat larger than in similar modern animals of the same size. Claims have been made concerning the use of stone tools by these apes, but this is seriously doubted by several paleontologists. Although considered by many evolutionists to be important in human evolution, these creatures are not men, even though written descriptions may label them as man-apes.

Olduvai Gorge in East Africa has proved to be a veritable treasure-trove for paleontologists and anthropologists. A great many fossils are seen scattered over the slopes of this gulley that has been water cut into a filled-in lake or valley of pre-Pleistocene or Pleistocene times. Several types of prehistoric elephants (mastodons, dinotheria, and types allied to the Indian elephant), one-toed and three-toed horses, rhinoceroses, hippopotamuses, pigs, primitive antelopes, and giant giraffes are found here. Dr. L. S. B. Leakey discovered the human remains (if indeed they are human) after years of fossil hunting in Africa.

From a study of the research literature on the material from East Africa one gets the distinct impression that miscellaneous fragmentary remains of a number of specimens are being found in about the same level. To attempt to build a composite (*Homo habilis*) on the basis of this material is highly questionable, and this proposal by Leakey and his associates has been seriously challenged by a number of eminent anthropologists. It is much too soon to assess fully these findings.

It seems especially appropriate to use caution when reading material on this subject, since so much personal opinion can be involved in interpreting the simian (apelike) or human characteristics of a skull or skeleton. Perfectly human characteristics are overlooked, while points that depart from modern normalcy are stressed, especially if they concern a character more strongly developed in apes. In this area there is a crying need for objective evaluation. It would be a great contribution to creationists if a qualified person could be encouraged with financial support to devote time to detailed research on this subject.

The controversy over Java man was one of the most heated in the history of science. The secretive way in which Eugene Dubois, a Dutch physician, kept the first *Pithecanthropus* pieces for years, allowing only a few privileged persons to see them, did not help reduce the confusion. Was it ape or human? Dubois himself changed his mind at least once, ending up with the published opinion that it was not human (von Koenigswald, 1956, p. 55). The discovery later of several more skulls or parts thereof, helped clear the air. It now is a little more certain that Java man was human. The sloping forehead and receding chin are considered apelike, but these features are not unseen today. The teeth are quite human in form, and the cranial capacity was near the low end of the range for modern humans. Cranial capacity cannot be used as a reliable index of intelligence, although there may be a rough relationship.

What can be said of these remains? Are they links in an evolutionary series? Many more links will be needed before an evolutionary chain is intact. The few extant links do not indicate evolution any more than they do degeneration. Could these remains represent primitive and degenerate human beings who wandered away from the centers of civilization, lapsed gradually into a crude and degraded social and economic culture that included cannibalism? The bashed-in skulls of these finds in Africa, Java, and China all indicate this possibility.

A fact that needs to be established is the contemporaneous existence of modern-type humans with so-called men-apes and ape-men. Such specimens probably have been located, but have been explained away or ignored. A case in point is a well-preserved skeleton of a normal human found at a low level of Olduvai Gorge. Its appearance at this level has perplexed paleontologists, but an attempt has been made to explain this situation by theorizing that the partial filling of Olduvai Gorge with sediments during late Pleistocene times created a shallow valley where the inhabitants of that time buried their dead. In recent times the Olduvai River cut away most of this valley sediment, but small patches of these sediments remain on the slopes of the present gorge, and the skeleton was probably in these sediments but at a level that looked like original Pliocene or early Pleistocene (von Koenigswald, 1956, p. 174). Whether this is so or not (some authorities question this explanation) cannot be determined without detailed survey of the area, and even then it may not be possible to settle the matter. There is a distinct possibility, however, that the man whose skeleton was uncovered was contemporaneous with *Homo habilis,* or nearly so.

Solo man found in river gravels six miles from Trinil, the location of the first fragments seen by Dubois, was perhaps located at a different level. Rivers are notoriously changeable, moving their courses from one position to another, eroding one bank, depositing materials at another, and then reversing the process. It is again entirely possible that these early dwellers in Java were not as far removed chronologically from Java man as is generally thought.

It was the prevailing opinion for many years that Neanderthal was in the direct line of evolution to modern man. The discovery some years ago of a number of skeletons with modern features buried near Neanderthal remains in the Mount Carmel region of Palestine proved such conclusive evidence of the contemporaneity of these two types that this opinion regarding Neanderthal man has changed. He is now considered by evolutionists to be a dead-end branch off the main line of evolution from ape to man. A foot recently found in Olduvai Gorge on a level comparable with *Zinjanthropus* and *Homo habilis* is almost identical to the modern human foot. These are four examples of possible contemporaneous existence of modern-type man with so-called primitive man. Several workers in the field of human evolution have expressed the opinion that humans of modern morphology (the *sapiens* type) go back as far as the Pliocene or farther (Lever, 1958, p. 151). Aside from these four, other human remains, especially the Swanscombe, Dénise, and Kanjera skulls, found in strata that may be contemporaneous with Java and Peking man, have supported this view, because these skulls are not significantly different from the *Homo sapiens* skulls.

Adequate study of the problem will probably lead to the conclusion that modernlike man will prove to be contemporaneous with these degenerate forms of man. Although we do not know what Adam looked like, and should not use our own physiognomy as a criterion, we know that he did not have a degenerate, apelike appearance.

The evidence of humans of superior size and intellectual capacity is not abundant, though a few remains may qualify. Several fragments of jaws of large size have been found in Europe and in Java. If the humans to whom these jaws originally belonged were proportioned in keeping with the massive jaws, they would be somewhat larger than modern man. One estimate of eight feet three inches was made for one of the Java jaws (von Koenigswald, 1956, p. 113).

More spectacular but still fragmentary are the giant teeth found by von Koenigswald in Chinese drugstores. If these teeth are human and are any indication of the size of the person, he may have been 11½ feet tall and have weighed between 880 and 1,320 pounds (von Koenigswald, 1956, p. 113). Several other miscellaneous fragments consisting of upper or lower jaws and portions of the skull have been considered abnormally large. Reports of large human footprints have been given in several sources, but questions concerning their authenticity have arisen. Until positive and clear-cut confirmation is available, these evidences cannot be given much weight, even though they may be genuine fossils.

In recent years anthropologists have become increasingly perplexed concerning the criteria for separating man from ape. Some of the characteristics formerly considered limited to man have been noticed on the skeletons of the Australopithecine fossils, which are unquestionably apes and not man. Investigators are deciding that it is almost impossible to decide whether a specimen is from man or ape unless there is considerably more than the meager fragments upon which most of the descriptions are based. Le Gros Clark says: "Probably the definition of 'Man' will ultimately have to rest on a functional rather than an anatomical basis, the criteria of humanity being the ability to speak and make tools" (Le Gros Clark, 1955, p. 73).

Neanderthal Man Straightens Up

Neanderthal man and Cro-magnon man are not a very useful support for evolution, for they are so much like modern human beings. This is especially true since the recent discovery that the classic descriptions of Neanderthal man were based in large part on the remains of a Neanderthal skeleton of a man suffering from severe osteoarthritis. Straus and Cave (1957) make the following comments:

"There is thus no valid reason for the assumption that the posture of Neanderthal man of the fourth glacial period differed significantly from that of present-day men. This is not to deny that his limbs, as well as his skull, exhibit distinctive features— features which collectively distinguish him from all groups of modern men. In other words, his 'total morphological pattern,' in the phraseology of Le Gros Clark (1955), differs from that of 'sapiens' man. Yet there is nothing in this total morphological pattern to justify the common assumption that Neanderthal man was other than a fully erect biped when standing and walking. It may be that the arthritic 'old man' of La Chapelle-aux-Saints, the postural prototype of Neanderthal man, did actually stand and walk with something of a pathological kyphosis; but, if so, he has his counterparts in modern men similarly afflicted with spinal osteoarthritis. He cannot, in view of his manifest pathology, be used to provide us with a reliable picture of a healthy, normal Neanderthalian. Notwithstanding, if he could be reincarnated and placed in a New York subway—provided that he were bathed, shaved, and dressed in modern clothing— it is doubtful whether he would attract any more attention than some of its other denizens."

This case should not be left without again referring to a point mentioned earlier. Boule's description (1911-1913) of the La Chapelle-aux-Saints skeleton rather well fixed opinion with respect to Neanderthal posture for many years. How did he arrive at these decisions? Some of the obvious pathological deformities seem to have been overlooked entirely or, if mentioned, were not considered in the reconstruction of the posture. The reasons for this are hidden in the lines of this further quotation from Straus and Cave (1957):

"In any event, it is certain that some of Boule's contemporaries regarded Neanderthal man as ancestral to all later hominid forms, and under the influence of the intellectual or philo-

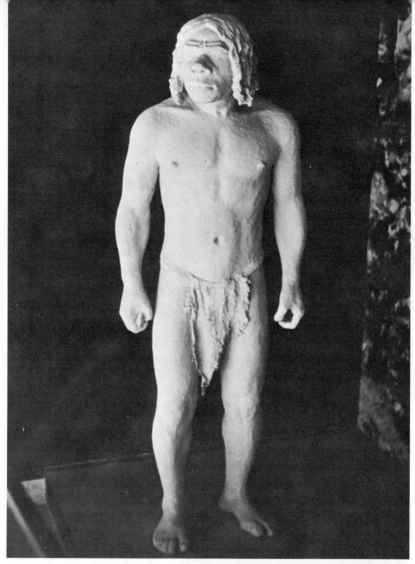

Fig. 20.2 Neanderthal man, in the museum near the original discovery site.

sophical climate in which their studies of human evolution were conducted, it was but natural for them to expect him to be more simian and more imperfect, both cerebrally and posturally, than the later forms of humanity which succeeded and replaced him. This is not an unusual phenomenon. The story of the Piltdown hoax is an even more striking example of the influence of prevailing philosophical climates on scientific thought (Straus,

1954). It seems unlikely, moreover, that we are free from similar influences at the present time. Some of the current appraisals of the Australopithecinae may well prove to be a case in point."

The chronological placing of these men must be considered. There is no value in attempting to assign specific dates, since the paleontological evidence is insufficient. It is probable, however, that none of these mentioned thus far (except perhaps the large remains) are pre-Flood remains. This conclusion is reached by considering the places in which the fossils have been found, the morphology of the skulls, and the animals associated with them. Fossils found in caves could hardly be pre-Flood. Peking, Neanderthal, and Cro-magnon man would be excluded from the possibility of pre-Flood age for this reason. Java, Solo, and East Africa man have been found in river gravels or sediments containing Pleistocene animals that are most likely post-Flood.

Before leaving the topic of primitive man, it would be negligence not to include a short discussion of Piltdown man, *Eoanthropus dawsoni*. In 1912 Charles Dawson found the remains of several skulls in gravel near Piltdown, Sussex, England. From then until 1953 these fragments were considered among the evidences for primitive man, the product of an intermediate branch of evolution from ape to man. Careful examination of the bone pieces at that time revealed the startling information that the whole thing was a fabrication, a hoax perpetrated by Dawson, probably, to achieve recognition. The skulls were collections of pieces, some human and some not. One skull had a human skull cap but an ape lower jaw. The teeth had been filed and the front of the jaw broken off to obscure the simian origin. Some fragments used had been stained to hide the fact that the bones were not fossil, but fresh. In drilling into the bones, researchers obtained shavings rather than powder, as would be expected in truly fossilized bone. Consequently, since 1953 Piltdown man has been removed from the evolutionary hall of fame!

REFERENCES

Bates, Marston. 1961. Man in nature. Prentice-Hall, Inc., Englewood Cliffs, N.J. 116 pp.

Boule, M. 1911-1913. Fossil men. Oliver and Boyd, Edinburgh. (English translation, 1923.) 504 pp.

Brace, C. L. 1964. The fate of the "classic" Neanderthals: A consideration of hominid catastrophism. Current Anthropology, February.

Clark, Harold W. 1946. The new diluvialism. Science Publications, Angwin, California, pp. 171-188.

Current Anthropology. 1965. The origin of man 6 (4):342-446. A collection of several important reprinted and original articles relevant to the new finds in Olduvai Gorge, East Africa.

Dart, Raymond A. 1959. Adventures with the missing link. Harper and Brothers, New York. 255 pp.

Klotz, John W. 1955. Genes, Genesis, and evolution. Concordia Pub. House, St. Louis. 575 pp.

Koenigswald, G. H. R. von. 1956. Meeting prehistoric man. The Scientific Book Club, London. 216 pp.

Le Gros Clark, W. E. 1955. The fossil evidence of human evolution: an introduction to the study of palaeo-anthropology. Univ. of Chicago Press. 181 pp.

————. 1965. History of the primates. Phoenix Books. The Univ. of Chicago Press. 127 pp.

————. 1959. The antecedents of man. Edinburgh Univ. Press, Edinburgh. 374 pp.

Lever, Jan. 1958. Creation and evolution. Grand Rapids International Pub., Grand Rapids, Mich. 244 pp.

Marsh, Frank L. 1950. Studies in creationism. Review and Herald Pub. Assn., Washington, D.C., pp. 350-366.

————. 1967. Life, man, and time. 2d ed. Outdoor Pictures, Escondido, California, pp. 192-211.

Robinson, J. T. 1965. *Homo 'habilis'* and the Australopithecines. Nature 205 (4967): 121-124.

Romer, Alfred Sherwood. 1945. Vertebrate paleontology. 2d ed. Univ. of Chicago Press. 687 pp.

Straus, William L., Jr. and A. J. E. Cave. 1957. Pathology and the posture of Neanderthal man. Quarterly Review of Biology 32:348-363.

Tax, Sol (Ed.). 1960. The evolution of man. Univ. of Chicago Press. 473 pp.

Weidenreich, F. 1943. The skull of *Sinanthropus pekinensis:* A comparative study on a primitive hominid skull. Pal. Sinica, new ser. D, No. 10.

Weiner, J. S. 1955. The Piltdown forgery. Ox. Univ. Press, New York. 214 pp.

GLACIATION

"The waters are hid as with a stone, and the face of the deep is frozen."

Job 38:30

Fig. 21.1   A great glacier in the St. Elias Mountains, Yukon, Canada.

Fig. 21.2   A lateral moraine left by Athabaska Glacier, Alberta, Canada.

CHAPTER TWENTY-ONE

Rivers of Ice

In 1840 Louis Agassiz, one of the most interesting scientific characters of the nineteenth century, published his *Etudes sur les Glaciers*. Prior to this time a few geologists and mountaineers had become convinced that glaciers once acted more widely in sculpturing the mountain valleys than at present. However, the book by Agassiz was the first widely read work on the subject, and it generated considerable excitement, as well it should. The "ice age" concept, which appears to have originated with Agassiz, must have startled many people. Today we are accustomed to thinking of a time of extensive glaciation in the remote past, but in those days it seemed incredible that masses of ice could have covered large portions of northern Europe and North America.

Because of the "ages" usually associated with glaciation, there was formerly a tendency in Adventist circles to view this theory with skepticism. Perhaps only within the past 25 years has the idea of continental glaciation been generally accepted by Adventist scientists and educated laymen. Part of the delay in the incorporation of this concept into our historical sequence for the earth was due to a rather steady insistence in denominational writings that the evidences of glaciation could all be explained by water action. Some writers outside the church were of the same opinion, as may be seen by Howorth's monumental volumes, *The Mammoth and the Flood* (1887), *The Glacial Nightmare and the Flood* (1893), and *Ice or Water* (1905), scholarly works that contended that glacial evidences were ac-

15

tually evidences of a deluge. As a matter of fact, the evidences of glaciation are very clear and cannot be accounted for by the workings of water. Modern glaciers are in the process of leaving unmistakable marks and deposits that serve as keys to the interpretation of similar phenomena in areas not presently occupied by glaciers.

The Glaciers of Today

In order to understand this topic it is necessary to consider some of the evidences and mechanics of glaciation. First let us examine modern glaciers, and then the evidence for past continental glaciers.

If a helicopter were to drop us off at the upper end or source of a mountain glacier, and we were to walk down the glacier to, and beyond, its end (terminus), the following features might come to our attention. A glacier must be fed by a source of snow accumulation. This usually consists of a snow field located at an elevation where snowfall is heavy and accumulation exceeds melting. As snow becomes covered by successive seasons of snowfall it changes slowly into a granular texture and eventually into nearly solid ice, which may be milky or bluish in appearance. As the ice moves downslope it pulls away from the head of the canyon (unless it is a large glacier that overlies completely the topography), taking with it some boulders and rocks embedded in the ice. This action, if continued, will eventually pluck out a depression in the side of the mountain (a cirque). Closely adjacent cirques and those that have dug in from both sides of a mountain or range create cockscomb peaks and ridges between them (Fig. 21.5).

Walking down a glacier may not be an easy task, because of the unevenness of the surface. Crevasses may block the way and make detours necessary. These are usually caused by stresses in the ice resulting from elevation changes on the surface of the ground below the ice and bending of ice around corners. The walls of the canyon may show scouring and grooves where the glacier filled the canyon to a higher level in past times. Feeder glaciers may cascade from adjacent valleys and join the main flow. When this occurs, median moraines consisting of long lines of rock and soil may define the boundary between the ice of the main glacier and that of the smaller, "feeder" glacier. This material is dragged out from the sides of the canyon that confines the small glacier (Fig. 21.1).

The same action is occurring along the sides of the main glacier, but this is not so noticeable except at the end of the glacier where these materials are deposited as long ridges (lateral moraines), often well beyond the terminus of the present glacier (Fig. 21.2). There also may be a terminal moraine, but this will probably be less clear because it is breached and broken down by streams fed by the melting of the glacial ice. The lateral and terminal moraines are often well enough developed to confine meltwater from the receding glacier. These lakes usually have the characteristic blue-green color of glacial lakes because of the rock powder suspended in the water.

In some cases it is possible to step off the thin lip of the glacier onto the scoured floor of the canyon, but in most instances the end of the glacier is a cliff of ice and the polished or scoured floor of the canyon is covered with debris brought down by the glacier. If our trip has taken us down a relatively large glacier we may notice that the lower end is broken up into blocks of ice of various sizes, and that gravel is being washed in between, and even over, these blocks. When they melt, depressions are left in the terrain (kettles) and a hummocky appearance is often seen (kames). Glacial deposits are generally not sorted unless they have been worked by the stream issuing from the ice.

Large boulders are often strewn on the surface of a glacier where they have come to rest after falling from the surrounding canyon walls. Similar blocks may also be incorporated into the ice at the bottom of the glacier, and moved along. Such boulders deposited over the surface of the ground by a retreating glacier are known as glacial erratics (Fig. 21.4). Before being dropped

227

by the melting ice, they may have left gouges and grooves in the valley floor where they were dragged along. Near Conway, New Hampshire, there is a granite erratic weighing close to 10,000 tons.

An interesting formation resulting from glacial action is the esker, which is usually associated with large or stagnant glaciers. An esker is a ridge of glacial deposit that often runs across country with little regard for normal drainage patterns or elevations. Generally, it will run roughly parallel to the direction of the flow of the ice, and will traverse hills and valleys. The esker is thought to be formed by streams running in tunnels under the ice. Materials are deposited on the floor of the stream tunnel while the ice above is melted. When the glacier retreats, a long twisting ridge is seen on the surface of the ground.

Mountains that have been glaciated in the past have characteristic U-shaped valleys, rounded domes, and polished rocks. Yosemite National Park with its domes and polish illustrates these features well. Yosemite Valley has been reworked by streams, so that the U-shape is not so evident. The floor is now flat and covered with vegetation. Canyons that have been cut entirely or mostly by water are usually V-shaped.

If the glacier down which we hiked flowed into the sea, we would have noticed icebergs forming at the terminus. There the

Fig. 21.3 Glacial polish in southern Ontario, Canada.

Fig. 21.4 An erratic boulder dropped in northwest Washington by a retreating glacier. Granite boulder on metamorphic rock.

blocks break away from the end, which has pushed into deep water far enough to float. If the water is shallow the bottom of the glacier will gouge the floor of the valley and produce moraines similar to those already described, except for the fact that they are below the surface of the water. Rising sea levels during the past several thousand years have allowed the oceans to pour into the coastal valleys now vacated by glaciers. Some of these fiords still have glaciers at their heads. British Columbia, Alaska, Norway, and Greenland have this type of coastline.

Resorting to our imaginary helicopter again, let us fly to Antarctica or Greenland and settle on the great sheet of ice. Continental glaciers cover the mountains and plains of practically all of Antarctica, and much of Greenland. The Antarctic ice sheet is one and one-half times as large as the United States and covers 4,860,000 square miles. The smaller Greenland ice cap covers about 670,000 square miles. Together, the two contain 96 per cent of the world's glacial ice and blanket nearly 10 per cent of the total land area of the globe. The Antarctic and Greenland ice sheets both reach elevations of 10,000 feet or more. If these masses of ice were melted and returned to the sea the level would rise nearly 100 feet (Flint, 1963, p. 261).

Glaciers move east and west through the mountains of Greenland from the high dome of ice resting in the center of the island.

229

They carry with them rock debris, which is deposited at sea when the glaciers calve (form icebergs) and eventually melt. Before melting they may travel as far as 1,800 miles in two and one-half years. Greenland has more than 100 glaciers that continually drop icebergs into the sea. Icebergs produced by glaciers of Antarctica may be as much as 100 kilometers long and may rise 90 meters above the water. This would mean that they are about 800 meters thick. Cores taken from large ice islands in the Arctic Ocean indicate that these icebergs have been floating there for many years. They circle around and around and seldom get out into the Atlantic or Pacific. The summer thawing and the winter accumulation of snow produce a layering of the ice that can be counted like rings in a tree.

Occasionally large glaciers become stagnant. Piedmont glaciers, as they are then called, come about by the coalescence of several glaciers or the spreading out of a glacier onto the valley or plains beyond the mountains. The Malaspina piedmont glacier of Alaska covers an area of approximately 1,500 square miles. Large sections of it are mantled by rock and soil. Trees grow undisturbed on it, and one would not suspect the presence of a glacier if erosion had not exposed the ice lying below the trees and soil. In 1962 I flew over the St. Elias Mountains, which are the source of the glaciers that produce the Malaspina. It is understandable how such a large glacier has been pushed out so far onto the low coastal plains when the extent of the glaciation of the St. Elias Mountains is seen. This glaciation compares with that of Iceland, and is the third or fourth most extensive glacial area in the world today.

Glaciers of the Past

Have large glaciers covered portions of the earth's surface in the past that are now completely devoid of glaciers? Was there an ice age, and if so, when did it occur? The first requirement in settling this problem is to examine the evidence advanced for past large-scale glaciation.

The ice sheets that formerly covered a large area of North America are said to have reached south to a latitude of 38°. Today much of the formerly glaciated land is heavily populated, and it is difficult to visualize such extensive glacial development. Past glaciation is determined mainly from the evidence of glacial erosion and deposition. The Canadian shield of crystalline bedrock is largely scoured rock with glacial drift, a few eskers, many lakes, and extensive areas of lake sediments caused by former obstruction of the drainage. In southern Ontario the drift is thicker, and moraines and drumlins occur.

In the United States, particularly in the region south and southwest of the Great Lakes, the glacial drift is thick on top of sedimentary bedrock. Rugged moraines, pitted outwash plains, eskers, and vast fields of drumlins are found in that region. The exact boundary of glaciation in southwestern Wisconsin consists of an end moraine of glacial drift. Moraines are common in the plains States.

In the central West several lines of moraines may be observed, one behind another, with kettles, kames, and drumlins. Terminal moraines consist of fragments of every conceivable size, heterogeneously mixed. The deposit is unsorted and un-

Fig. 21.5 Extensive glaciation in the St. Elias Mountains of Yukon.

stratified, and contains few organic remains. The mass consists of debris carried on top of the glacier, and materials frozen to the bottom or pushed along in front of it. Moraines can be traced almost entirely across the continent. Note this old but accurate statement from a geology textbook:

"A very conspicuous feature of the Wisconsin drift is the great terminal moraine, or rather morainic belt, which itself records many episodes in the history of the ice. The moraine has been traced all across the continent; beginning in the island of Nantucket, it passes through the islands off the south coast of New England and New York, Martha's Vineyard, Block Island, Long Island, and Staten Island, to the mainland of New Jersey, which it crosses northwestward into Pennsylvania, running to the New York border, but turns southwest at nearly a right angle and reaches almost to the Ohio River at Cincinnati. In an irregular sinuous line it crosses the States of Indiana, Illinois, and Iowa, and thence northwestward through the Dakotas into Montana, where it nearly follows the international boundary line to the mountains of the Pacific Coast" (Scott, 1932, vol. II, p. 403; see also Fig. 21.6).

Most erratic boulders were carried only short distances, but many have been transported by glaciers for hundreds of miles. Chunks of copper torn from the Upper Peninsula of Michigan have been found as far south as Missouri, a distance of at least 600 miles. Boulders of an unusual conglomerate containing jasper, found throughout Ohio, have been traced to outcrops of rock on the northern shore of Georgian Bay in Canada. Finland's most important copper mine was discovered in 1910 by tracing ice-transported boulders of copper ore to their source. In glacial deposits of Wisconsin, Michigan, Ohio, and Indiana, isolated diamonds have been found. As yet the source is unknown, but it is thought to be somewhere in central Canada.

Erratics can be traced to their source by comparing their composition with that of the apparent source, and by boulder trains. These trains are a series of erratics that appear as a line

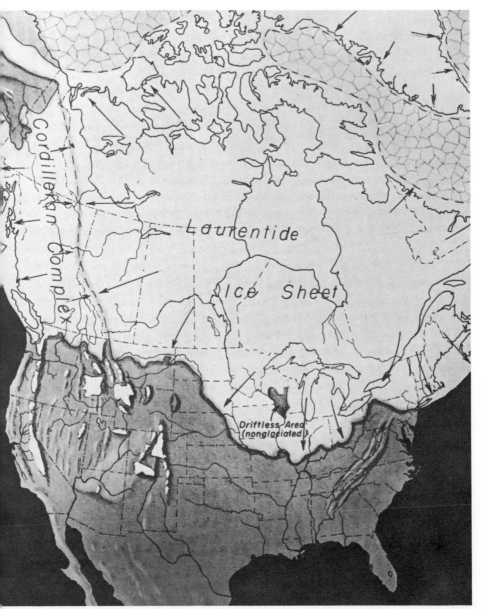

Fig. 21.6   The extent of past glaciation in North America.

stretching downvalley from their source, as a fan-shaped pattern with the apex toward the point of origin. By mapping these boulder trains we can get a good idea of the direction the ice flowed, as well as the source of the boulders.

Displaced Rivers

The displacement of the Ohio and Missouri rivers is one of the evidences of the southern extension of glaciers. These rivers show that drainage has been altered over a large area.

"The present channels of the Missouri and Ohio, which for many miles follow the approximate edge of the vanished glacier, record the glacial blocking of northward-flowing stream courses with diversion of their waters to a position along the margin of the glaciers. The Milk and Yellowstone rivers were not always tributary to the Missouri. They formerly drained to Hudson's Bay, as shown by till-filled channels. The present course of the upper Missouri is the channel cut by the waters as they were diverted across low divides along the margin of the glacial ice" (Gilluly, et al., 1959, p. 244).

The Ohio River has a similar history, and is seen to be somewhat younger than the drainage patterns associated with it to the south. The present course of the Ohio River is a combining of new tributaries from the north which were forced to join it, and old preglacial streams entering from the south. A large river called the Teays originated in preglacial times in the eastern Appalachian Mountains and flowed north and west in a great arc until it drained into what is now the Mississippi River valley. This river valley with many of its tributaries was filled in with glacial debris and obliterated. Its channel can be traced today, but only a few small streams still follow sections of the great river valley.

The Columbia River was also forced out of its normal channel. When ice blocked a northward bend of its course it spilled over a low place and flowed southward, forming the Grand Coulee of Washington. As the ice retreated the river again returned to its normal course toward the northwest and left the canyon dry. There are many evidences of the river's erosion, such as the lakes and falls in the canyon, and parallel canyons that were apparently alternate courses. This canyon had its origin in the area of the present dam bearing the same name.

When glaciers lay across north central Canada the drainage into Hudson Bay was blocked. The lake that collected behind this natural dam has been named Lake Agassiz. The lake covered parts of Manitoba, North Dakota, and Minnesota. The extremely flat nature of the terrain is typical of a lake bed, and the shore lines can be traced. When the ice melted back sufficiently to allow drainage to the north Lake Agassiz disappeared, except for numerous smaller lakes. Lake Winnipeg and Lake Manitoba are two of the larger remaining bodies of water. The Red River now sluggishly winds its way northward across this old lake bottom, sometimes flooding when melting snows exceed the rate of drainage.

The Great Lakes of the north-central United States constitute the largest continuous body of fresh water in the world. They cover 95,000 square miles and receive water from an area of about three times that size. These lakes are drained by the St. Lawrence River and by a man-made canal connecting Lake Michigan to the Mississippi River. The land now under water was probably a great network of valleys. A huge continental glacier advanced southward, covering the entire area to a speculated depth of 5,000 feet. There is indication that the tremendous weight of this ice (2,000 pounds per square inch) caused a down-warping of the land into a huge "saucer" measuring close to 2,000 miles across, and that this "saucer" is springing back, now that the great weight of ice has been removed.

As the glaciers melted, lakes were formed and were drained southward by rivers whose beds are now above the present levels of the lakes. Eventually, the glacial ice melted enough to free the St. Lawrence River and drop the water level.

In many ways it is possible to study the effects of the great glaciers of the past on the surface of the earth. Water does not produce these results, and cannot be suggested as a causative agent. Modern glaciers have provided us with the key to unlock the mystery of these surficial features produced in prehistoric times by continental glaciers. In the next chapter the problem of four different Pleistocene glaciations and the possible causes of climatic changes necessary to bring on glaciation will be considered.

REFERENCES

Charlesworth, J. K. 1957. The quaternary era with special reference to its glaciation. 2 vols. Edward Arnold (Publishers), London. 1699 pp.

Clark, Harold W. 1946. The new diluvialism. Science Publications, Angwin, California, pp. 132-170.

Daly, R. A. 1934. The changing world of the ice age. Yale Univ. Press, New Haven.

Dyson, James L. 1962. The world of ice. Alfred A. Knopf, New York. 305 pp.

Field, William O. 1955. Glaciers. Sci. Am. 193 (3):84-92.

Flint, R. F. 1963. Glacial and Pleistocene geology. John Wiley and Sons, New York. 553 pp.

Gilluly, James, A. C. Waters, and A. O. Woodford. 1959. Principles of geology. W. H. Freeman and Co., San Francisco, pp. 220-253.

Howorth, Henry H. 1887. The mammoth and the flood. Sampson Low, Marston, Searle, and Rivington, London. 464 pp.

———. 1905. Ice or water. vols. 1, 2, 3. Longmans, Green, and Co., London.

———. 1893. The glacial nightmare and the flood. vols. 1, 2. Sampson Low, Marston and Co., London.

Kingery, W. D. (ed.). 1963. Ice and snow. The Mass. Inst. Tech. Press, Cambridge. 684 pp.

Moore, Raymond C. 1958. Introduction to historical geology. 2d ed. McGraw-Hill Book Co., Inc., New York, pp. 495-526.

Scott, William B. 1932. An introduction to geology. vols. 1, 2. The Macmillan Co., New York.

Zeuner, F. E. 1959. The Pleistocene period, its climate, chronology and faunal succession. Hutchinson, Scientific and Technical, London.

CHAPTER TWENTY-TWO

Climatic Conditions
of the Past

THE PREVIOUS CHAPTER has recounted numerous evidences of much glaciation at some time in the past. What circumstances gave rise to so frigid a climate? This question has perplexed many geologists, and a number of theories have been advanced to account for it. Most of these theories have not been widely accepted by students of Pleistocene geology, nor, because they postulate long periods of time, are they acceptable to us either. There are reasons to believe that the onset and retreat of glaciation was relatively rapid.

Volcanic Dust

One theory concerns the suspension in the upper atmosphere of fine volcanic ash from violent eruptions. Such ash can remain in the air for several years and cut down the amount of solar radiation that reaches the surface of the earth. The penetration of the atmosphere by the sun's radiation may be reduced by water vapor, carbon dioxide, ozone, and dust. In times of high humidity half of the sun's heat is absorbed by a cloudless sky, while a cloud cover may reflect more than 70 per cent of the sun's rays. Dust may reduce solar radiation received by the earth by as much as 20 per cent. After the eruption of Krakatau in 1883, Pelee and Santa Maria in 1902, Katmai in 1912, and Agung in 1963, a reddish-brown corona hung around the sun as a result of volcanic dust in the atmosphere. Brilliant red sunsets were common, sometimes for two or three years following the explosions. A shell of volcanic dust is some thirtyfold more effective in shutting out solar radiation than it is in keeping terrestrial radiation in. In other words, the veil of dust produces an inverse greenhouse effect, and if the dust were indefinitely maintained, the ultimate equilibrium temperature of the earth would be less than it is when no such veil exists (Humphreys, 1929, p. 576).

The total amount of dust necessary to diminish solar radiation by 20 per cent, an amount presumably needed to cause an ice age, is surprisingly small—only 1/700th to 1/1500th of a cubic mile, depending on the size of the dust particles (Humphreys, 1929, p. 579). This is not a large amount. One one-thousandth of a cubic mile would be equal to about 5 million cubic yards. There are numerous indications that greater quantities of volcanic dust than this have been thrown into the air in the past. Three or four times the number of currently erupting volcanoes would depress the temperature from one to two degrees centigrade, enough—given adequate precipitation—to initiate an ice age.

Volcanic activity in prehistoric times was evidently so violent that in the western part of North America there must have been an almost continuous line of erupting cones. In one small area, between the Feather and Pit rivers in northern California, more than 150 cones have been counted, averaging about three miles apart. They were not necessarily all in action at once, but it is plain that there must have been a large number belching forth dust and ashes simultaneously. The Aleutian Islands have been the center of great volcanic activity in the not-far-distant past. Glacier Peak and Mount Mazama (Crater Lake) in the Cascade Mountains of Oregon and Washington blew up clouds of ash that spread east and north, settling in marshes and bogs. These layers of ash have been identified in cores taken from a number of bogs, indicating that Glacier Peak and Mount Mazama were active after the retreat of the continental glacier in northern Washington.

Abbot (1913) calculated that 0.280 calories per square centimeter per minute was the heat loss by reflection in the summer of 1912. Other recent years showed a loss of only about 0.05. It would appear that the difference between .05 of earlier years and .280 of 1912 was caused by the eruption of Mount Katmai. The difference of a little over .20 calories might produce a fall of 7 degrees centigrade in the temperature of the earth as a whole, according to Abbot, if there were no counteracting influences such as altered cloudiness and nighttime radiation of the earth's heat.

A decrease in temperature of 7 degrees centigrade over a period of several years would greatly influence weather conditions as a whole. Humphreys (1929, pp. 567-598) suggested that the average temperature of the earth may have been several degrees centigrade lower than at present, during the time when the activity of great volcanoes was most intense. He estimated that the temperature of the earth would have to be lowered only one to two degrees centigrade to cause the spreading of polar ice caps to include most of Canada and some of the northern States, provided the pattern of precipitation was favorable.

"Contrary to popular opinion, a glacial period would not require long cold winters, but rather cool, damp summers. Low summer temperatures and heavy precipitation are the prerequisites for the growth of glacier ice. . . . Temperature is not the only factor involved in glaciation. At present, Siberia has sufficient cold to support extensive glaciers, but there is nothing in that vast region to correspond to the Greenland ice-cap. The reason lies in the absence of moisture in Siberia. In order for glaciation to occur, abundant precipitation is a more potent factor than low temperatures" (Clark, 1946, p. 139).

In checking to discover whether there actually was a lowering of the temperature, Abbot (1913) found that the high-altitude weather stations of southwestern Europe all reported a drop below normal temperatures beginning in July, 1912, one month after the eruption of Mount Katmai in Alaska.

An interesting example of what can happen when the sun's heat is reduced by volcanic dust is the summer of 1816, famous as the year without a summer. Colton (1943, p. 668) states that snow fell to a depth of six inches in New England during June. People wore overcoats and mittens on the Fourth of July. August 29 registered 37 degrees. This unusual summer was probably caused by the accumulation of dust from the three great volcanic explosions of 1812, 1814, and 1815.

From the viewpoint of the diluvialist, contemporaneous heavy precipitation and extensive volcanism are not difficult to visualize. The breakup of the earth's crust by a universal deluge of great magnitude initiated extensive volcanic outbursts that have gradually tapered off to the comparative quiet of modern times. The amount of precipitation following an event of this kind would doubtless have been ideal for the establishment of continental glaciers.

Climatic Fluctuations

Another possible cause of glaciation is major climatic fluctuations. The factors governing these fluctuations are not clear, but sun spots and tides, along with a number of others, have been suggested. Otto Pettersson, a renowned Swedish oceanographer, proposed that major weather fluctuations have occurred, which he attributed to tides (Carson, 1954, p. 136). He found that deep ocean waves, not visible on the surface, were found to be controlled by the tides. When the tidal pull was strong, greater deep ocean waves were produced. Less tidal attraction produced shallower waves. The periods of maximum tidal effect as proposed by Pettersson are approximately 1,850 years apart, with a period of minimal tidal action midway between (Fig. 22.1). There are also shorter periods of 9, 18, and 36 years between minor periods of stronger tidal action. Modern weather records generally support these shorter periods. The most recent

Fig. 22.1 Pettersson's tidal cycle and rainfall for North America (after Brooks, 1949).

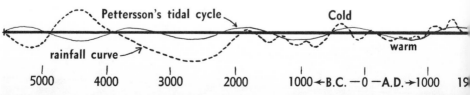

period of maximum tidal effect occurred around A.D. 1450. The two previous periods occurred roughly 1,800 and 3,600 years before that, or about 450 and 2250 B.C. Periods of minimum tidal effect occurred midway between these times.

The exact nature of the effect on climate of stronger or weaker tides is not known, but it is proposed that stronger tides move warm water under the polar caps. This, presumably, would partially break up the polar ice and cause it to drift southward, disrupting the warm ocean currents and prevailing weather patterns, and producing floods, cold damp weather, and heavy snowfalls. This theory regarding the effect of the tides on climate may be questioned, but it is probable that 1800-year or other long periods of climatic cycles have been in operation and have had a significant influence on climate.

The most recent period of severe winter conditions was during the 1400's, when the lowlands of Holland and Belgium experienced the most devastating storms and floods in history. Wolf packs are reported to have crossed the ice from Norway to Denmark. Travel across the ice was common. Icelandic records indicate distressing weather conditions, and it was not much before that when the Vikings abandoned their northern sailing routes, and the colonies in Greenland and Newfoundland vanished. Even normally mild Southern Europe felt the sting of inclement climate.

Previous cold periods in the 1800-year cycle are too far back for much accurate historical checking. Legends, mythology, shifting of trade routes, and migrations of Teutons, Cimbrians, Druids, and "barbarians" do, however, suggest difficult living conditions in northern areas.

The mild period that should lie between 450 B.C. and A.D. 1450 was the time when Vikings and Irish monks sailed freely in the northern seas. Colonies were established in Greenland, where it would now be difficult to maintain a livelihood. Excavations by the Danish Archaeological Expedition showed clearly that the colonists of Greenland experienced a warmer climate.

An arrow shaft found under a retreating glacier in Norway was dated approximately A.D. 500.

According to this theory, we should presently be moving into a warm phase of the cycle. There is ample information to indicate that this is true. It is beyond the scope of this chapter to detail these evidences, but they can be listed briefly as follows:

1. Greater navigation in the far north, especially around the top of North America.

2. Pack ice around Iceland only a century ago.

3. The greater northward movement of southern birds.

4. Cod now off the coast of Greenland.

5. Warm-water fish never reported before off the coast of Iceland.

6. Glaciers in most parts of the world retreating.

7. A longer growing season in Iceland and Norway.

Brooks (1949) gives an interesting graph showing the correlation of the Pettersson cycle with the actual weather as measured in the North American continent, by tree ring counts, pollen analyses, and other valid methods of measurement. The correlation is remarkable. Of interest also is the fact that the correlation disappears completely at a point closely equivalent to the generally accepted date of the Genesis Flood (Fig. 22.1).

Since this chapter is concerned chiefly with the question of "ice ages," let us return to a closer look at the chronology of glaciation. The mountains of northwestern Washington contain the largest number of active glaciers in the United States outside of Alaska. A study of these glaciers (Long, 1955) has revealed some interesting facts regarding their past history.

It is obvious to anyone who visits these glaciers that there has been considerable recession in recent years. Boulder glacier, on the east side of Mount Baker, occupied a position considerably in advance of its present position some time ago. Three terminal moraines indicate three recent advances. Calculations based on tree-ring counts and the amount of time lapse required for tree seedlings to become established on the exposed glacial trough give dates of approximately A.D. 1750 for the oldest of the three advances. Some trees growing on the edge of the 1750 lateral moraines and beyond the end of the terminal moraine are 500 or more years old, indicating that the 1750 maximum had been maintained for perhaps several hundred years. The tremendous size of the moraines would also indicate that the ice maintained equilibrium for many years at this level of advance. This advance could have become established during the A.D. 1450 cold maximum.

This advance does not represent the farthest glacial penetration, however. Farther down the valleys are other moraine deposits, obviously of great age, the extent of glaciation being much greater than the A.D. 1750 advance. These evidences of glaciation have been referred to the end of the "Pleistocene ice age," which is assigned a date of approximately 10,000 years by glaciologists. Ten thousand years is not acceptable to creationists who accept the Genesis record literally. This glacial advance could have occurred during the preceding maximum (450 B.C.), a glaciation that was much more extensive.

Again we must say that these deposits well down in the valleys are not the most extensive spread of glacial evidences. There is overwhelming observational evidence that at some time in the distant past, glaciers lay over much of northwestern Washington and were not confined to the mountains. The San Juan Islands in the northern portion of the Puget Sound are extensively glaciated, and clearly show glacial grooves and erratic boulders, as well as major scouring and shaping. This glaciation no doubt occurred when most of Canada and the northern States were covered with a continental glacier or glaciers. Such extensive ice coverage could be assigned to the first maximum soon after the Genesis Flood.

In areas that were not glaciated, the weather cycles were felt by changes in precipitation and temperature. It is interesting and somewhat significant to note the close correlation between the weather cycles and the floor layers of Sandia Cave in New

Mexico, where much archeological excavation has been done even though the cave is small (Fig. 22.3). From the present floor of the cave to the bedrock of the mountain in which it is located, the archeologist passed through the following layers:

1. Dry accumulations of recent origin containing Puebloan artifacts.

2. A layer of calcium carbonate in the form of a crust deposited under wet conditions.

3. A Folsom cultural level in what was obviously another dry period.

4. A sterile level of yellow ochre that is laminated and water laid.

5. The Sandia cultural level representing another dry period.

6. A sterile layer of clay representing another wet period immediately following the formation of the cave (Hibben, 1955).

Multiple Glaciations

It is generally accepted as a fact among glaciologists that there have been four or more major periods of glaciation. According to the American and European names, they are as follows:

1. Wisconsin—Würm
2. Illinoisian—Riss
3. Kansan—Mindel
4. Nebraskan—Günz

Fig. 22.2   Glacial trough now exposed on Mt. Baker, Washington.

Fig. 22.3 Sandia Cave, New Mexico.

The oldest of these (the Nebraskan) is said to have occurred a million years ago, and the ending date for the youngest (the Wisconsin) is given as 8,000 or 10,000 years ago.

The reasons for proposing four glaciations in the Pleistocene period are summarized as follows: From the Midwestern States eastward, weathered and oxidized so-called glacial tills are found. These are sometimes stratigraphically below the fresh, more-or-less unweathered Wisconsin glacial tills. Remains of plants are found between these tills, suggesting that interglacial periods existed when much warmer climatic conditions favored the growth of vegetation.

The effects of the Wisconsin glaciation are abundant and far overshadow the evidences of the other three. There may be some question over the validity of the gumbotills and other glacial deposits used to support glaciations previous to the Wisconsin. A thorough field study must be done (to my knowledge as yet undone by any Adventist scientist) before any definite statement can be made. The point that is even more open to question, however, is the amount of time between these glacial periods. Could these three (or four, if the Nebraskan is accepted) glacial periods represent merely retreats and advances of one major ice sheet? A number of glaciologists have held that there was only one great glaciation, with major retreats and advances that are wrongly interpreted as four discrete major glacial periods.

Some of the main considerations used as arguments in favor of one major glaciation are itemized below. It is beyond the scope of this book to delve into this aspect in detail. A number of references dealing with the concept of one major glaciation are listed in the references at the end of the chapter.

1. The so-called glacial deposits and evidences for those previous to the Wisconsin are insignificant and atypical as compared with those left by the Wisconsin ice sheets.

2. Since these evidences of earlier glacial periods are found along the margins of the obvious last glaciation, it is questioned why two or more glacial periods separated by complete deglaciation should have had such similar geographical coverage.

3. The so-called interglacial faunas are not reliable indications of interglacial periods with warm climatic conditions, because glaciers are often found only a short distance from forests, heavy vegetation, and even subtropical rain forests (New Zealand). Minor advances often send the snouts of these glaciers into and over forests and other vegetation. This phenomenon would also have been present, at least in some areas, with a continental ice sheet.

4. Differences in weathering and oxidation of glacial soils and deposits are held to be owing to various local factors, such as differences in weather conditions, permeability of the deposits, source areas, and the presence of residual soils in the original deposits (Charlesworth, 1957, pp. 911-929).

At this time it is not possible to settle the question of multiple glaciations. There is no valid reason for not considering these four glacial advances as fluctuations of one major glaciation, which would require far less time than would be necessary for the build-up and retreat of four separate ice sheets, with interglacial warm periods. Most Adventists usually limit post-Flood time to four or five thousand years.

Before leaving the topic of glaciation, let us consider briefly the so-called Precambrian and Permian glaciations. If valid records of Precambrian glaciers do occur in the geologic column, they might be accounted for by pre-Flood glaciation. (Here I have recourse only to geologic literature. Field research in many different areas of the world is sorely needed.) We do not know whether conditions favorable to the formation of glaciers existed anywhere in the world before the Flood. The Paleozoic fossil floras seem to indicate relatively uniform subtropical conditions. Genesis 3:21 states that God provided Adam and Eve with coats of skins. The context suggests that He did so because they were ashamed of their nakedness. But according to *Patriarchs and Prophets,* page 61, it might also have been because of variation in the atmospheric temperature that set in. Debris dropped from floating icebergs is said to have been the source for some Precambrian glacial deposits. This phenomenon would not be incompatible with the theory of a universal Genesis Flood.

Permian glaciation, however, is another matter, and the validity of these glacial remains and evidences needs to be carefully evaluated, and the stratigraphy verified. The tillites, which are considered to be indurated glacial deposits, may have some other origin. But this can be determined only by careful field study.

REFERENCES

Abbot, C. G. 1913. Do volcanic explosions affect our climate? Nat. Geog. Mag., February.

Brooks, C. E. P. 1949. Climate through the ages. McGraw-Hill Book Co., Inc., New York.

Carson, Rachel L. 1950. The sea around us. The New American Library of World Literature, Inc., New York, pp. 136-144.

Charlesworth, J. K. 1957. The Quaternary era. vols. 1, 2. Edward Arnold (Publishers) Ltd., London. 1700 pp.

Clark, Harold W. 1946. The new diluvialism. Science Publications, Angwin, California, pp. 132-170.

Colton, F. Barrows. 1943. Weather works and fights for man. Nat. Geog. Mag. 84 (6):641-670.

Dunbar Carl O. 1960. Historical geology. John Wiley & Sons, Inc., New York. 500 pp.

Field, William O. 1955. Glaciers. Scientific American. September.

Flint, Richard Foster. 1963. Glacial and Pleistocene geology. John Wiley & Sons, Inc., New York. 553 pp.

Hibben, F. C. 1955. Specimens from Sandia Cave and their possible significance. Science 122 (3172):688.

Humphreys, J. W. 1929. Physics of the air. 2d ed. McCraw-Hill Book Co., Inc., New York, pp. 562-615.

Long, William A. 1955. What's happening to our glaciers! Scientific Monthly. August.

Nairn, A. E. M. 1961. Descriptive palaeoclimatology. Interscience Publishers Inc., New York. 380 pp.

Schwarzback, Martin. 1963. Climates of the past. D. Van Nostrand Co., Ltd., London. 328 pp.

Zeuner, Frederick E. 1962. Dating the past. Methuen &. Co. Ltd, London. 516 pp.

Fig. 23.1 Cliffs of Grand Coulee, a former channel of the Columbia River.

Fig. 23.2 Scoured surface of the volcanic plateau of eastern Washington.

CHAPTER TWENTY-THREE

The Story of a River

THE COLUMBIA RIVER originates in the Rocky Mountains of British Columbia and flows for 1,270 miles through British Columbia, Washington, and Oregon into the Pacific Ocean near Astoria, Oregon. From glacier-fed Columbia Lake in British Columbia the river flows northward, bends around the Selkirk Mountains, passes through the Arrow Lakes, and then enters the United States. Not long after entering the State of Washington it turns abruptly toward the west and skirts the northern and western edges of the great lava beds of the Columbia Plateau until, unable to find another way, it flows over and through the plateau, cutting deep canyons through barrier after barrier of faulted mountains and anticlinal hills (see Fig. 23.3).

Any pre-Flood river would probably have been obliterated by that event. The Columbia River would appear to follow a drainage pattern that was established after the Flood. Its original course is not well known. It flowed through a granite-domed countryside that apparently supported a wide variety of plant life. Granite hills are seen protruding into the basalt in the region of one of the great trenches cut by the river (the Grand Coulee). Its former course may have led to the Puget Sound, but under any circumstances its channel will be difficult to trace, because it lies under thousands of feet of basaltic lava.

Displacement by Volcanism

Perhaps volcanic upheavals began during the Flood and continued for hundreds of years. The basalt, molten and extremely

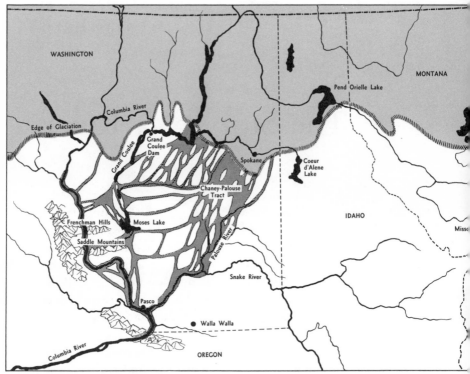

Fig. 23.3   Eastern Washington and adjacent area.

hot, seared and destroyed everything in its way. As it cooled, hexagonal columns up to several feet in diameter sometimes formed. These are a familiar feature of the landscape in the canyons of the lava country. Many times the lava poured out of fissures in the ground and spread out in flat layers for many miles in all directions. The great basalt flows filled the channel of the river and pushed it farther and farther northward and westward. During this time of widespread volcanic disturbance torrential rains, which usually accompany volcanic eruption, probably washed out many trees and shrubs from both mountains and lowlands, and swept them down the streams into ponds and lakes dammed by the encroaching lava.

As the lava entered the lakes, great quantities of steam arose and the debris of trees and brush was covered. Pillow lava, a typical formation produced by molten lava falling into water, can be seen at several places along the present canyon of the Columbia River, and in road cuts. Most remarkable are the numerous specimens of petrified wood now found in central Washington near the Columbia River. More than 200 species, the greatest number found in one location anywhere in the world, have been identified (Brockman, 1954). The museum of the State park at Vantage, Washington, contains a spectacular display of petrified woods ranging from semitropicals such as *Eucalyptus* and *Taxodium* (bald cypress) to conifers similar to those growing in the forests of Washington today. These plants provide a glimpse of the flora of eastern Washington at that time, and indicate that the climate was quite different from the dry conditions of today.

In Washington and Oregon the basaltic flows spread far to the west. The river was not able to move along the edge of the lava, but cut into it. Through the years the gorge in the lava has been eroded deeper, until today many canyon walls well over 1,000 feet can be seen (Fig. 23.1). Several layers of basalt are exposed in the walls of the canyon. Some time after the last basalt lava flow had spread out, faults and folds in the plateau formed. Frenchman Hills, Saddle Mountains, Horsehaven Hills, and others along the present course of the river are now breached by canyons.

Displacement by Glaciation

For the next act in the Columbia River drama we turn to the basalt plateau southeast of Grand Coulee Dam. Gouged into its surface are great canyons, dry cataracts, and waterways unequaled anywhere (Figs. 23.5 and 23.6). Harlen Bretz, who began a study of this region in 1921, proposed that a fantastic quantity of water swept over the plateau and eroded most of the canyons in a short time (Bretz, 1923). Three other explanations were suggested in opposition to a theory so startling as this proved to be. Where did all the water come from? But for a number of years after

251

Fig. 23.4 The Columbia River, now controlled by a series of dams, flows quietly to the sea near Astoria, Oregon.

Bretz's several papers were published, no satisfactory answer to the question was available.

An Amazonlike river would be required to provide the mass of water—up to nine miles wide and several hundred feet deep— that scoured a 75-mile waste across the depressions and low divides to the Snake River (the Chaney-Palouse Tract; see Fig. 23.3). Only water of unbelievable force and magnitude could produce gigantic ripple marks with wave lengths of 200 feet (Bretz, Smith, and Neff, 1956). River bars of gravel up to 400 feet high would require the water to be at least that deep, because bars are developed only within the water. Plunge pools 300 feet deep could be dug only by the hydraulic force and turbulence of a great amount of water passing over the lip of the cataract. The evidence also strongly indicates that these magnificent floods were repeated a number of times.

Since 1910 remnants of a large Pleistocene lake—called Lake Missoula—have been recognized in the western valleys of Montana (Pardee, 1910). In 1942 this author published a paper describing giant ripple marks related to this evidence. A large area of western Montana drains northwest into Pend Oreille Lake in Idaho—and water dammed up in Lake Missoula would have to rise more than 2,500 feet to find any other outlet. The Clark Fork River, which drains the area formerly occupied by Lake Missoula, flows into Pend Oreille Lake. There is no natural obstruction across this canyon mouth. What stopped this northwest flow and backed the water up so high?

During Pleistocene times favorable climatic conditions were piling up great quantities of snow in the mountains of Canada and northern Washington and Idaho. Glaciers began to push down the mountain valleys and out onto the flatlands. Through the years the snows were maintained, and the ice increased and pushed relentlessly southward. Now, both the Columbia and the Clark Fork were menaced by an advancing wall from the north as irresistible as the lava. Molten, fiery lava had pushed north; now solid, frigid ice was to push south. Grinding and rumbling forward like a great bulldozer, the glaciers covered and destroyed everything in their path. Lakes backed up against the ice wherever rivers and streams were dammed. Ice was the obvious dam that pushed past Clark Fork mouth and blocked the outlet. It scoured out Pend Oreille Lake to a depth of 1,800 feet. A lake gradually rose behind the impounding ice, until 500 cubic miles of water were being held back (Pardee, 1942).

One of the four theories (Hobbs, 1943) is completely unacceptable because it requires a glacial lobe extending far south into eastern Washington, a condition that is not supported by field data except for erratic boulders. These can be explained by the transport of boulders by icebergs broken off from the terminus of the ice sheet and rafted down the glacial waterways.

According to still another theory, monumental iceberg dams (not glaciers) plugged up the Columbia and other streams well south of glaciation and backed water into the preglacial channels of the plateau. When the dams weakened, water rushed down-

Fig. 23.5 Palouse River canyon, a deep scour in the basalt plateau.

stream, scouring out the prominent scabland topography of today. That such has happened is not beyond possibility, especially on a minor scale, but it cannot account for some of the evidence without postulating gigantic ice jams several miles wide and up to 500 feet high across some of the major divides in the area. This is as fantastic as Bretz's original flooding concept, and does not fit the facts as well.

Flint (1938), who studied the area between Cheney near Spokane and Palouse on the Snake River (called the Cheney-Palouse Tract), concluded that glacial streams had filled in waterways with gravel, causing normal rivers and channels of moderate size to spill over divides and thus produce the amazing network of channels (anastomosing channels), which constitute one of the unique and most puzzling features of the scablands (Fig. 23.2). Later cutting of the streams removed most of the gravel. Since the introduction of this concept, further facts have come to light, especially the discovery of gigantic ripple marks on a number of the large gravel bars, thereby eliminating this suggestion as a serious possibility. Only great quantities and depths of water would transport icebergs large enough to carry granite boulders weighing several tons and leave them stranded on divides between waterways and in high channels. The original theory, that of flooding by great quantities of water, thus comports most closely with the evidence.

Although present Pend Oreille Lake drains to the northwest, a broad, natural passageway exists southwest toward Spokane and the Columbia Plateau. A reconstruction of what occurred may be somewhat as follows. When the great head of water in Lake Missoula proved too great for the ice dam to contain, it gave way, allowing a tremendous quantity of water mixed with giant blocks of ice to be deflected by the front of the ice sheet toward the southwest, where it roared into the Spokane Valley and out onto the basalt plateau. The failure of the glacial dam may not have been so dramatic. Water flowing over the top of the dam when the lake had filled may have cut a channel into the ice that grew larger and larger until an overwhelming torrent was being released. Although the volume of water was greater than the Columbia Valley could contain, not even part of the water could pass on around the big bend of the Columbia, because it too was blocked by ice. There was no other way for the water than southward and westward across the basalt flats, in great interlacing fingers and fronts of water. How long the flood continued is difficult to determine accurately, although Pardee (1942) calculated that the rate of discharge of the impounded water was nearly 9½ cubic miles per hour, which would have emptied the lake in two days. It is possible that some of the water from Lake Missoula may have left the blocked canyon of the Clark Fork by seepage and tunneling under the ice dam.

Current glacial lakes that are periodically flushed of water are reported from British Columbia, Alaska, and other areas. Knudsen (1951) reports on George Lake near Anchorage, Alaska, which discharges itself nearly every year. Meltwater raises the water level in the spring until it spills over the low end of Knik

Fig. 23.6 Grand Coulee, temporary outlet for a dammed river.

Glacier into Knik River and the Pacific Ocean. As the erosion channel in the ice grows deeper and wider, the water roars out faster and with more force until the lake is drained. With the return of cold weather and the movement of Knik Glacier, the drainage canal is closed until the following spring. It is no more than speculation to suggest that Lake Missoula drained annually, but this is a possibility. The stratification of glacial silt and the obvious sequence of erosional and depositional phenomena record at least eight or ten floods and probably a number more.

Normal meltwater from the glacial front would swell the Columbia and other streams to a great extent, but would be insufficient to produce the effects seen in the Columbia Plateau. Some greater source, suddenly released, is needed, and Lake Missoula with its weak dam meets this need.

Probably one of the last channels to convey glacial water, other than the Columbia River itself, was the Grand Coulee, which trends south-southwest from the site of Grand Coulee Dam and has the lowest head of any of the channels leading across the basalt plateau. When water first spilled over the south bank of the Columbia Valley at this point, it began erosion that quarried a 42-mile canyon up to 900 feet deep (Fig. 23.6), which is divided in the middle by a short section of uncanyoned flats. Approximately 11 cubic miles of material were taken out by the water and deposited in the Quincy Basin, beyond the mouth of the Lower Grand Coulee and in other areas farther south. A cataract escarpment of great size that developed in the Upper Grand Coulee receded until it cut through to the Columbia River valley and was lost. Another great fall began in the Lower Canyon and retreated upcanyon to the present location of Dry Falls, a spectacular scenic spot where the visitor gets some concept of the vastness of the forces in operation (Fig. 23.7).

The "dry falls" were definitely not dry while the water funneled through this canyon. Water 40 times the volume and 3 times the height of Niagara dropped into the canyon below. The water cut mighty notches in the wall of the Columbia River valley where it re-entered the river west of the Quincy Basin. Water also drained south around the Frenchman Hills and Saddle Mountains, some of it not entering the Columbia again until near the present site of the town of Pasco, more than 125 miles from the

Fig. 23.7 Dry Falls, the remains of the ancient Columbia's mighty plunge.

head of Grand Coulee. All along the way it scoured out deep canyons and labyrinthine channels—scabland topography of spectacular dimensions. Gravel piles were dumped into the mouths of canyons coming from the east out of the Cheney-Palouse Tract, indicating that this diversion of Columbia River water was still in operation after the others had dried up.

Finally climatic conditions improved sufficiently to cause the glacial sheet to retreat northward. With one final display of its frightful power, the river broke through the weakened and retreating Okanagan Lobe, and the water thus impounded upstream rushed down the old river valley. Since the water was dammed up to the level of the head of Grand Coulee, 650 feet above the present level of the river, the volume of water was great. The resulting flood would have been much greater than what would result if Grand Coulee Dam should fail. Gravel bars were flung across the mouths of the now-dry scabland channels and waterways where they entered the Columbia. The roaring falls in the Grand Coulee grew silent as the water dropped to a trickle and stopped. Today the dry escarpment with a few blue lakes in the bed below and in the canyon beyond are all that remain, but they mutely speak of an action that must have been a tremendous spectacle. All that remains of the glacier are piles of moraine and rows of erratic boulders spread along the rocky fields and dry wastes west of the deep canyon walls of Grand Coulee.

A Record of Past Life

From the bottom of the canyon of the Grand Coulee, now deserted by the river, the unusual remains of ancient plant and animal life exposed by the erosion of the river in the dry, dark basalt cliffs are not readily evident. One of the most unusual fossils ever found lies buried in the lava part way up the cliff beside Blue Lake. A rhinoceros, dead and bloated, lay in a shallow lake. The advancing lava overwhelmed the carcass but surprisingly did not destroy it. The water or wet mud cooled the magma sufficiently to form pillows of lava, which molded around the shape of the animal. Eventually when the animal disintegrated, the near perfect form of the body was left in the basalt cliff. This most unusual fossil was discovered by rock collectors who crawled into the mold through a small hole at the rear of the cavity. Erosion of the cliff exposed this fascinating evidence of a prehistoric animal that lived during the time of the volcanic buildup of the plateau. Now a person can climb inside and wonder at the freak circumstances that make it possible to crawl into the interior of a prehistoric animal!

The report of a mold of a rhinoceros in basalt seemed so ridiculous that a team of geologists from the University of California (Chappell, Durham, and Savage, 1951) went to the Grand Coulee to check the report. Fragments of bone and teeth were tentatively identified as *Diceratherium,* a prehistoric genus of rhinoceros. These men were convinced of its authenticity and concluded that the reason the animal was not destroyed by the great heat of the lava was because it lay in water, which caused the formation of pillow lava as described above. They made a plaster-of-Paris cast of the inside of the cavity, cut it into sections, removed it from the hole, and reassembled it outside. Its resemblance to a bloated rhinoceros is not coincidental. Even the folds of skin around the neck of the animal left their marks on the lava and were noticeable in the plaster cast.

At a lower level a few hundred feet away, molds of large trees in both vertical and horizontal positions can be seen. One of the upright tree molds is so large that a person can stand inside with outstretched arms and scarcely touch the two walls.

The dammed-up Columbia, now much smaller but still a mighty river, has little opportunity to manifest its power. Only in Canada and west of the Cascade Mountains can the waters be seen moving through the canyons. Each dam backs water up to the next. Man has tamed the river. Now the great glaciers have gone and the lava boils up from the earth no longer. The river has been put to work for man. Only by studying the canyons of the great river, looking for the telltale evidences left by volcanoes and glaciers, and pondering the remains of plants and animals, can man unravel the fantastic and fascinating story of this river.

REFERENCES

Bretz, J. Harlen. 1923. Glacial drainage on the Columbia Plateau. Geol. Soc. Am. Bull. 34:573-608.
————. 1932. The Grand Coulee. Am. Geog. Soc. Special Pub. No. 15.
————. 1959. Washington's channeled scabland. Bull. 45. Division of mines and Geology, Olympia, Washington. 57 pp., 36 figs., 4 pls.
Bretz, J. Harlen, H. T. U. Smith, and George E. Neff. 1956. Channeled scabland in Washington: new data and interpretations. Geol. Soc. Am. Bull. 67 (8): 957-1049, 25 figs., 16 pls.
Brockman, C. Frank. 1954. The story of the petrified forest. State Parks and Recreation Commission, Olympia, Washington. 16 pp., 11 figs.
Chappell, Walter M., J. Wyatt Durham, Donald E. Savage. 1951. Mold of a rhinoceros in basalt, Lower Grand Coulee, Washington. Geol. Soc. Am. Bull. 62 (8): 907-918.
Flint, R. F. 1938. Origin of the Cheney-Palouse scabland tract. Geol. Soc. Am. Bull. 49:461-524. 11 figs., 10 pls.
Hobbs, W. H. 1943. Discovery in Eastern Washington of a new lobe of the Pleistocene continental glacier. Sci. 98:227-230.
Knudsen, Don C. 1951. Alaska's automatic lake drains itself. Nat. Geog. Mag. 99 (6):835-844. 10 figs.
Pardee, J. T. 1910. The glacial Lake Missoula, Montana. Jour. Geol. 18:376-386.
————. 1942. Unusual currents in glacial Lake Missoula, Montana. Geol. Soc. Am. Bull. 53:1569-1600.

ORIGINS AND TIME

"In the beginning God created the heaven and the earth."

Genesis 1:1

Fig. 24.1 The Earth from Lunar Orbiter V at a distance of 214,806 miles, in orbit around the Moon, August 8, 1967. India is in the center, with Arabia to the left. Africa, the Mediterranean Sea, Turkey, Greece, and Italy are clearly visible at the far left. Night has fallen over the Pacific Ocean at the right.

CHAPTER TWENTY-FOUR

In the Beginning—God

THE HUMAN MIND is unable to comprehend infinity. When a child I curled up in the big overstuffed chair in the living room, deeply engrossed with the concepts of limitless time and space. After working myself into considerable agitation over these thoughts, I shook my head as though to awaken from a bad dream and ran off to play. Years have brought maturity, but I am no nearer being able to resolve this situation, which I accept by faith, although astronomy and mathematics now make some of the dimensions of time and space more comprehensible than they were then.

"Everything human has a beginning. He alone who sits enthroned the sovereign Lord of time, is without beginning or end. The opening words of Scripture thus draw a striking contrast between all that is human, temporal, and finite, and that which is divine, eternal, and infinite. . . . Genesis 1:1 affirms that God is before all else and that He is the one and only cause of all else" (1BC 207).

Man has always been curious about the origin of matter and life, but aside from the record found in the Bible, little can be known. Those who have not had opportunity to know God's Word, or who reject its inspiration, have formulated various theories concerning the origin of matter. It is not our purpose to discuss these theories, but to review Seventh-day Adventist thinking on the subject.

Matter is here understood to mean the basic substance that makes up the structure of the minerals and organic materials of which the earth is composed. The discovery of nuclear fission in recent years has focused attention on energy and matter. Man has made only slight progress toward changing energy into matter. More spectacular has been his ability to change mass associated with matter into energy, by nuclear fission and fusion. The atomic bombs that were dropped over the cities of Hiroshima and Nagasaki took more than 200,000 lives. Although the material actually involved in the explosions over Japan could easily have been carried by one man, the amount of energy in that matter was tremendous.

Obviously, at least as much energy was required to create the matter, as was released at the time of the explosion. As a matter of fact, more than 1,000 times as much energy was required to create the matter involved in uranium fission, because nuclear fission is only a reorganization of matter that releases approximately 0.09 per cent of the energy that would be available if the matter involved were completely annihilated. If the creation of so small an amount of matter required so much energy, how much energy was required to create the world? It would be equivalent to the energy given off by our sun in 44 million years.

"He spake, and it was . . . ; he commanded, and it stood fast" (Ps. 33:9). With this concept of the power of God's spoken word, the following statement takes on new meaning: "The creative energy that called the worlds into existence is in the word of God. This word imparts power; it begets life. Every command is a promise; accepted by the will, received into the soul, it brings with it the life of the Infinite One. It transforms the nature and re-creates the soul in the image of God" (Ed 126).

What happened on the first day of creation week? Was matter, along with light, the subject of God's attention on this day, or was matter already in existence? On this there has been a diversity of opinion as far back as the pioneers of the church. For representative statements supporting the concept that matter was already present when God began His creative work recorded in Genesis 1, see the *Review and Herald* for April 6, 1897, and the *Signs of the Times* for July 7 and August 25, 1898. For statements affirming the creation of the substance of the earth during creation week, see the *Review and Herald* for February 5, 1867, and April 7, 1874.

Both points of view recognize that God created the matter that composes our earth, and that when He did so He was not indebted in any way to pre-existing matter. Both likewise acknowledge the integrity of creation week as consisting of six literal days, and the sanctity of the Sabbath as a memorial of it. The only difference between the two viewpoints is whether or not there had been a primordial creation of matter prior to creation week. This difference of opinion has arisen from the fact that passages in the Bible and the writings of Ellen G. White that appear to deal with the subject can, with equal fairness, be understood either way.

The root of the problem lies in the import of the opening declaration of Holy Writ: "In the beginning God created the heaven and the earth. And the earth was without form, and void; and darkness was upon the face of the deep" (Gen. 1:1, 2). Is reference here to a divine act and to the condition of our planet prior to the first day of creation week, or to the first divine act on that first day and to the state of our planet when God began the series of great creative acts recorded in the remainder of the chapter? Does the phrase "in the beginning" refer to the first moments of creation week, to creation week itself, or to a point of time before creation week? Does the word "created" refer to the production of materials that had no prior existence, or to their rearrangement as a suitable abode for man and to the myriad forms of life upon the earth? Does "heaven" mean the starry universe, or the atmospheric heavens above the surface of the earth? Does the "earth" refer to our planet as a whole, or to its surface features and the living things upon it?

A further question arises as to how the original (vowelless) Hebrew of Genesis 1:1-3 should be translated—as in the King

James Version (above), or as it reads in the Anchor Bible: "When God set about to create heaven and earth—the world being then a formless waste, with darkness over the seas and only an awesome wind sweeping over the water—God said, 'Let there be light.' And there was light." * Both are valid renderings of the original Hebrew text, the difference between them being the result of supplying different vowels to the consonants in which the Hebrew Scriptures were originally written. As a matter of fact, there is no way of knowing today which of the two translations comports most closely with the meaning Moses intended these words to convey. It might be said that the King James translation tends to favor the idea that God created the basic substance of our planet on the first day of creation week, and the Anchor Bible the idea that He did so prior to day one. However, neither translation necessarily precludes either view, and the ultimate choice between the two depends on the sense in which the words "beginning," "created," "heaven," and "earth" are to be understood.

The question, then, is: What meaning did the inspired writer intend these words to convey? In modern parlance the word *earth* denotes our planet as a whole, including all of the matter that composes it. On the other hand, we are told that "God called the dry land Earth," in contradistinction to "the gathering together of the waters," which He called "seas" (Gen. 1:10). Furthermore, Moses informs us that the Flood destroyed "the earth" (Gen. 9:11), and other inspired writers declare that in the future God will "create new heavens and a new earth" (Isa. 65:17; cf. 2 Peter 3:13; Rev. 21:1). Clearly, by "earth" the Bible writers appear to refer to the surface of our planet, not to the planet itself.

In the Bible the word "heaven (s)" is used variously to refer to the atmospheric heavens, to the starry heavens visible from the earth, and to the Paradise of God. But in every instance in

---

* From GENESIS (*Anchor Bible*), translated and edited by E. A. Speiser. Copyright © 1964 by Doubleday & Company, Inc.

which the couplet "heaven (s) and earth" occurs in a context where the writer makes clear the sense in which he uses the terms, reference is always to the atmospheric heavens and to the surface of the earth, not to the starry universe and to our earth as a planet. Noteworthy examples are Hebrews 1:10, 11 and 2 Peter 3:7, 10, which declare that the heavens and the earth will be "burned up" and "shall perish." To our knowledge, no one holds that the planet earth and the starry universe will be destroyed in the great conflagration of the last day.

The word "create" is used in Genesis 1 of the divine acts by which God produced marine creatures (v. 21) and man (v. 27). Yet it is evident in both instances that at the moment of their creation God made use of matter already in existence (Gen. 1:20, 21; 2:7, 17). As a matter of fact, the same is true of all forms of plant and animal life mentioned in the creation account, as the Bible itself plainly states. It is therefore evident that the word "create," as the inspired writer himself uses it later in Genesis 1 and 2, can refer to the reorganization of materials already in existence to produce the material component of living things, and not necessarily to the origination of these materials themselves.

In summary, it is possible to read Genesis 1:1: "In the beginning [of the first day of creation week] God created [brought into existence] the heaven [starry universe] and the [planet] earth." It is equally valid to read: "In the beginning [creation week] God created [formed] the [atmospheric] heaven and the [surface of the] earth." The former would have reference to the creation of the basic substance of the earth on day one of creation week; the latter would refer to the series of divine acts recorded in the remainder of the chapter, without saying anything about the time when the basic substance of the earth was brought into existence.

At this point let us examine the statement of Exodus 20:11, that "in six days the Lord made heaven and earth, the sea, and all that in them is." To the modern mind this may at first glance appear to include the basic, inorganic material composing our planet, as well as all living things. But again, as with Genesis 1:1, 2, such was evidently not the intention of the inspired writer, for the observations made above with respect to the words "heaven (s)" and "earth" apply here, as well. In its original sense the Exodus passage could read: "In six days the Lord made heaven [the firmament or atmosphere, Gen. 1:8] and earth [the dry-land portion of the earth's surface, Gen. 1:10], the sea [or water portion of the earth's surface, Gen. 1:10], and all that in them is [all living things in heaven, earth, and sea]." Like its counterpart in Genesis 1, this statement can refer to the organizing of the surface features of the earth, including the atmosphere and the sea, which had been "without form," and the filling with living things of that which had been "void" of life. Like Genesis 1, Exodus 20:11 leaves unanswered the question as to *when* God created the basic substance out of which He formed the surface features of the earth. The Bible does not specifically say whether this took place as the first creative act of day one of creation week or prior to that time.

The only Ellen G. White statements that explicitly deal with the origin of matter are *Education,* page 126, and *Testimonies,* volume 8, page 258: "The theory that God did not create matter when He brought the world into existence is without foundation. In the formation of our world, God was not indebted to pre-existing matter." (With slight variations in wording, the same concept is expressed also in MH 414; *Signs of the Times,* March 13, 1884; Manuscript 117, 1897.) None of these statements, however, specifies *when* the basic substance of our earth was created, but simply that God did create it.

A number of E. G. White statements may at first glance appear to assign the creation of the basic substance of the earth to the first day of creation week. Take, for instance, this from *Patriarchs and Prophets,* page 111: "Like the Sabbath, the week originated at creation, and it has been preserved and brought down to us through Bible history. . . . Six days were employed in the work of creation; upon the seventh, God rested, and He then blessed this day, and set it apart as a day of rest for man."

If it is assumed that the expression "the work of creation" includes the origination of matter, as well as its organization, then it would be fair to conclude that this statement assigns the creation of matter to the six days of creation week. If, on the other hand, this expression refers to the creative activity described in Genesis 1 as taking place during the six working days of the first week, it could be concluded (on the basis of what has been said above) that the statement provides no clear guidance on the subject of *when* matter itself was created. The same alternatives are implicit in a number of other E. G. White statements.

At least one other statement by Ellen G. White may appear to be weighted in favor of the opinion that the earth already existed as a planet but was "without form and void" when God began the work of creation week. This occurs in a passage dealing with the millennium: "That the expression 'bottomless pit' represents the earth in a state of confusion and darkness is evident from other scriptures. [Gen. 1:2 where the same Greek word is translated "deep."] Concerning the condition of the earth 'in the beginning,' the Bible record says that it 'was without form, and void; and darkness was upon the face of the deep.' Prophecy teaches that it will be brought back, partially at least, to this condition" (GC 658). But, like the passages cited above, this statement does not actually say what it may at first appear to say, and so does not settle the question.

Several statements refer to the "foundations of the earth," of which this is representative: "When the foundations of the earth were laid, then was laid the foundation of the Sabbath also" (1T 76). This statement depends, in turn, on the meaning of the phrase "foundations of the earth." If this refers to, or includes, the inorganic material of the earth, then obviously the matter that makes up the earth sphere was created on day one. Since "foundations of the earth" is a Biblical expression, the answer to our question depends on the sense in which the Bible writers use it. Take, for instance, Job 38:4: "Where wast thou when I laid the foundations of the earth?" Or, "Of old hast thou laid the foundation of the earth: and the heavens are the work of thy hands. They shall perish, but thou shalt endure: yea, all of them shall wax old like a garment; as a vesture shalt thou change them" (Ps. 102:25, 26; cf. Heb. 1:10, 11). Or, "The channels of the sea appeared, the foundations of the world were discovered, at the rebuking of the Lord, at the blast of the breath of his nostrils" (2 Sam. 22:16; cf. Ps. 18:15; Deut. 32:11; Ps. 82:5; Isa. 24:18; Micah 6:2). An examination of these texts makes clear that "the foundations of the earth" were laid by God, but that they will shake, be moved, wax old like a garment, and perish. Then fire burns them up. In Micah 6:2 the phrase is in poetic parallelism with "mountains."

In summary, to the ancients "foundations of the earth" were the hidden parts of the ground—that which lies beneath the mountains, that shakes in earthquakes, that is covered by the seas. This part of matter, which composes the earth's crust, was involved in the work of creation recorded in Genesis 1 regardless of the presence or absence of matter before creation week. The statement may or may not refer to all subterranean matter. Again two interpretations are possible.

A number of incidental arguments could be mentioned on both sides of the question. For instance, one person may say that it is not like God to leave the work of creation half finished for millions of years, but another will point to Mars, whose surface is still apparently "without form and void." With respect to questions such as the time when God created the basic substance of our earth, our only safe course is to accept God's Word for what it says, no more and no less, and to let the Bible be its own interpreter. On points for which Inspiration has provided no positive guidance it is best to suspend judgment, and to build solidly on those truths that are clearly revealed. We should also be tolerant of other points of view on such matters.

The Age of Organic Matter

The existence of inorganic matter before creation week may be an open matter, but there can be no question relative to animals and plants (organic matter). The idea that living things existed on earth prior to creation week is altogether incompatible with a literal interpretation of Genesis 1.

Attempts have been made to reconcile the evolution theory with the Bible story of creation by calling each day of creation a long period of time. Seventh-day Adventists emphatically reject this view. Any view that allows many thousands or millions of years for existence of life on the earth would most probably lead, ultimately at least, to the day-age concept. Attempts to maintain the integrity of creation week in the face of eons of time by saying that creation week concerned the Garden of Eden only, or that life existed before creation week but was all destroyed prior to that event, cannot be defended. The sequence of fossils in the crust of the earth—sea animals on the lowest level, lowland plants and reptiles next, and mammals, birds, and man last—must be explained by those who hold to long ages for life upon the earth either as an evolutionary sequence, or as a series of progressive creative acts by God interspersed by much time. It is only logical for those who accept the latter possibility to equate it with the creation sequence recounted in the first chapter of Genesis. This brings them back again to the idea that the Biblical narrative refers to the days of creation as long, indefinite periods of time. It would appear to be nearly impossible to believe in great ages since the beginning of creation week and at the same time to believe in literal creation days.

The Bible and the writings of Ellen G. White clearly indicate that the organic features of the earth are not hundreds of thousands or millions of years old. Nor are they *exactly* 6,000 years old. How much latitude should be given to such words as "nearly," "about," et cetera, that are sometimes associated with Mrs. White's remarks on the 6,000-year age of the earth is a matter for personal study. But one point is clear—the earth is only a few thousand years old—very young indeed in contrast to the great eons of time given in geological literature.

We can affirm with certainty those truths about creation that are clearly revealed—that God "spoke and it was," that He fashioned this earth in six literal days, and that He rested on the seventh day and set it apart as a memorial of creation.

REFERENCES

Allen, B. F. 1963. Earth's origin during creation week. The Naturalist 23 (2): 36-40; 23 (3):25-31; 23 (4):22-28.

Brown, R. H. 1958. The creation of elementary matter. The Ministry, February.

————. 1964. Key words in the Genesis account of creation. The Ministry, February.

Clark, Robert E. D. 1961. The universe: plan or accident? Muhlenberg Press, Philadelphia. 240 pp.

Gilkey, Langdon. 1959. Maker of heaven and earth. Doubleday and Co., Inc., Garden City, New York. 311 pp.

Hoen, Reu E. 1951. The Creator and his workshop. Pacific Press Pub. Assn., Mountain View, California, pp. 1-21.

Marsh, Frank Lewis. 1950. Studies in creationism. Review and Herald Pub. Assn., Washington, D.C., pp. 127-155.

————. 1967. Life, man, and time. 2d ed. Outdoor Pictures, Escondido, California, pp. 30-73.

Morris, Henry M. and John C. Whitcomb. 1961. The Genesis flood. The Presbyterian and Reformed Pub. Co., Philadelphia. 518 pp.

Nichol, F. D. 1964-1965. How old is the earth? The Review and Herald, December 3, 10, 17, 24, 31, January 7.

Seventh-day Adventist Bible commentary, the. 1953. vol. 1. Review and Herald Pub. Assn., Washington, D.C.

Surburg, Raymond F. 1959. In the beginning God created. In Darwin, evolution, and creation. Paul A. Zimmerman, ed. Concordia Pub. House, St. Louis, Missouri, pp. 36-80.

White, Ellen G. 1903. Education. Pacific Press Pub. Assn., Mountain View, California, pp. 128-134.

————. 1913. Patriarchs and prophets. Pacific Press Pub. Assn., Mountain View, California, pp. 44-51; 111-116.

————. 1945. Spiritual gifts. vol. 3. Facsimile Reproduction. Review and Herald Pub. Assn., Washington, D.C., pp. 33-35; 90-95.

Zimmerman, Paul A. 1959. The age of the earth. In Darwin, evolution, and creation. Paul A. Zimmerman, ed. Concordia Pub. House, St. Louis, Missouri, pp. 143-166.

CHAPTER TWENTY-FIVE

Radioactive Time Clocks*

By R. H. Brown

IT IS THE PURPOSE of this chapter to outline basic features of the various methods of inorganic radioisotope dating briefly but with sufficient detail to enable the reader to form his own judgments concerning the significance of radioisotope age determinations.† Although an introductory course in chemistry, or equivalent independent reading, is a desirable preparation for the study of this chapter, those who do not have this background can, with the aid of a good dictionary or the glossary on pages 485-500, obtain insights which should prove helpful in resolving many apparent conflicts between requirements of prophetic revelation and the results of scientific investigation.

The natural occurrence of radioactive material that spontaneously decays into material with different characteristics provides a possible means for determining the time interval since the formation of such matter, or the time interval since an event that altered the relative abundance of the isotopes within a mineral sample. The daughter/parent isotope pairs that have been used as chronometers for the dating of minerals are argon-40/potassium-40, calcium-40/potassium-40, strontium-87/rubidium-87, osmium-187/rhenium-187, lead-208/thorium-232, lead-207/uranium-235, lead-206/uranium-238, and lead-206/lead-210.

---

* Some readers may wish to pass directly to page 295 where a simplified abstract of this technical topic appears.

† Radioisotope ages cited in this chapter are those assigned by scientists working in this area and are not to be considered as representing either actual ages or the opinion of the author.

In the simplest and most usual radioisotope dating procedure it is necessary to obtain values for the present concentration of parent radionuclide and its stable daughter-product, the half-life of the parent nuclide, and the concentration of the stable daughter-product at the time of the event that is being dated. With knowledge of these quantities the radioactive age is given by

$$t = \frac{T}{.693} \ln \left(1 + \frac{D}{P}\right) \tag{1}$$

where t = radioactive age or time since the event that is to be dated,

T = half-life of the parent radionuclide,

D = number of atoms of the stable daughter-product that have accumulated per unit of sample in time t,

P = number of atoms of parent radionuclide per unit of sample at present, and

in=natural logarithm=2.3026 times the common logarithm.*

The present concentration of parent radionuclide and its daughter-product can usually be determined with precision by analytical chemistry techniques (activation analysis, absorption spectrometry, emission spectrometry, X-ray spectrometry, as well as wet-chemistry procedures) combined with mass spectrometry, which frequently utilizes isotope dilution techniques.

The Half-life

The half-life of the parent nuclide is determined by observing with a radiation counter the number of radioactive

---

* Using the subscript "i" to denote initial concentration at zero time, equation (1) derives from the more familiar equation for radioisotope decay as follows:

$$P = P_i \, e^{-.693 \frac{t}{T}} \qquad e^{+.693 \frac{t}{T}} = 1 + \frac{D}{P}$$

$$D = P_i - P = P e^{+.693 \frac{t}{T}} - P \qquad .693 \frac{t}{T} = \ln\left(1 + \frac{D}{P}\right)$$

$$\frac{D}{P} = e^{+.693 \frac{t}{T}} - 1 \qquad t = \frac{T}{.693} \ln\left(1 + \frac{D}{P}\right).$$

transformations per unit time in a measured quantity of the nuclide. With this observation, the length of time in which one-half a given quantity of the parent nuclide will decay to its daughter nuclide can be obtained by direct computation.

The half-life of a nuclide is related to the elementary forces involved in the existence of matter, and is a direct consequence of the basic characteristics of the material universe. While there is no absolute basis for affirming that nuclear half-lives do not change in course of time, it can be confidently stated that such a change is comparable to variation, with time, of such fundamental phenomena as gravitation, electrical interaction, or the speed of light. It is improbable that the basic forces involved in the maintenance of the entire structure and behavior of the physical universe should be subject to large variation. The uniform nature of the radiation reaching earth from the vast reaches of the universe argues strongly against the hypothesis that atomic and nuclear binding forces are subject to time variation which would make radionuclide half-lives unreliable units of measurement.

Table 1 gives the most precise values currently available for the half-lives of the principal radionuclide geochronometers (Hart, 1966; Hirt, *et al.*, 1963). The numbers that follow ± signs in this tabulation give the range in which the "true" value for the half-life lies, with a confidence of 68 chances out of 100.

Table I

HALF-LIVES OF RADIONUCLIDE GEOCHRONOMETERS

NUCLIDE	HALF-LIFE (Years)
Potassium-40	
decay to calcium-40	$(1.47 \pm 0.07) \times 10^9$
decay to argon-40	$(1.19 \pm 0.04) \times 10^{10}$
combined decay	$(1.31 \pm 0.07) \times 10^9$
Rubidium-87	$(4.7 \pm 0.3) \times 10^{10}$
Rhenium-187	$(4.3 \pm 0.5) \times 10^{10}$
Thorium-232	$(1.39 \pm 0.03) \times 10^{10}$
Uranium-235	$(7.13 \pm 0.25) \times 10^8$
Uranium-238	$(4.51 \pm 0.01) \times 10^9$

Thus (4.7 ± 0.3) x 10^{10} for the half-life of the rubidium-87 to strontium-87 transition means that the odds are considered to be 68 out of 100 that the actual half-life of rubidium-87 lies between 44 and 50 billion years. The odds are 95 out of 100 that the actual half-life of this nuclide lies within twice as great a range—41 to 53 billion years—and less than three out of one thousand that it lies outside a range three times as great—38 to 56 billion years.

Research on the lifetimes of excited states in atomic nuclei at the Westinghouse Research and Development Center has been cited in support of the contention that radioisotope ages may have no significance because radionuclide half-lives are subject to large variation. However, this Westinghouse research project concerned the lifetimes of above-normal energy states in some of the most stable nuclides in existence—iron-57 and tin-119 (Ruby and Ferber, 1964). The lifetimes of these energy states were predictably prolonged a few per cent by placing the atoms in an intense field of appropriate gamma radiation. Ruby and Ferber's experiments confirm an understanding of nuclear characteristics that assures us that the half-lives of long-lived radionuclides are among the most dependable physical constants in the universe. (See also Malliaris and Bainbridge, 1966.)

Major Assumptions

Major uncertainties do enter into radioisotope dating through the assumptions that must be made concerning the concentrations of parent radionuclide and daughter-product at the time of the event being dated, and concerning loss or gain of parent nuclide and daughter-product during the subsequent history of the specimen. Loss or gain of nuclides involved in a determination of radioactive age may come about through the action of heat and water. Loss of gaseous elements, as well as migration of other elements with enrichment in some portions of a mineral body and depletion in others, can take place even at temperatures much below the melting point. Ground water can carry radioactive or radiogenic material into rock, as well as dissolve these materials away. As much as 30-50 per cent of the uranium, thorium, and lead in granite has been shown to be accessible to leaching by acid and hence susceptible to removal and transfer in any geological process (Russell and Farquhar, 1960, p. 109). For these reasons it is desirable to use for inorganic radioisotope dating, a specimen taken from the interior of solid rock that gives no evidence of having been subjected to high temperature or the action of ground water since the event that is to be dated.

The daughter element is generally assumed to have been initially present in the same isotopic composition that presently characterizes it in minerals that do not contain the parent radionuclide and do not give evidence of having been associated with the parent nuclide in the past. Strontium/rubidium dating provides a good illustration of this critical assumption. Whenever strontium is found not associated with rubidium, it appears as 0.56 per cent Sr^{84}, 9.86 per cent Sr^{86}, 7.02 per cent Sr^{87}, and 82.56 per cent Sr^{88}. One study of Texas geology reports minerals containing rubidium that have associated strontium that is as high as 93 per cent Sr^{87} (Wasserburg *et al.*, 1962). All the strontium-87 in excess of the amount in the ratio 7.02/9.86 with the strontium-86 present is assumed to be radiogenic, that is, produced by radioactive decay of associated rubidium-87. It is the amount of radiogenic strontium-87 that would be used for the term D in equation 1 above in order to compute the strontium/rubidium age of a mineral—the time for the observed excess of strontium-87 to accumulate, on the assumption that the sample experienced no gain or loss of rubidium-87 or strontium-87 during this period.

The determination of an argon/potassium age entails a somewhat more involved approach. Earth's atmosphere is 0.93 per cent argon, which is 0.337 per cent A^{36}, 0.063 per cent A^{38}, and 99.60 per cent A^{40}. When a mineral sample is melted, argon-40, which is released in the ratio 99.60/0.337 with argon-36, is designated as "atmospheric" argon, and is assumed not to be a decay product of potassium-40 originally contained in the sample. The "atmospheric" argon in a mineral could be the result of

277

infusion from the atmosphere and/or gas dissolved in the mineral at the time of its formation. The amount of argon-40 in excess of the "atmospheric" argon-40 is assumed to be the daughter-product of potassium-40 that was originally contained in the mineral. The argon-40 content of potassium-bearing minerals that have been studied ranges from 100 per cent "atmospheric" (Hawaiian basalt; Run No. KA 1218) to 1.5 per cent "atmospheric" (Sanidine from tuff on Drinkwater Pass, Oregon; Run No. KA 1225; Evernden, *et al.*, 1964a).

In determining the argon/potassium age of a sample the difference between the concentrations of argon-40 and "atmospheric" argon-40 is used for the term D in equation 1. For P one must use the fraction of the contemporary concentration of potassium-40 that will decay by orbital electron capture to form argon-40, and for T it is necessary to use the half-life for the combined decay of potassium-40.

In ideal cases the argon/potassium age of a sample is either the time since the sample was formed (no potassium or radiogenic argon gain or loss during its history), or the time since it was last heated sufficiently to expel its entire argon content (no potassium or radiogenic argon gain or loss since a complete argon loss). The observations that have been made up to the present indicate that in the absence of heating, radiogenic argon loss may be expected to be very small in micas, in the order of 30 per cent in potash feldspars, and as much as 70 per cent in plagioclase feldspars (Webster, 1960).

Uranium and Decay Products

The geochronometers thorium-232, uranium-235, and uranium-238 each have helium and an isotope of lead as the stable end products. Radioisotope age determinations have been based on the helium content of mineral specimens, but due to the poor retentivity of rocks for helium, such determinations have very limited value (Knopf, 1949; Cook, 1957; Damon and Green, 1963).

To determine a lead/uranium or a lead/thorium age it is necessary to know how much of the appropriate lead isotope in a sample has accumulated from radioactive decay during the interval involved. Since the isotopic composition of lead is subject to wide variation from locality to locality and specimen to specimen, even among minerals that do not contain uranium or thorium, it is difficult to estimate with assurance the isotopic composition of the lead in a uranium- or thorium-bearing specimen at the time of a remote significant event. The following tabulation of data from Russell and Farquhar (1960, pp. 40, 136, 137, 163) shows the range that has been observed in the ratio of the radioactively related lead isotopes 206, 207, and 208 to nonradioactively related lead-204 in common lead.

Table II
ISOTOPE RATIOS FOR COMMON LEAD

(Data from Russell and Farquhar, 1960)

Source	Relative Proportions of Isotopes Present			
	204/204	206/204	207/204	208/204
Meteorite from Henbury, Australia	1.00	9.55	10.38	29.54
Rosetta Mine, Union of South Africa, Toronto, Sample No. 193	1.00	12.54	14.16	32.47
Ozone Mine, Thunder Bay region, Ontario, Toronto, Sample No. 854	1.00	18.32	15.89	37.15
Quirke Mine, Sault Ste. Marie region, Ontario, Toronto, Sample No. 988	1.00	79.82	24.25	71.29

The Ozone Mine sample described in Table II is typical of terrestrial lead. It is generally assumed by geochemists and geophysicists that terrestrial leads are a mixture of primordial lead (lead as it first appears in an original creation) and leads that have accumulated from the radioactive decay of uranium and thorium. Lead from iron meteorites that show no traces of uranium or thorium contains the lowest observed relative amounts of radioactively related isotopes and is assumed to represent primordial lead. From an average of data on meteorite lead, the composition of primordial lead is assumed to be 29.71 parts lead-208, 10.42 parts lead-207, and 9.56 parts lead-206 to one part lead-204 (Anders, 1962). In defense of this identification of primordial lead, Russell and Farquhar (1960, p. 40) state: "The isotope ratios for a number of elements have been shown to be identical in meteorites and in the earth. This includes both uranium and potassium, which have naturally occurring radioisotopes. In the case of elements that vary in isotopic composition in terrestrial materials as a result of natural isotope fractionation, the average terrestrial values agree well with meteoritic values."

Table III
ISOTOPE RATIOS FOR VARIOUS LEADS

Type of Lead	Relative Proportions of Isotopes Present			
	204/204	206/204	207/204	208/204
Primordial Lead	1.000	9.56	10.42	29.71
Typical Common Terrestrial Lead	1.000	17.9	15.6	38.0
Lead in West Texas Zircons	1.000	177.5-	28.45-	61.4-
(Wasserburg, et al., 1962)		905.7	81.2	166.0

Table III gives a comparison between the isotopic composition assumed for primordial lead, found to be typical of common terrestrial lead, and observed in a mineral that is rich in uranium and thorium. The data in Table III show that there are minerals for which the amount of radiogenic lead is so great that estimates of its quantity will not be critically affected by relatively large uncertainties in the composition of primordial lead. One would expect to obtain satisfactory lead/uranium and lead/thorium ages for samples of such minerals.

Before considering actual radioisotope ages that have been derived by the three direct methods involving lead isotope analysis (lead-208/thorium-232, lead-207/uranium-235, and lead-206/uranium-238) it would be desirable to review the principles of the lead/lead dating technique. Equation (1) may be converted from logarithmic to exponential form and written

$$D = P \left(e^{.693 \left(\frac{t}{T} \right)} - 1 \right) \qquad (2)$$

In terms of the number of lead-206 atoms per unit of sample (Pb^{206}) produced by uranium-238 that has decayed to a present concentration expressed as U^{238}, equation 2 becomes

$$Pb^{206} = U^{238} \left(e^{0.1537t} - 1 \right) , \qquad (3)$$

in which t is expressed in billions of years. For the lead-207 produced by decay of uranium-235 one similarly obtains

$$Pb^{207} = U^{235} \left(e^{0.972t} - 1 \right) . \qquad (4)$$

Noting that regardless of its source, natural uranium has been found to contain 137.7 parts uranium-238 to one part uranium-235, the ratio of equation 4 to equation 3 becomes

$$\frac{Pb^{207}}{Pb^{206}} = \frac{1}{137.7} \left(\frac{e^{0.972t} - 1}{e^{0.1537t} - 1} \right) . \qquad (5)$$

Equation 5 provides a means for determining a radioisotope age without a uranium analysis or an absolute determination of lead content. All that is required is a relatively simple mass spectrographic determination of the lead-207/lead-206 ratio. It should be noted that equation 5 requires the ratio of the lead-207 and the lead-206 that are in excess of primordial lead. A convenient tabulation of the solution of equation 5 for t as a function of the ratio of lead-207 to lead-206 is given by Russell and Farquhar (1960, p. 103).

Since thorium, uranium, and lead may be readily transported by the action of water and the result of high temperature, the effect of possible gain or loss of both parent and daughter nuclides should be kept in mind when comparing radioisotope ages. Loss of the parent element during the time period involved produces an apparent time span greater than the true one. Loss of daughter element, or continuous loss of any intermediate element, results in an apparent age which is less than the true age. Lead-206/uranium-238 ages are more sensitive to loss of parent or daughter elements than are lead-207/uranium-235 ages. The lead-207/lead-206 method, however, is highly insensitive to losses of uranium or lead. A 30 per cent loss of uranium or lead will not affect the lead-207/lead-206 determination of a one-billion-year time period more than approximately 5 per cent. Furthermore, uranium or lead losses which occur within the last 1/100 of the time interval (10 million years out of a one-billion-year period) will have no effect on the lead-207/lead-206 age determination.

The reader who is particularly interested in these considerations is advised to consult the graphical presentations of error produced in lead/uranium age determinations by losses in uranium or lead that are presented in connection with the discussion on page 106 of Russell and Farquhar's book (1960).

When parent and daughter nuclides are separated by intervening members of a radioactive series, time periods cannot be measured by the methods discussed in the preceding paragraphs unless these periods have been characterized by radioactive equilibrium. In radioactive equilibrium all radioactive members of the daughter nuclide series are decaying at the same rate as the parent nuclide which heads the series. Following isolation of the nuclide that heads a radioactive series, radioactive equilibrium is not established until a time equal to approximately three half-lives of the longest-lived daughter nuclide in the series. The time required to reach equilibrium is approximately 750,-000 years for uranium-238 decay, 100,000 years for uranium-235 decay, and 20 years for thorium-232 decay. Not all uranium ores are in radioactive equilibrium, notably certain carnotites from the Colorado Plateau, but most primary radioactive ores that have not been exposed to weathering are found to be in equilibrium and therefore suitable for age measurement (Moorbath, 1960).

In addition to methods that have been outlined above, uranium-bearing minerals are dated from measurement of the ratio of lead-206 to its 21-year half-life parent, lead-210. In radioactive equilibrium, uranium-238 will be present in a ratio with respect to lead-210 equal to the ratio of the half-life of uranium-238 to the half-life of lead-210 (Kulp, Broecker, and Eckelmann, 1953; Gojković, Deleon and Červenjak, 1963).

As a result of the surface breakup associated with the Genesis Flood and orogenic activity since that time, earth's surface today contains a mixture of material placed on the surface of the planet by the creative activity during the second through sixth days of creation week, and material that was below the surface at the end of the third day of creation week. Aside from interesting speculations concerning the isotopic composition and degree of radioactive equilibrium that characterized the minerals in earth's crust on the first day of creation week, we should not, in view of the exposure to water and/or heat that much of this material experienced during and after the Genesis Flood, expect agreement among all the various independent methods of determining a radioisotope age for any sample we might investigate. A given degree of heating or exposure to chemical action could not be expected to influence equally the argon-40/potassium-40 age, the strontium-87/rubidium-87 age, the osmium-187/rhenium-187 age, the lead-208/thorium-232 age, and the lead/uranium ages.

Furthermore, if the original formation of a mineral involved slow cooling, various mineral components and their associated radioisotopic sequences would be isolated at different times. At the time a radioactive parent nuclide was isolated in a solidification, some portion of the previously accumulated daughter nuclide(s) might be included, with the result that the radioisotope age for the crystals thus formed would be greater than the time since solidification. Hence, we should expect agreement between various radioisotope ages for a mineral specimen to be exceptional, rather than general experience.

Table IV
AGES OF CEYLON ZIRCONS
(from Damon and Green, 1963)

Method				
	Pb^{206}/U^{238}	Pb^{207}/U^{235}	Pb^{207}/Pb^{206}	Pb^{208}/Th^{232}
Age in millions of years	540 ± 12	544 ± 16	555 ± 30	538 ± 25

The data in Table IV for the age of gem-quality zircons from Ceylon by four different methods illustrate the amount of agreement, or concordance, that is often encountered in radioisotope dating.

Table V
DISCORDANT URANIUM-LEAD AGES FROM THE WEST ORE BODY OF THE ACE MINE, SASKATCHEWAN
(from Russell and Farquhar, 1960, p. 105)

Toronto number	Chemical analysis		Isotopic analysis				Age in millions of years		
	%Pb	%U	$\%Pb^{204}$	$\%Pb^{206}$	$\%Pb^{207}$	$\%Pb^{208}$	Pb-206/ U-238	Pb-207/ U-235	Pb-207/ Pb-206
348	3.18	16.5	0.055	87.90	9.89	2.15	1,140	1,350	1,710
349	9.70	40.3	0.014	89.50	9.87	0.60	1,430	1,580	1,790
352	1.04	11.0	0.089	86.64	9.99	3.29	590	830	1,630
354	6.30	33.8	0.03	89.55	9.43	0.99	1,210	1,380	1,660
355	5.87	30.1	0.034	89.53	9.73	0.70	1,180	1,370	1,700

(Representative samples taken across a single ore body)

Table V illustrates the discordance that is generally characteristic of lead/uranium ages. The ages given in this table should be studied carefully in connection with the foregoing comments on the effects a loss of uranium or lead has on the ages obtained

Table VI

SOME NEARLY CONCORDANT AGES FROM NORTH AMERICA*

(from Tilton and Hart, 1963, p. 359)

Rock	Mineral †	Pb^{206}/U^{238}	Pb^{207}/U^{235}	Pb^{207}/Pb^{206}	Pb^{208}/Th^{232}	Sr^{87}/Rb^{87}	Ar^{40}/K^{40}
Beartooth Mountains, Montana							
Pegmatite A	U	2600	2640	2700			
Pegmatite B	M					2800	2470
Pegmatite B	F					2700	
Rainy Lake, Ontario (Rice Bay)							
Gneiss A	Z	2450	2600	2730			
Gneiss B	B					2630	2520
Gneiss B	M						2600
Viking Lake, Saskatchewan							
Pegmatite	U	1850	1880	1910	1670		
	B					1970	1780
Keystone, South Dakota							
Pegmatite	U	1580	1600	1630	1440		
	L					1650	1380
	M					1730	1550
Wilberforce, Ontario							
Pegmatite	U	1020	1020	1020	1000		
	Z	900	930	1000	990		
	B					1030	960
Shenandoah National Park, Virginia							
Gneiss	Z	1070	1100	1150	1110	880	800
	B						900
Pegmatite	H						
	F					980	
Bear Mountain, New York							
Gneiss	Z	1140	1150	1170	1030		
	B					880	780
Granite	Z	960	990	1060	850		
	B					930	840
Llano, Texas							
Granite	Z	970	1020	1120			
	Z	950	990	1070	890		
	B					1100	1060
Spruce Pine, North Carolina							
Pegmatite	U	385	390	400±50			
	U	370	375	420±50			
	M					375	335
	F					385	

* The ages listed in this table (in millions of years) are those assigned by standard radio-active dating procedures.

† B, biotite; F, potassium feldspar; H, hornblende; L, lepidolite; M, muscovite; U, uraninite; Z, zircon.

by the various lead/uranium dating techniques. The discordances in Table V indicate varying amounts of lead loss from a set of samples with a corrected radioisotope age of approximately 1,700 million years.* It has been demonstrated that radioactive zircon crystals may rapidly lose up to 80 per cent of their lead content with less than 2 per cent loss of uranium when subjected to a superheated sodium chloride solution (Pidgeon, O'Neil, and Silver, 1966). The evidence suggests that the zircons described in Table IV crystallized more recently than the uranium ore described in Table V. The average lead-207/lead-206 age for the West Texas zircons described in Table III is 1,200 million years.

Table VI gives a comparison of six independent methods of radioisotope dating for samples from nine different geographical areas. Similar examples of radioisotope age agreement are available for other localities (Tilton and Hart, 1963). In a study of disagreement between argon/potassium and strontium/rubidium ages, Kulp and Engles (1963) report agreement in 154 samples and disagreement in 22 samples of muscovite and biotite from Australia, South Africa, Europe, and North America with radioisotope ages ranging from 16 million to 2,600 million years.

Additional evidence of material from the "foundations of the earth" (Job 38:4) that may have been brought into existence by creative activity preceding that which is described in the first chapter of Genesis is provided by what are known as extinct isotopes. All possible radioactive nuclides that have a half-life greater than 100 million years have been found in earth minerals. Uranium-235 is the shortest half-lived member of this group ($T=713$ million years). No nuclide with a half-life less than 100 million years has been found in earth minerals unless it is supported by a process now in operation. Examples of such processes are the production of 5730-year carbon-14 by cosmic ray interaction with the upper atmosphere and the production

---

* The radioisotope ages listed in this chapter are not necessarily equivalent to existence duration in terms of solar years.

of 1620-year radium-226 by the radioactive decay of 4.51 billion-year uranium-238.

Table VII lists extinct nuclides that have half-lives greater than one million years. Technetium is produced in nuclear reactors, and has been observed spectroscopically in some stars (Merrill, 1952). Iodine-129 is also produced in nuclear reactors, and evidence for its prior existence, as well as that of plutonium-244, has been found in both earth minerals and meteorites (Cherdyntsev, 1961, p. 81; Fleischer, *et al.*, 1967).

Table VII

EXTINCT NUCLIDES

WITH HALF-LIVES GREATER THAN 10^6 YEARS

Nuclide	Half-life in Millions of Years
Beryllium-10	2.7
Manganese-53	2
Technetium-97	2.6
Technetium-98	1.5
Palladium-107	7
Iodine-129	16
Cesium-135	2.0
Samarium-146	50
Hafnium-182	9
Lead-205	30
Uranium-236	23.9
Plutonium-244	76
Curium-247	≥40

The available data clearly indicates that during the past half billion years there has been no creation of unsupported radionuclides with half-life less than 100 million years in earth or in the meteors of our solar system. In a specific creation that shaped the surface of a planet and covered it with organic life there would be no need for material of this nature. It is difficult to see why God in a general creation of matter, a galaxy, or a solar system would bring into existence all nuclides with half-life greater than 100 million years and eliminate all those with a shorter half-life.

Long before discovery of the scientific principles on which radioisotope dating is based some Seventh-day Adventist ministers and scholars had concluded that the basic substance of the earth came into existence through a manifestation of God's creative power earlier in the history of the universe than the activity encompassed within the Genesis creation week (see *Signs of the Times,* July 7, 1898, p. 432; Aug. 25, 1898, p. 535). Debate based on inferences drawn from reading into the few Bible statements and E. G. White comments related to this question, more meaning than the writers intended to convey or than could be communicated by the vocabulary available to these writers, is futile.

In attempting to account for the results obtained by radioisotope dating techniques, or to ascertain the true import of God's communications with man in the language of men, it must be borne in mind that a God with the capacity to cover, in a moment, the surface of a planet with an essentially infinite variety of vegetation containing incomprehensible numbers of previously nonexistent organic molecules, can also in a moment either call into existence or reorder the relatively simple atoms and crystals that make up the inorganic structure of the whole planet or any portion of a planet. The acceptance of the Sabbath as presented in the fourth commandment of the Decalogue involves a recognition that God is distinguished by such capacities. The study of radioisotope dating does not properly involve rejection or acceptance of the Deity as presented in the Bible, or the integrity of the means used by God to communicate with man. Rather, in such a study one can obtain a broader and deeper appreciation of the manner in which God has worked in the creation and maintenance of the physical universe.

There need be no conflict between conclusions drawn from radioisotope dating of inorganic material and the basic requirements of the Bible. However, problems may appear concerning situations in which fossils are associated with minerals which can be dated by radioisotope techniques. Such minerals may be volcanic material, igneous intrusions into deposits containing fossils, or sedimentary deposits overlying, or interbedded with, fossiliferous material (Faul, 1954; Knopf, 1949). Those who seek support for a millions-of-years-long evolution of organic life on earth will assume that radionuclide-bearing minerals associated with fossils were brought into such association free of daughter-products. Accordingly, the accumulated radiogenic daughter-nuclides may be assumed to provide a measure of the time lapse since the radioactive mineral came in contact with the fossil material. One who seeks harmony between scientific observation and a straightforward acceptance of the book of Genesis may, with equal plausibility, assume that these radioactive minerals contained previously acquired daughter-products along with parent nuclides at the time they were brought into association with organic material.

Argon-Potassium Dating

Some defenders of conservative Biblical interpretation have endeavored to resolve problems presented by association of radioactive material with fossils by suggesting that during the Genesis Flood, God disrupted the nuclei of atoms in the earth so that radioisotope ages have no time significance. This suggestion leaves serious problems concerning the agreement among numerous independent radioisotope ages that is generally observed (*e.g.*, see Tables IV and VI), and concerning the regular increase of radioisotope ages for extrusive and intrusive igneous material that seems to be characteristic of increasing depth (see following paragraph). According to this suggestion one should expect to find evidence for decay of nuclides that are not now radioactive. No such evidence is known to exist, even though there is abundant evidence of past decay of nuclides that are now radioactive.

Tertiary volcanic ash beds and basalt flows in the John Day Basin of Oregon have argon/potassium ages that increase regularly and progressively with depth into the local geologic column. These argon/potassium ages range from 6.4 million years for the stratum immediately under surface alluvium, through 15.4 mil-

19   289

lion years for Columbia River basalt, to 36.5 million years for volcanic material overlying deposits assigned as Cretaceous. Fossil flora and fauna are found throughout this column (Evernden and James, 1964b). On the basis of argon/potassium and strontium/rubidium ages for minerals selected from geologically classified strata, a time scale has been developed that ranges from 1.5 million years for Pleistocene deposits to 570 million years for lower Cambrian material (Harland, *et al.*, 1964). The development of this time scale is based on the assumption that radiogenic daughter-products were completely removed when the selected minerals were brought into association with fossil-bearing deposits. More study should be made to determine whether or not it is a universal characteristic for radioisotope ages of strata in a restricted locality to increase as one goes to successively lower layers, as has been shown to be the case in the John Day region.

The testimony of the book of Genesis and the Gospels of Matthew and Luke does not support the assumption of complete removal of daughter-products when inorganic radioactive material has been brought into association with plant and animal remains. The book of Genesis positively affirms that man and other high forms of earth's organic life have been coexistent for all but at most three days of earth's history, and no reasonable interpretation of the Hebrew and Greek words translated "son" can force the genealogies of the Bible to span a period of 36 million years, or even one million years.

John J. Naughton and colleagues from the Hawaiian Institute of Geophysics, in describing lava that erupted from Hualalai volcano in Hawaii in 1801 and contains minerals with argon/potassium ages as great as 3 billion years, comment: "It is noteworthy that argon is retained in the crystal voids despite the high temperature environment where diffusion losses would be expected" (Naughton, Funkhouser, and Barnes, 1966, p. 197).

An attractive hypothesis concerning argon/potassium observations is that degassing was generally more complete for each successive volcanic outflow during the Genesis Flood and the readjustment of earth's crust that followed. Another hypothesis worthy of consideration suggests that successive volcanic outflows may have come from magma that contained progressively less radiogenic argon. Much patient investigation may be required before a fully satisfactory understanding of the radiogenic content of volcanic material is developed.

Attempts to Date Marine Deposits

In addition to the methods outlined in the foregoing portions of this chapter, procedures have been developed for determining radioisotope ages of marine deposits containing radioactive daughter-products that are not maintained in equilibrium ratios with parent uranium in sea water. The assumptions required in these procedures are more involved than those for the relatively simple and direct methods based on measurement of the concentrations of a radioactive parent nuclide and the related stable daughter nuclide. The basic measurement in marine deposit dating techniques may be the relative proportion of 80,-000 year half-life thorium-230 (ionium) to parent uranium-238 (Broecker, 1963), 248,000 year half-life uranium-234 to parent uranium-238 (Thurber, 1962), or 32,480 year half-life protoactinium-231 to thorium-230 (Rosholt et al., 1961). Table VIII outlines the steps in the radioactive formation of protoactinium-231 and thorium-230.

Specification of a radioisotope age on the basis of thorium-230/uranium-238 and uranium-234/uranium-238 ratios requires assumptions concerning the uranium and thorium isotope content of sea water at the time the deposit was formed. Sea water presently has an excess of uranium-234 and a deficiency of thorium-230 with respect to radioactive equilibrium, a condition suggesting that the sea does not retain thorium but has in the past experienced an injection of thorium containing the isotope thorium-234, which decays with a 24.1 day half-life to uranium-234. Thorium-230/uranium-238 and uranium-234/ura-

Table VIII
URANIUM RADIOACTIVE-DECAY SERIES

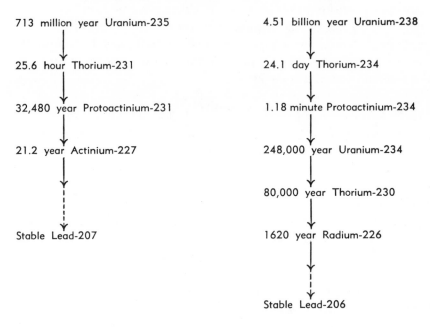

713 million year Uranium-235

25.6 hour Thorium-231

32,480 year Protoactinium-231

21.2 year Actinium-227

Stable Lead-207

4.51 billion year Uranium-238

24.1 day Thorium-234

1.18 minute Protoactinium-234

248,000 year Uranium-234

80,000 year Thorium-230

1620 year Radium-226

Stable Lead-206

nium-238 ages are based on the assumption that sea water has always contained the uranium and thorium isotopic ratios that characterize it at present. Recent analysis has revealed approximate equilibrium between the uranium-234, thorium-230, and uranium-238 in pre-Pleistocene marine carbonate (Veeh, 1966). This observation can be taken to indicate that uranium-238 and its daughter-products may have been in approximate equilibrium in sea water before, and possibly for a short time after, the Genesis Flood.

Protoactinium-231/thorium-230 ages are based on the relative production rates of these isotopes from parent uranium rather than on assumptions concerning their concentration at the time of marine deposit formation, and may, therefore, be expected to have a more secure correlation with real time than do other

Fig. 25.1   Zircon crystals.

marine-deposit radioisotope ages. If the chemical reactions are such as to maintain equal residence times no greater than approximately one thousand years for protoactinium and thorium in sea water, protoactinium-231 and thorium-230 may be expected to be present in the ratio 0.0460/1 and be absorbed in the same ratio on particles incorporated into marine deposits.* Due to the shorter half-life of protoactinium-231, the protoactinium-231/thorium-230 ratio of a chemically isolated deposit will become smaller with the passage of time, decreasing by a factor of one-half every 54,600 years.

If a deposit to be dated by the protoactinium-231/thorium-230 method contains uranium, it is necessary to subtract the amounts of uranium-supported protoactinium-231 and thorium-230 before computing the ratio appropriate for age determination. This correction is made by assuming that a sample that contains uranium also contains all uranium daughter-products in radioactive equilibrium with the parent uranium present. If the uranium contained in a sample is not in equilibrium with its daughter-products, the assumed correction for uranium-supported protoactinium-231 and thorium-230 will be too large. An excessive correction for uranium-supported decay products reduces protoactinium-231/thorium-230 ages that are below roughly 70,000 years and extends those which are greater.

Protoactinium-231/thorium-230 ages for *Globigerina*-ooze sediments in the Caribbean Sea presented by Rosholt, *et al.* (1961), when recalculated on the more precise 32,480-year value

---

* If the protoactinium-231 and thorium-230 concentrations are expressed in terms of uranium concentrations that would provide equivalent levels of radioctivity, this ratio is stated as 2.46/1, rather than 0.0460/1. Expressed in "uranium units" the protoactinium-231/thorium-230 concentration ratio would be 1/1 under conditions of radioactive equilibrium with parent uranium.

for the half-life of protoactinium-231, range uniformly from 8,200 ± 3,000 years at 10 - 17 centimeter depth, to 160,000 ± 30,-000 years at 591 - 595 centimeter depth. The testimony of Genesis accordingly indicates a need for further research on the assumptions involved in this dating technique. It would seem that disturbed conditions existing since the Genesis Flood must have formed marine sediment with initial protoactinium-231/thorium-230 ratios less than the expected 0.0460/1.

The assumption that protoactinium-231/thorium-230 ages are equivalent to absolute age for the Caribbean cores described by Rosholt, *et al.* (1961) yields sedimentation rates that are lower during the past 10,000 years than during any other interval over the 160,000-year range. During the first 47,000 years of this range the average sedimentation rate was approximately three times greater than during the last 10,000 years. This trend is in accord with a stabilization that would be expected following the upheaval of earth's crust and the loss of its vegetation cover at the time of the Genesis Flood. Although a compression of the protoactinium-231/thorium-230 time scale into the limits allowed

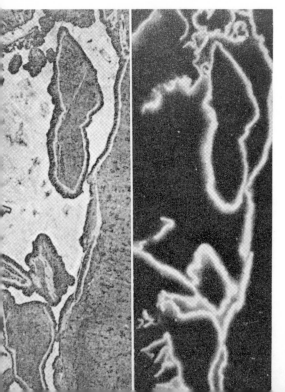

by the book of Genesis might be expected to increase the ratio between early and recent sedimentation rates, no hypothesis of this nature is warranted until a detailed correspondence between absolute age and protoactinium-231/thorium-230 age is available for each locality.

In accord with the principle that "the book of nature and the

Fig. 25.2 A radioactive ore (left) and its autoradiograph (an exposure produced by its own radioactivity).

written word shed light upon each other" (PP 115), an understanding of radioisotope dating can assist one in avoiding unwarranted interpretation of inspired testimony, and a recognition of the insights given through prophetic ministry can assist one in identifying incorrect assumptions underlying the interpretation of radioisotope data. There is need for extensive research by adequately qualified geochemists who recognize the complementary testimony of the book of nature and the written Word. Areas in great need of such investigation are radioisotope dating of volcanic material, intrusive material, and marine deposits.

One should not expect research on radioisotope dating to produce compulsive evidence for historical accuracy throughout the book of Genesis. God compels no one, and may be expected to require faith commensurate with knowledge, as much from the most highly informed geochemist, geologist, or geophysicist as from the unlettered convert who has had no access to scientific information.

This chapter may appropriately conclude with emphasis concerning the need, when speaking on scientific topics such as radioisotope dating, to avoid statements that might lessen respect for direct testimony of the Bible on the part of fair-minded individuals who are well informed in the areas concerned. The assurance that "the book of nature and the written word shed light upon each other" provides ample basis for confidence that sound viewpoints of Biblical truth will accommodate basic related observations in the physical and biological sciences in a manner to win respect from a well-informed, honest mind.

Abstract of the Chapter

Radioisotope dating is based on the rate at which one nucleus (nuclide) spontaneously transmutes into another which has different characteristics. Radioactive change proceeds toward less complex structure, and is a consequence of the nature of the basic forces on which the existence and behavior of matter depends. Accordingly, the rates of radioactive disintegration might logically

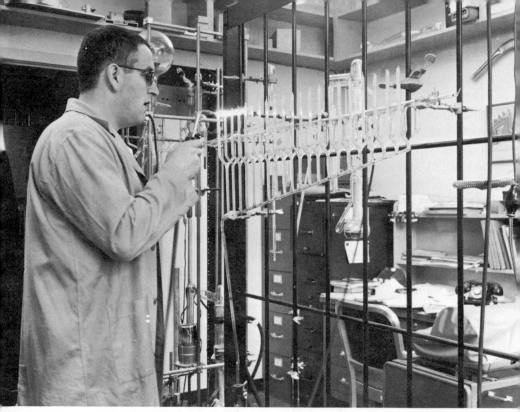

Fig. 25.3 A typical radioisotope dating laboratory, with a physicist dating a specimen by the potassium-argon process.

be expected to be as constant and dependable as the basic characteristics of the physical universe, and, therefore, reliable as units of time measurement.

When allowance is made for the chemical action and heating to which minerals may have been subjected, inorganic radioisotope ages determined by as many as seven independent methods are generally found to be in essential agreement. The presence of exceedingly long-lived radioisotopes and the absence of unsupported short-lived radioisotopes in earth and meteoritic material is consistent with the results obtained by radioisotope dating techniques. These facts support the contention of many exegetes, that most of the statements concerning the creation of earth which come to us from inspired sources refer only to a modification of the planet's surface and its adornment with plant and animal life. The testimony of inspired writers is that pre-existing matter is not essential to such creative activity. Furthermore, this testimony carries the implication that large quantities of previously nonexistent elementary matter may have been created during the immediate events involved in the placement of life on earth.

Radioisotope dating of volcanic materials and marine deposits appears to contradict inspired testimony concerning the duration of earth history. This contradiction, it should be noted, is at the level of interpretation, rather than that of direct laboratory or field observation. Radioisotope dating of volcanic flows and eruptions is based on assumptions concerning degassing at the time of volcanic activity, which have recently been shown not to be valid in all cases. Radioisotope dating of marine deposits is based on presently unverifiable postulates concerning the radioisotope content of ancient sea water. Further research is needed on the potassium/argon dating of volcanic material, and on radioisotope dating of marine deposits, in order to correlate the testimony obtained from a study of nature and that given by Inspiration.

REFERENCES

Anders, Edward. 1962. Meteorite ages, Reviews of modern physics 34:287-325. This paper is essential reading for anyone who is strongly concerned with radioisotope dating.

Broecker, W. S. 1963. A preliminary evaluation of uranium series inequilibrium as a tool for absolute age measurements on marine carbonates. Jour. Geophys. Res. 68:2817-2834.

Chemical and Engineering News. 1964. Half-lives of tin-119 and iron-57 prolonged. June 22.

Cherdyntsev, V. V. 1961. Abundance of chemical elements. The University of Chicago Press, Chicago.

Cook, Melvin A. 1957. Where is the earth's helium? Nature 179:213.

Damon, P. E. and W. D. Green. 1963. Investigations of the helium age dating method by stable isotope-dilution techniques. *In* Radioactive Dating. International Atomic Energy Agency, Vienna, pp. 55-71.

Evernden, J. F., D. E. Savage, G. H. Curtis, and G. T. James. 1964[a]. Potassium-argon dates and the Cenozoic mammalian chronology of North America. Am. Jour. Sci. 262:145-198.

Evernden, J. F. and G. T. James. 1964[b]. Potassium-argon dates and the Tertiary floras of North America. Am. Jour. of Sci. 262:945-974.

Faul, Henry. 1954. Nuclear geology. John Wiley Co., New York, pp. 269, 280.

Fleischer, R. L. and P. B. Price, *et al.*, 1967. Tracks of heavy primary cosmic rays in meteorites. Jour. Geophys. Res. 72 (1):355-366.

Gojkovic, S., G. Deleon, and Z. Cervenjak. 1963. Dating of some uranites from Yugoslav localities by the Pb^{206}/Pb^{210} method. *In* Radioactive Dating. International Atomic Energy Agency, Vienna, pp. 105-110.

297

Harland, W. B., *et al.*, editors, 1964. The phanerozoic time scale. Geological Society of London.

Hart, S. R. 1966. Current status of radioactive age determination methods. Transactions Am. Geophysical Union 47 (1):280-286.

Hirt, B., W. Herr, and W. Hoffmeister. 1963. Age determinations by the rhenium-osmium method. *In* Radioactive dating. International Atomic Energy Agency, Vienna, pp. 35-43.

Knopf, Adolph. 1949. Time in earth history. *In* Genetics, paleontology, and evolution. Glenn L. Jepsen, Ernst Mayr, and George Gaylord Simpson, eds. Princeton Univ. Press, Princeton, New Jersey.

Kulp, J. L. 1961. Geological time scale. Science 133:1105-1114.

Kulp, J. L., W. S. Broecker, and W. R. Eckelmann. 1953. Age determination of uranium minerals by the Pb-210 method. Nucleonics 11:19-21.

Kulp, J. L. and Joan Engels. 1963. Discordance in K-Ar and Rb-Sr isotopic ages. *In* Radioactive Dating. International Atomic Energy Agency, Vienna, pp. 209-238.

Malliaris, A. C. and Kenneth T. Bainbridge. 1966. Alteration of the decay constant of Te^{125m} by chemical means. Physical Review 149:958-964.

Merrill, P. W. 1952. Spectroscopic observations of stars of class S. Astrophysical Journal 116:21 (abstract).

Moorbath, S. 1960. Radiochemical methods. *In* Methods in geochemistry. A. A. Smales and L. R. Wagner, eds. Interscience Publishers, Inc., New York, pp. 247-296 (specifically p. 284).

Naughton, John J., John C. Funkhouser, and I. Lynus Barnes. 1966. Fluid inclusions in potassium-argon age anomalies and related inert gas studies. Transactions Am. Geophysical Union 47 (1):197 (abstract).

Pidgeon, R., J. O'Neil, and Leon T. Silver. 1966. Uranium and lead isotopic stability in a melamict zircon under experimental hydrothermal conditions. Science 154:1538-1540.

Rosholt, J. N., *et al.* 1961. Absolute dating of deep-sea cores by the Pa^{231}/Th^{230} method. Jour. of Geol. 69:162-185.

Ruby, S. L. and R. R. Ferber. 1964. Scientific paper 64-8c2-115-Pl. Westinghouse Research and Development Center, Pittsburgh. September 1.

Russell, R. D. and R. M. Farquhar. 1960. Lead isotopes in geology. Interscience Publishers, Inc., New York. 243 pp.

Signs of the Times. 1898. Pacific Press Pub. Assn., Mountain View, Calif. Editorial on p. 432 of July 7; question corner on August 25.

Thurber, D. L. 1962. Anomalous U^{234}/U^{238} in nature. Jour. Geophys. Res. 67:4518-4520.

Tilton, G. R. and S. R. Hart. 1963. Geochronology. Science 140:357-366.

Veeh, H. Herbert. 1966. Th^{230}/U^{238} and U^{234}/U^{238} ages of Pleistocene high sea level stand. Jour. Geophys. Res. 71:3379-3386.

Wasserburg, G. J., *et al.* 1962. A study of the ages of the Precambrian in Texas. Jour. Geophys. Res. 67:4021-4047.

Webster, R. K. 1960. Mass spectrometric isotope dilution analysis. *In* Methods in geochemistry. A. A. Smales and L. R. Wagner, eds. Interscience Publishers, Inc., New York, pp. 202-246 (specifically p. 236).

White, E. G. 1890. Patriarchs and prophets. Pacific Press Pub. Assn., Mountain View, California. 793 pp.

CHAPTER TWENTY-SIX

Radiocarbon Dating

By R. H. Brown

RADIOCARBON LABORATORIES have determined ages for organic material that in many instances appear to be in conflict with the specifications concerning earth history given by the book of Genesis and endorsed by the gospel writers and the apostle Paul in the New Testament. There is therefore need for intensive and careful study of radiocarbon dating to find the agreement that we can expect between the book of nature and the written Word.

The human mind attempts to integrate and summarize its observations into generalized principles and viewpoints, a procedure that is necessary to the development of understanding and ability. An investigator naturally tends to harmonize the information available to him with his general world view. As a consequence of their cultural and educational background, the world view of most radiocarbon specialists is based on uniformitarianism and progressive evolutionary development of life. In dealing with some of the information provided by carbon-14 analysis, a person who begins with commonly accepted uniformitarian viewpoints may unintentionally be following a more difficult and devious path in his attempt to attain to a full understanding than the person who makes the Bible his guide. Where scientific investigation and inspired testimony both bear upon a subject, a sincere search for truth will result in a clearer and more complete understanding of both.

Those who are leading out in the development and application of carbon-14 dating techniques are men and women of high ideals, intensely devoted to finding truth and meticulous in their attempt to distinguish between speculation and firmly substantiated evidence. With carbon-14 dating, as with many other areas of human thought, the dogmatism with which speculative conclusions are advocated commonly increases in direct proportion to the dogmatists' distance from prime sources of information, and in inverse proportion to his own knowledge and understanding.

The Formation of Carbon-14

Before considering some recent developments in the field of radiocarbon dating, many readers may appreciate a brief survey of the physical phenomena involved. Stars eject into space some of the matter of which they are composed. This ejected matter consists of hydrogen, small amounts of helium, and traces of more complex atoms. Some of the atoms in this ejected matter have undergone forces that strip away their outer negative electric charge (electrons) and that accelerate the remaining positively charged nucleus to extremely high speeds. These high-speed atomic nuclei that drift through interstellar space are called primary cosmic rays.

Earth is constantly bombarded from all directions with these primary cosmic-ray particles, which have sufficient energy to break up atoms they encounter on reaching the upper levels of earth's atmosphere. The breakup of nitrogen and oxygen atoms by primary cosmic rays produces neutrons and atoms of carbon, boron, beryllium, helium, hydrogen, and possibly lithium. Neutrons are uniquely effective agents for producing atomic transmutation. The most frequent reaction produced by neutrons in air transmutes nitrogen into carbon with 14 units of mass, making it 16½ per cent heavier than an ordinary carbon atom (which has 12 units of mass), and radioactive (that is, unstable).

Some 22 pounds of radioactive carbon are produced per year

in earth's upper atmosphere as a result of reactions produced by primary cosmic rays. This radioactive carbon is oxidized to carbon dioxide, which is mixed throughout the atmosphere by air currents and utilized by plants along with nonradioactive carbon dioxide to form carbohydrates. The high solubility of carbon dioxide in water transfers a large portion of earth's radioactive carbon to the oceans. Radioactive carbon is distributed through all living material as a result of the dependence of animal life upon plant food.

Death of a plant or an animal terminates the processes by which its tissue structure receives carbon-14 from the environment. Since carbon-14 is unstable and spontaneously converts to nitrogen, the remains of once-living material will, with the passage of time, contain progressively smaller amounts of carbon-14. Laboratory measurements on known amounts of radioactive carbon have established within an uncertainty of less than 100 years, that in 5,730 years half of an initial amount of carbon-14 will decay into nitrogen. As a result, 5,730-year-old remains of plants and animals would be expected to contain half as much radioactive carbon as they did at death.

Changes in the Carbon-14, Carbon-12 Ratio

For convenience, data on the radioactive carbon content of a sample is reported by specifying a "radiocarbon age." The radiocarbon age describes the relative amount of radioactive carbon in the sample, in terms of the relative amount of radioactive carbon in an oxalic acid standard supplied by the U.S. National Bureau of Standards.* The NBS oxalic acid standard of carbon-14 activity is adjusted to provide a reference based on the average carbon-14 activity of wood that was growing in A.D. 1850. The strength in which the NBS standardized oxalic acid is supplied is such that 95 per cent of its specific radiocarbon activity is equivalent to the specific radiocarbon activity to be expected

---

* As used in this chapter the term "radiocarbon age" designates the amount of radioactive carbon present, and in no way implies that such "ages" beyond approximately 2000 B.C. are to be accepted as indicating real, chronological time.

from wood growing in A.D. 1950 under conditions that prevailed in A.D. 1850. The radiocarbon age of a sample is the number of years that would be required for the specific radiocarbon activity level defined by the NBS oxalic acid standard to decay to the specific activity level measured in the sample.

Radiocarbon ages are based on a 5,568 year half-life for carbon-14 decay (the average of early less precise measurements), rather than on the more accurate value of 5,730 years. This is done in order to avoid confusion in comparing recent determinations with the large number of radiocarbon ages that appeared in the literature during the time when 5,568 years was the best available value for carbon-14 half-life. Since the radiocarbon time scale is arbitrary and does not directly measure real time, there is no need for basing it on an absolutely accurate determination of half-life. Those who are unhappy with the 5,568 year half-life convention can convert radiocarbon ages to a 5,730-year-based scale with a simple multiplication by 1.03. A sample with a specific radiocarbon activity equal to one-half of 95 per cent of the specific radiocarbon activity of the NBS oxalic acid standard is assigned a radiocarbon age of 5,568. The radiocarbon date for the time when this sample ceased to exchange carbon with its environment would be 5,568 B.P. (before present), or 3,618 B.C. (5,568 B.P.—A.D. 1950). In summary it may be said that radiocarbon ages are based on a 5,568 year half-life and are standardized against pre-industrial-revolution conditions (A.D. 1850), and that A.D. 1950 is used for the zero point on the radiocarbon time scale. (Stuiver and Suess, 1966; Editorial Statement, *Radiocarbon,* vol. 8, 1966; Half-Life Statement, *Proceedings of the Sixth International Conference on Radiocarbon and Tritium Dating.*)

The reasons for basing radiocarbon ages on conditions in A.D. 1850 are of interest. Since A.D. 1850 man has introduced into earth's atmosphere large amounts of carbon dioxide produced by the use of fossil fuels—coal, oil, and natural gas. These fossil fuels contain a negligible amount of carbon-14 and are described as of "infinite age" on the radiocarbon time scale. During the 100-year period between A.D. 1850 and A.D. 1950 use of fossil fuels released infinite-age carbon equivalent to approximately 11 per cent of the total carbon presently contained in the atmosphere. Had this contribution of nonradioactive carbon been confined to the atmosphere it would have reduced the radiocarbon activity of the atmosphere by approximately 10 per cent. The actual decrease experienced (Suess effect) was only approximately 3 per cent (Houtermans, 1967), indicating that a large portion of the carbon released to the atmosphere by man's use of fossil fuels has been absorbed in the ocean (95 per cent of the carbon in earth's carbon dioxide exchange system is contained in the ocean). From A.D. 1950 to A.D. 1964 use of fossil fuels contributed carbon equivalent to approximately 6 per cent of the present atmospheric carbon content (Suess, 1955; Dyck, 1966).

Another factor related to human activity that influences the radiocarbon concentration in the atmosphere is the release of

Fig. 26.1   Carbon purification apparatus in a radiocarbon dating laboratory.

neutrons by atomic reactors and nuclear weapons. As a result of the Russian thermonuclear tests the relative amount of carbon-14 in earth's atmosphere approximately doubled between 1962 and 1965 (Thommeret and Thommeret, 1966; Burger and Libby, 1966). Thorough mixing of bomb products was expected to increase the radiocarbon activity throughout earth's atmosphere to a level possibly three to four times greater than it was prior to 1962. Factors in the mixing of various components of earth's carbon dioxide exchange system that are not quantitatively understood appear to have limited the atmospheric radiocarbon activity peak resulting from bomb products to the approximate doubling that has already been experienced (Libby, 1966a; Fergusson, 1966; Tauber, 1967).

By using as a "contemporary" reference the most recent radiocarbon activity level that has not been significantly affected by human activity, radiocarbon ages can more readily be used in studies of the past. The most accurate value for the "contemporary" activity level is now considered to be 13.6 disintegrations per minute per gram of plant or animal carbon (Libby, 1966a).

The Accuracy of Carbon-14 Dating

The measurements made in a radiocarbon laboratory do not determine historical ages or dates. The laboratory procedures only determine the amount of radioactive carbon which a sample contains at present. As described in the foregoing portion of this chapter, this amount of radioactivity is conveniently specified in terms of a radiocarbon age. The historical time lapse since a given specimen was part of a living organism that exchanged carbon with its environment, is an interpretation based in part on its radiocarbon age. The postulation of a date or age associated with the sample requires an assumption concerning the relative amount of radioactive carbon in the environment that supported the life of the organism from which the sample has been derived.

Sagebrush sandals found in Fort Rock Cave in the southern part of central Oregon have a radiocarbon age of 9,300. If the relative percentage of radioactive carbon in earth's atmosphere during the growth of the sagebrush from which these sandals were made was the same as it was in A.D. 1850, these sandals were made from sagebrush harvested 9,579 solar years ago.* There is no proof that these sandals were made 9,579 years ago, for radiocarbon ages can be reliably correlated with solar time only over the past 3,500 or possibly 4,000 years (approximately to the time of Moses or Abraham; Libby, 1966b).

Major research effort is being directed toward developing reliable correlations between radiocarbon age and historical age. If the relative amount of radioactive carbon in the atmosphere had been at the A.D. 1850 level throughout the time life has existed on earth, radiocarbon ages, when adjusted to the 5,730 year half-life, would be identical with historical age. Tree-ring dating has established a precise and reliable chronology extending back to 59 B.C. By measuring the radiocarbon activity in precisely dated wood fibers, a chart can be prepared for converting radiocarbon age into historical age over the past 2,000 years (Stuiver and Suess, 1966). Such a chart (see Fig. 26.2) shows fluctuations in the relative amount of carbon-14 in the atmosphere during this period, but these fluctuations appear to have been limited within a range of less than five per cent of the A.D. 1850 level. Because of the fluctuations in the atmospheric carbon-14 activity and the difficulties in standardizing one radiocarbon laboratory against another, the minimum uncertainty in any radiocarbon age is commonly considered to be plus or minus 100 years (see *Radiocarbon*, vol. 8, 1966, pp. 27, 213, 240, 340, and 453). Accordingly, if there are no contamination problems, the historical age of a sample that has a radiocarbon age no greater than about 2,000 years may confidently be considered to lie within a range of uncertainty equal to plus or minus twice

---

* Multiplying 9,300 by 1.03 to convert from the 5,568-year scale to the more precise 5,730-year scale.

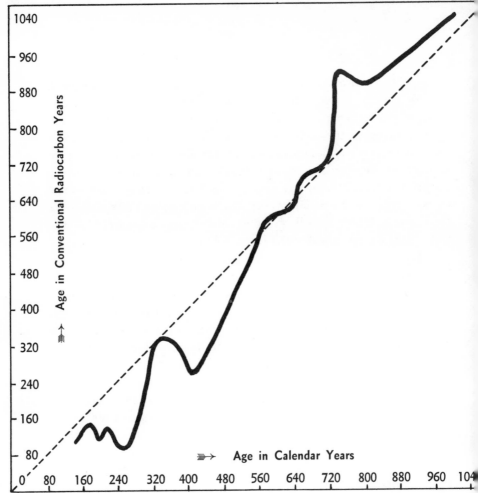

Fig. 26.2 The relation between radiocarbon ages and true ages for the past millennium. From A.D. 1000 to 250 B.C., radiocarbon years are generally about 50 to 100 years older than true ages. (From Minze Stuiver and Hans E. Suess, Radiocarbon 8:537-538.)

the uncertainty specified for the radiocarbon age, provided this range is no less than plus or minus 200 years (see *Radiocarbon* 8:256).

The foregoing statement must be qualified for samples that contain carbon derived from more than one period of history. A mud turtle from the Montezuma Well in Arizona that died in early A.D. 1961 was found to have an apparent radiocarbon age of approximately 15,000 years. This age is consistent with the radiocarbon age of the turtle's food supply, which obtained most of its CO_2 from water rather than from the atmosphere, artesian spring "fossil" water that had a radiocarbon age of 21,420 (Haynes, *et al.*, 1966).

Attempts to derive historical age from radiocarbon age yield increasingly uncertain conjectures for samples older than 2,000 years. By the use of bristlecone pine wood fiber, a tree-ring sequence extending to about 5100 B.C. has been developed (Ferguson, 1968). The establishment of a precise long-term growth-ring sequence with bristlecone pine wood is difficult because all sections of a given tree do not grow simultaneously. An attempt must be made to match the growth patterns for various portions of individual trees, as well as to compare sections from a large number of trees. Attempts to correlate bristlecone pine tree-ring sequences with radiocarbon ages indicate that either ring counting has overestimated the age of ancient bristlecone pine material by 500 to 1,000 years or the relative amount of carbon-14 in the atmosphere prior to 2000 B.C. was in the order of 10 per cent greater than the A.D. 1850 level (Damon, *et al.*, 1966; Ferguson, 1968).

Aside from the information supplied in the book of Genesis and the Ellen G. White comments thereon, there is at present no firm basis for inferring historical age for any sample with a radiocarbon age greater than 3,500 to 4,000. Commenting on

Fig. 26.3 A bristlecone pine in the White Mountains of California.

radiocarbon data for the eastern middle European paleolithic material, Dr. László Vértes, of the Hungarian National Museum, says: "From the present until about 25-28,000 radiocarbon years ago, the data are congruent; earlier data than these are inconsistent, and chaotic—a fact that is all the more striking as the contradictions appear just in that period from which the bulk of analyses are available: the time between 30,000 and 45,000 C^{14} years" (Vértes, 1966).

Studies conducted in the C-14 laboratory at the University of Uppsala indicate that "infinite" age material may give a radiocarbon age between 32,000 and "infinite" (greater than 40,000), depending on the method of sample preparation (Olsson, 1966). While Dr. Olsson's studies were conducted with Tertiary Age oyster shells (geological age at least one million years), her findings together with the observations of Dr. Vértes indicate that any radiocarbon age greater than 28,000 should be regarded with liberal skepticism. Added to the difficulties of counting low-level radioactivity (one gram of 28,500-year-old carbon would average only one carbon-14 disintegration every two and one-half minutes), very old samples present problems due to critical but uncertain contamination with modern carbon, which is easily acquired during collection, handling, and laboratory preparation.

Those who accept the Genesis account as inspired and historically valid interpret the radiocarbon age for ancient material, such as the Tertiary oyster shells referred to above, anthracite coal, mineral oil, natural gas, et cetera, to indicate that earth's atmosphere before the Genesis Flood had a relative carbon-14 activity no greater than 1/100, and possibly as low as 1/1000 of the level that became established by 1500 B.C. (A relative carbon-14 activity of 1/128 the contemporary level corresponds to decay over seven half-lives, or a radiocarbon age of 39,976: $2^7 = 128$; $7 \times 5,568 = 39,976$.)

Although up to the present no basis has been found for precise and reliable conversion between historical age and radiocarbon ages greater than 3,500, radiocarbon age determinations in the 4,000 to 30,000 range do, nevertheless, give important support to the book of Genesis. With a particularly appropriate figure of speech, a leading archaeologist states: "W. H. Libby, in developing radiocarbon dating . . . dropped the equivalent of an atomic bomb on archaeology" (Johnson, 1966). Radiocarbon dating of spruce trees buried by glacial advance in Wisconsin has forced geologists to reduce the presumed time that has elapsed since major glacial advance, from 25,000 solar years to 11,400 radiocarbon years. Assuming a one-to-one correspondence between radiocarbon years and solar years results in a drastic compression of the time span that previously had been considered available for the development of Western civilization (Putnam, 1964).

The remarkable scarcity of objects clearly associated with human activity, and which have radiocarbon ages in excess of 12,-000, suggests that the human population has grown from a small beginning in a short period of time. It is highly significant that the greatest radiocarbon ages firmly related to human activity are provided by material from the Middle East, the Ukraine, and the Mediterranean basin (Haynes, 1966; Smith, 1966; Vogel and Waterbolk, 1967). Radiocarbon ages for the oldest evidences of man indicate that earth was populated as the result of a migration that spread out in all directions from the Middle East, and that reached the Western Hemisphere by way of Alaska. Radiocarbon dating has established that the recent glacial periods in Northern Europe and Northern North America were coincident, that the earliest appearance of man in North America coincided closely with the latest advance of glacial ice across Wisconsin, and that both North America and Northern Europe were settled rapidly after the first appearance of man in these regions (Libby, 1956).

A recent survey of radiocarbon dates indicates that by the time corresponding to a radiocarbon age of 7,200, farming had been established throughout a strip approximately 10 degrees latitude in width extending from Greece across southern Asia

Minor to Iran; during the succeeding period of time represented by a span of 1,200 "years" on the radiocarbon time scale, farming extended over the Nile Delta, Northern Egypt, Babylonia, and Central Europe; and by the time corresponding to a radiocarbon age of 5,000, farming had become established in Northwestern Europe, Northwestern Africa, and the Ukraine (Clark, 1966). Data is lacking concerning the spread of agriculture eastward from Babylonia, but there are in India remains from the highly developed Harappa culture that have radiocarbon ages as great as approximately 4,300 (Agrawal, 1966). This culture developed elaborate irrigation facilities, and had a written language that appears to be unrelated to the writing of subsequent Asian cultures and that modern man has thus far been unable to decipher.

The limited time suggested by radiocarbon dating for the spread of human population and for the development of ancient civilization has led many individuals whose world view is not based on the information given in the Bible to seek support for the postulate that in the ancient past earth's atmosphere contained a greater relative amount of carbon-14 than it has over the 3,000-year period up to A.D. 1850. (Every doubling of the initial relative amount of carbon-14 in a specimen over the relative amount that characterizes material living in A.D. 1850 would add 5,730 solar years to the difference between the historical age and the radiocarbon age of the specimen, if the historical age is greater than a radiocarbon age based on assumed initial conditions equivalent to those which existed in A.D. 1850.) Search for firm evidence to support a higher carbon-14 level in the ancient atmosphere has not been fruitful.

Since primary cosmic ray particles are deflected away from earth by its magnetic field, the role of this field in carbon-14 production rate has been investigated (Elsasser, *et al.*, 1956; Kigoshi, 1966). Detailed calculation indicates that a complete disappearance of earth's magnetic field would no more than double the present carbon-14 production rate, with consequent extension of the time indicated by the oldest radiocarbon dates by no more than 6,000 years.

A higher level of carbon-14 activity would be brought about by an increase in the primary cosmic ray activity. Since studies of the cosmic ray effects in meteorites indicate that the cosmic ray flux in the solar system has remained close to its present level over a period of time many orders of magnitude greater than that with which radiocarbon dating is concerned (Libby, 1966a), the only possibility for a large increase in the relative amount of carbon-14 appears to be through a reduction in the amount of nonradioactive carbon in the atmosphere. An addition of 17,190 solar years to the historical age of ancient material in this manner would require a reduction of the atmospheric carbon dioxide to one-eighth its present concentration (17,190$=$3 x 5,730; $\frac{1}{2}$ x $\frac{1}{2}$ x $\frac{1}{2}=\frac{1}{8}$). Since only 0.053 per cent by weight of earth's atmosphere is carbon dioxide at present, and the fossil record indicates a much more extensive and more luxurious life than is now supported by earth, a significant reduction of atmospheric carbon dioxide below the present level does not appear to be a reasonable postulate.

It seems much more suitable to think of earth's ancient atmosphere as characterized by a higher, rather than a below-modern, carbon dioxide composition. Coal, oil, and gas reserves, limestone beds, shales, and vast amounts of organic materials scattered in gravel beds throughout the planet indicate that before the Flood the biosphere was many times richer in carbon than it is today. A plant or an animal that might have lived at a time when the biosphere contained the same amount of carbon-14, but eight times the amount of nonradioactive carbon characteristic of contemporary conditions, would at its death have a radiocarbon age of 17,190 "years" in comparison with contemporary materials. Earlier in this chapter evidence was presented that suggests that prior to the Flood the relative amount of radioactive carbon in earth's biosphere was at most 1/100 and possibly as low as 1/1000 of its present value. The reader must be cautioned that harmony

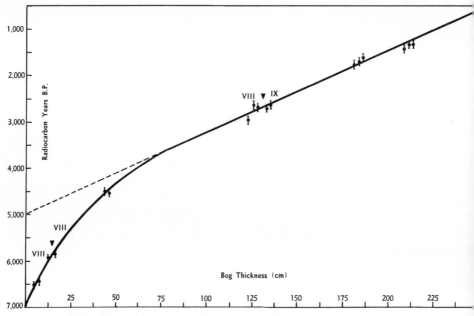

Fig. 26.4 Draved Mose peat bog growth plat.

between the historical requirements of the book of Genesis and
radiocarbon ages cannot be obtained by postulating a hundred
fold greater concentration of carbon dioxide in the pre-Flood atmosphere, since carbon dioxide becomes highly toxic when it
reaches unit per cent levels. It is the amount of carbon in the entire carbon dioxide exchange system, not the relatively small
amount contained in the atmosphere, that determines the
carbon-14/carbon-12 ratio with which we are concerned.

In connection with speculation concerning an increase in the
carbon-14/carbon-12 ratio since the Genesis Flood, the relationship plotted in Fig. 26.4 is of interest. The points on this plot are
radiocarbon ages of one-centimeter-thick slices of peat from a vertical section in the central part of Draved Mose bog in south Jut-
land, Denmark. The first point on the plot is for peat that lay at a
mean height of 4.5 centimeters above the underlying sand and
has a radiocarbon age of 6,500 ± 140 (Tauber, 1966).

All points plotted in Fig. 26.4 would cluster around the
straight portion of the solid line and the dashed extension of this
portion if radiocarbon age had always been directly proportional
to historical age and if the build-up rate of the bog, averaged over

312

Fig. 26.5 A peat bog in Nova Scotia.

periods in the order of 100 years'
duration, had been constant
throughout the history of the
profile. Since radiocarbon age
has been demonstrated to correlate closely with historical age
over the past 3,500 years, the data
at hand indicate that during this
period until at least 700 years
ago the center of bog Draved Mose has been building up uniformly at an average rate of 0.600 millimeter per year. Considering the various factors involved in peat-bog development, it is
surprising to find evidence for a uniform build-up over so large
a portion of post-Genesis Flood history.

The average build-up rate at the center of Draved Mose bog
appears to have been only 0.125 millimeter per 6,000 B.P. radiocarbon year during the initial accumulation under Pollen-zone
VII conditions, approximately one-fifth the average build-up rate
since 3,500 B.P. In seeking to interpret the data presented in
Fig. 26.4, one can postulate equivalence between radiocarbon age
and historical age over the past 7,000 years and infer initial
relatively slow growth of the peat over a 2,000-year period. One
can also postulate initial bog growth-rate equal to or greater than
that which has been characteristic over the past 3,500 years,
and infer that the carbon-14/carbon-12 ratio in the atmosphere
increased by possibly as much as 50 per cent during the time the
first 75 centimeters of the central bog section was built up.

A deeper portion of this bog in another site contains Pollen-
zone V material, which increased 40 centimeters in thickness (as

presently measured) during a 565-radiocarbon-year interval beginning 8,730 ± 160 radiocarbon years B.P. (Tauber, 1966, pp. 215, 216). The average build-up rate for this older material is approximately 0.7 millimeter per 8,500 B.P. radiocarbon year.

Because of large variations to be expected in conditions affecting the development of a peat bog, a wide variety of radiocarbon age versus bog-thickness profiles is to be expected. Analysis of the limited data presently available confirms this anticipation. A few profiles have been found which indicate relatively rapid growth per radiocarbon year prior to 3,000-4,000 B.P. (inverse to the pattern represented in Fig. 26.4). The most probable type appears to be either one that is approximately a straight line, or one that indicates relatively less rapid build-up per radiocarbon year during earlier growth as illustrated by Draved Mose. The Draved Mose data is compatible with a model for ancient climatic and atmospheric changes that involves initial relatively rapid bog build-up during a period that combines favorable moist climatic conditions with an increasing relative amount of atmospheric carbon-14. A more rapid initial growth rate than that experienced by Draved Mose could produce a straight-line or inverted profile of radiocarbon age verses bog thickness during a period of increasing relative amount of atmospheric carbon-14. Detailed studies of many peat bogs with this model in mind would be desirable.

While there are at present no scientific data to prove that any of the changes listed below have taken place, it is worth noting that each one is within the range of possibility and would *increase* the relative amount of radioactive carbon in the atmosphere over its pre-Flood level:

1. Reduction of earth's magnetic field from a pre-Flood intensity that kept most of the primary cosmic ray particles from interacting with the atmosphere.

2. Loss of an outer region of water vapor that absorbed primary cosmic rays and cosmic-ray-produced neutrons before they had opportunity to react with nitrogen in the atmosphere.

3. Removal by rains during and after the Flood of a large

portion of the carbon dioxide characteristic of the pre-Flood atmosphere, and conversion of this to precipitated carbonates and carbonates carried in solution by the post-Flood oceans.

It has been reliably estimated that the carbon in the earth that is not presently contained in minerals or fossils is distributed 86.2 per cent in solution in the oceans in a chemical form not directly associated with organic material, 8.7 per cent in organic material contained in the oceans, 3.5 per cent associated with organic life on land, and 1.6 per cent in the atmosphere (Dyck, 1966). Given the necessary changes in the carbon reservoir and/or the production rate of carbon-14, the historical requirements of the book of Genesis allow ample time for a transition from pre-Flood conditions to the contemporary carbon-14 specific activity level by the time of Moses, since the average residence time of carbon-14 in the atmosphere is approximately four years, and the mixing time of the carbon dioxide exchange reservoir, 25 years (Libby, 1966a; Schell, *et al.*, 1966; Young, *et al.*, 1968).

The development of radioactive dating with carbon-14 has brought both support and problems to those who accept a short duration of life on the earth. It is well to keep in mind the principle so well stated in the last three paragraphs of *Patriarchs and Prophets,* pages 115 and 116: "Science . . . brings nothing from her research that conflicts with divine revelation. . . . The book of nature and the written word shed light upon each other. . . . Those who take the written word as their counselor will find in science an aid to understand God." Continuing investigation of radiocarbon dating may be expected to bring greater harmony between the information God has given to us through the written Word and that through the natural world.

REFERENCES

Agrawal, D. P. 1966. C¹⁴ dates, Banas culture and the Aryans. Radiocarbon and Tritium Dating, Proc. Sixth International Conf. on Radiocarbon and Tritium Dating, National Bureau of Standards, U. S. Department of Commerce, Springfield, Virginia, pp. 256-263.

Burger, Rainer and W. F. Libby. 1966. UCLA radiocarbon dates V. Radiocarbon 8:467-497.

CREATION—ACCIDENT OR DESIGN?

Clark, Grahame. 1966. Radiocarbon dating and the spread of agriculture in the old world. Radiocarbon and Tritium Dating, pp. 232-242.
Damon, Paul E., Austin Long, and Donald C. Grey. 1966. Fluctuation of atmospheric C^{14} during the last six millenniums. Radiocarbon and Tritium Dating, pp. 415-428.
Dyck, Willy. 1966. Secular variations in the C^{14} concentration of Douglas fir tree rings. Radiocarbon and Tritium Dating, pp. 440-451.
Elsasser, W., E. P. Ney, and J. R. Winckler. 1956. Cosmic-ray intensity and geomagnetism. Nature 178:1226, 1227.
Ferguson, C. W. 1968. Bristlecone pine: science and esthetics. Science 159:839-846.
Fergusson, G. J. 1966. Radiocarbon and tritium in the upper troposphere. Radiocarbon and Tritium Dating, pp. 525-540.
Haynes, C. Vance, Jr. 1966. Carbon-14 dates and early man in the new world. Radiocarbon and Tritium Dating, pp. 145-164.
Haynes, C. Vance, Jr., Paul E. Damon, and Donald Grey. 1966. Arizona radiocarbon dates VI. Radiocarbon 8:4, 5.
Houtermans, J., H. E. Suess, and W. Munk. 1967. Effect of industrial fuel combustion on the carbon-14 level of atmospheric CO_2. Radioactive Dating and Methods of Low-Level Counting, International Atomic Energy Agency, Vienna, pp. 57-68.
Johnson, Frederick. 1966. The impact of radiocarbon dating upon archeology. Radiocarbon and Tritium Dating, pp. 762-784.
Kigoshi, K. 1966. Secular variation of atmospheric radiocarbon concentration and its dependence on geomagnetism. Radiocarbon and Tritium Dating, pp. 429-438.
Libby, W. F. 1956. Radiocarbon dating. Am. Sci. 44:98-112.
———. 1966[a]. Radiocarbon and paleomagnetism. Radiocarbon and Tritium Dating, pp. 348-356.
———. 1966[b]. Natural radiocarbon and tritium in retrospect and prospect. Radiocarbon and Tritium Dating, pp. 745-751.
Olsson, I. U. 1966. New experience on C^{14}-dating of tests of foraminifera. Radiocarbon and Tritium Dating, pp. 319-331.
Putnam, William C. 1964. Geology. Oxford University Press, New York, pp. 434-436.
Schell, W. R., A. W. Fairhall, and G. D. Harp. 1966. Measurements of carbon-14 in known age samples and their geophysical implications. Radiocarbon and Tritium Dating, Proc. Sixth International Conf. on Radiocarbon and Tritium Dating, National Bureau of Standards, U.S. Department of Commerce, Springfield, Virginia, pp. 397-405.
Smith, Philip E. 1966. Paleolithic radiocarbon dates from southwestern Europe and the Mediterranean basin. Radiocarbon and Tritium Dating, pp. 199-209.
Stenberg, Allan and Ingrid U. Olsson. 1967. Uppsala radiocarbon measurements VIII. Radiocarbon 9:471-476.
Stuiver, Minze and Hans E. Suess. 1966. On the relationship between radiocarbon dates and true sample ages. Radiocarbon 8:534-540.
Suess, Hans E. 1955. Radiocarbon concentration in modern wood. Science 122:415.
Tauber, Henrik. 1966. Copenhagen radiocarbon dates VII. Radiocarbon 8:213-234.
———. 1967. Copenhagen radiocarbon dates VIII. Radiocarbon 9:246-248.
Thommeret, J. and Y. Thommeret. 1966. Monaco radiocarbon measurements II. Radiocarbon 8:286-291.
Vértes, László. 1966. A comment on the C^{14} data of eastern middle European paleolithic, with suggestions for future standardization of radiocarbon age determinations. Radiocarbon and Tritium Dating, pp. 210-223.
Vogel, J. C. and H. T. Waterbolk. 1967. Groningen radiocarbon dates VII. Radiocarbon 9:119.
Young, J. A. and A. W. Fairhall. 1968. Radiocarbon from nuclear weapons tests. Jour. Geophys. Res. 73 (4):1185-1200.

THE FORMATION OF
NEW SPECIES

"He hath made every thing beautiful in his time."

Ecclesiastes 3:11

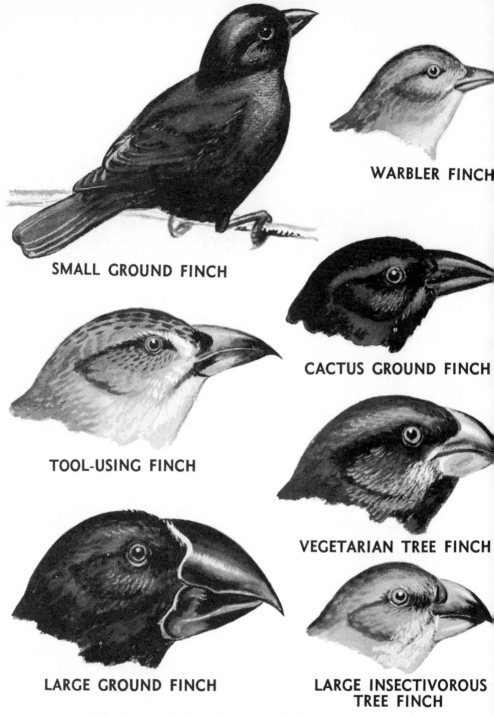

WARBLER FINCH

SMALL GROUND FINCH

CACTUS GROUND FINCH

TOOL-USING FINCH

VEGETARIAN TREE FINCH

LARGE GROUND FINCH

LARGE INSECTIVOROUS TREE FINCH

Fig. 27.1 Darwin finches illustrate speciation on the Galápagos Islands.

CHAPTER TWENTY-SEVEN

Are New Species Forming Today?

SINCE THE TURN of the century the science of genetics, the study of inheritance, has skyrocketed from a little known aspect of biology to perhaps the most significant and most quantitative of life sciences. The study of genetics has revealed principles and laws that have given the evolutionist the first concrete basis for micro-evolution. What problem does this pose for the creationist?

In order to understand the role of heredity in the formation of new species and varieties it is necessary to state a few basic principles and to define some of the terms used subsequently in this chapter. Every individual is composed of cells, each of which has a nucleus. The carriers (chromosomes) of the hereditary units (genes) are located in the nucleus. The reproductive cells (sperm and ova) likewise contain chromosomes, but only half as many as other cells. At the time of fertilization—when two reproductive cells unite—the normal number of chromosomes is restored to the cell and is maintained thereafter in the multiplication of cells that eventually form the adult body. It is obvious that each individual receives chromosomes from his father and from his mother; in fact, he receives equal numbers and similar kinds from each parent. The set of chromosomes from each parent contains genes for each characteristic governed by heredity.

If a person receives dominant genes for eye color (brown) from both parents, that person is said to be homozygous for eye color. If he receives dominant for eye color from one parent and recessive from the other parent, he will be heterozygous for eye color.

Occasionally a gene or a chromosome will become changed. If a change such as this in the reproductive cell becomes permanent, so that it is passed on from one generation to the next, it is referred to as a *mutation*. Mutations also occur in genes not located in reproductive cells, but these mutations are not inherited through successive generations.

In recent years naturally occurring mutations have been known to produce interesting variations in plants and animals. Among these are Ancon sheep with very short legs (Fig. 27.2), Concord seedless grapes, and navel oranges that are "seedless" because all the seeds are located in the rudimentary orange that constitutes the navel. By use of artificial means—especially X-radiation—man has been able to speed up the rate of mutations and produce unusual results in a wide variety of animals and plants. The large number of artificial mutations produced in the fruit fly (*Drosophila*); in corn; in *Neurospora* (a mold); and in other organisms has greatly advanced the study of heredity.

The world about us contains an almost limitless number of

Fig 27.2 **Ancon sheep illustrate a mutational change in leg length.**

living things; in fact, more new species are being named every day, and the number already runs to a million or more. Obviously one pair of each of the present-day species of land animals and birds could not have found lodging in the ark. What has happened to organisms since that time? According to *Spiritual Gifts,* volume 3, page 75, hybridization since the Flood has produced "almost endless varieties of species of animals."

It is significant that at a time when many biologists and most clergy were of the opinion that the species were fixed, Ellen G. White made this contrary statement; a statement that was undoubtedly "liberal" by the standards of her day. The correctness of her declaration will become more apparent as we progress through this chapter.

Mutations

Geneticists declare that the two main driving forces of evolution are mutations and recombinations. Let us consider mutations first. These may be of two types—sudden changes in the gene or sudden changes in the chromosomes caused by the loss of a part and the rearrangement of genes within the chromosome, or by the duplication of chromosomes and contained genes without subsequent segregation into separate chromosomes. Chromosomal mutations (aberrations) can bring about new forms by the reshuffling of existing characteristics, but this process is limited in its possibilities because no truly new gene is involved. The mutation of the gene is, therefore, the real mechanism of change, because it introduces into the gene pool of an individual, and subsequently into the population, a modified gene; a gene that has been changed in its molecular arrangement. The loss of a gene is also a mutation.

The following discussion is concerned mainly with interesting aspects of human metabolism that probably have arisen through gene or chromosomal mutations. Within the past 50 years man's curiosity has rewarded him with knowledge concerning what are called inborn errors of metabolism, and other genetically influenced disorders. Man now stands on the threshold of a new day in medical history. Research in the realm of heredity has opened a new chapter in the healing sciences. Already a vague picture has been sketched to show how the genes of chromosomes dictate the sequence of amino acids in the production of proteins and enzymes found in the body. It is the nature of the gene and its role in the production of these important chemical compounds that interests the student of genetics, as well as the student of evolution. The study of genetics leads to the obvious conclusion that if the evolution of an organism does occur, it must be able to pass on each new characteristic to the following generation. Thus, the traits of the parents must be conveyed to the offspring by means of the genes of the chromosomes. Should an accident occur to a gene, this change would be manifested in the production of important chemical compounds that the body uses in metabolism.

Such a change must then be passed on to the offspring in order to maintain it in the species. Usually, such a change or mutation of a gene in the species is deleterious. Some examples are found that are metabolic blocks to the utilization and synthesis of some chemicals important to life.

One such case involves a recessive inherited inability to utilize the simple sugar galactose (galactocemia). This sugar is found in milk, and children inheriting a double recessive gene for galactocemia (homozygous recessive) would inevitably be poisoned by the galactose. This inability to change galactose to glucose elevates the blood level of galactose and can consequently cause mental deficiency, cataracts, and other disorders in the developing child. The intermediate products in the metabolism of galactose to glucose are catalyzed by enzymes. Such a metabolic defect as galactocemia would be due to a loss of the ability to produce a specific enzyme necessary to convert galactose to glucose. This inability is due to a mutation.

It is interesting to note that the colon bacillus (*Escherichia coli*) also has the same enzyme pathway of reactions in convert-

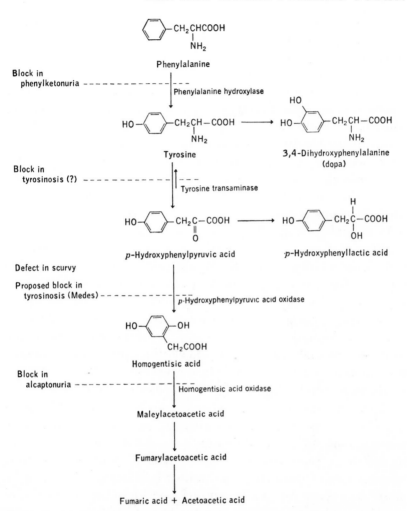

Fig. 27.3 Metabolic blocks in the oxidation of phenylalanine and tyrosine.

ing galactose to glucose. A mutant form of colon bacillus cannot utilize galactose because the microorganism lacks a specific catalytic enzyme. It is interesting that human beings follow the same pathways in the conversion of galactose to glucose.

Another metabolic disorder is very nearly the same as galactocemia. However, instead of a metabolic block occurring in the conversion of galactose to glucose, the disease phenylketonuria involves amino acid metabolism. The normal pathway in the metabolism of the essential amino acid phenylalanine to another amino acid tyrosine is catalyzed by a specific enzyme. Individuals who have both recessive genes (homozygous recessive) for phenylketonuria lack the ability to carry out the oxidation of phenylalanine; consequently, this amino acid must be metabolized through other pathways. This manifests itself in disruption of the alternate pathway and produces an abnormally high byproduct of phenylpyruvic acid, which in turn affects the individual's mentality (Fig. 27.3).

Both of these examples clearly show the deleterious effect of a gene mutation controlling the production of an enzyme. Protein synthesis likewise is regulated by the genes, and the mutation of a gene can affect the synthesis of a protein.

A change in a gene is usually a change for the worse. Such a change or mutation may alter the organism profoundly and bring on mental disorders, blood-clotting problems, abnormal hemoglobin, and even death. These gross effects may depend on a single alteration in the synthesis of an enzyme or protein.

Some mutations may appear to convey a benefit to the species —as in the case of sickle-cell anemia. Recent experimentation seems to point to the possibility of "gain" mutations that can occur in metabolic processes. This entire area of genetics is opening new avenues of research. Evolutionists considered genetics to be most important for understanding the supposed processes of evolution. The examples cited above from human genetics reveal how mutations are able to produce changes that are passed on from generation to generation. But, as we have said, most of these changes are detrimental. Changes that are not harmful are small. Without exception, the laboratory evidence from genetics that appears to support the theory of evolution does so only in the realm of microevolution (minor change).

If beneficial or harmless mutations are recessive in character they will not show up as a visible phenotypic expression until a later generation when an offspring can inherit the recessive character from both parents. If the population is small, the new gene will have much more opportunity to become incorporated into the gene pool. The population will probably not remain in a heterozygous condition, however, but will drift one way or the other to become homozygous again (genetic drift). Studies of small populations indicate that in a few generations the new character will either be eliminated or will become fixed in the population in place of the original gene.

One factor that played an important role in Charles Darwin's original theory was natural selection. Natural selection (survival of the fittest) is definitely an influencing factor in microevolution. Continuing with the discussion above, it can be seen that if environmental conditions favor the survival of individuals who have the new gene, that gene will be much more likely to become established in the population and supplant the old gene. It will not work the other way, however. A new gene is not likely to become established in the population if environmental factors are more severe for individuals with the new gene. Genetic drift will not operate against environmental pressures (natural selection).

Let us examine illustrations of mutations that have become established in the population. Many mutations of the fruit fly *Drosophila* have been produced and studied in genetics laboratories. Among these is a condition in which there is no pigment in the eye (the fly has white eyes). If this condition occurs in the wild, and if it were advantageous to the fly as compared to the normal eye color, eventually the entire population might become white-eyed. Actually the situation turns out to be the reverse, however. Female flies will not mate with the white-eyed males as long as normal-eyed males are available. Obviously this mutation could not become established under natural conditions, and the population would remain normal-eyed. This is a good example

Fig. 27.4 Peppered moths, showing industrial melanism.

of natural selection in operation—an example that does not involve the death of the organism; the characteristic is simply not perpetuated (Savage, 1963, p. 51).

One interesting case of natural selection resulting from environmental pressures influencing the survival of a characteristic in a population that has been given intensive study in England is referred to as industrial melanism. Before 1845, only white specimens of the peppered moth *(Biston betularia)* were known there, but in that year one black one was collected at Manchester. From that time until the present, black specimens have become more and more common until the present population is all black. However, this is true only in the industrial areas of England and not in the rural areas! The reason for this became apparent when it was noticed that the black moths were hardly noticeable on the soot- and coal-dust-covered trees; whereas, the white moths stood out plainly. These moths normally alight on the bark of trees that are black and devoid of lichens in the industrialized areas, but lighter colored and plastered with white crustose lichens in the rural, uncontaminated country (Fig. 27.4).

Recently, actual quantitative results have been obtained by releasing marked black and white moths in groves of trees in an industrial area and in a rural location. Visual observation and photographic records were obtained of the birds feeding on the conspicuous moths but missing the others. A count of the remaining moths, which were attracted with lights, revealed that 40 per cent of the black moths and 19 per cent of the white ones were recaptured in the soot-covered region. Six per cent of the black moths and 12.5 per cent of the white specimens were taken again in the unpolluted countryside. Obviously, the original supposition that natural selection was operating in favor of the dark moths in industrialized areas was correct. More examples of this same phenomenon have been found in other parts of Europe, and nearly 100 species of moths in the Pittsburgh region of the United States show industrial melanism.

Mutations involving changes in pigmentation are not uncommon, especially in organisms that have rapid reproduction. Albinism, a complete or partial absence of pigment, is quite frequently reported for many different kinds of animals and plants. It is likely that the dark phase of the moths involved in industrial melanism arose by mutation in recent times. In fact, mutations of this sort have probably been occurring repeatedly over hundreds and perhaps thousands of years, but were of no advantage to the animal until the industrial revolution began to cover the vegetation with dark dust and soot. Environmental pressure then caused the population to shift to the dark pigmentation phase.

One more illustration will be given of a mutation, and natural selection acting on its survival. A mutation in a human gene at some time in the past caused a change in the hemoglobin molecule. Especially when there is a lack of oxygen the red blood cell takes on the general appearance of a crescent moon or a sickle. With few exceptions, sickle-cell anemia is limited to Negroes. These sickle-shaped red blood cells are destroyed by the body, causing the individual to become anemic. Because of the lethal results of this disease, most individuals who carry both recessive genes for the abnormal hemoglobin die in childhood. Logically, such a gene trait would naturally decline in the population if the individuals thus affected die at an early age.

In some areas of Africa, however, as high as 40 per cent of the Negroes are carriers; that is, they have the heterozygous condition for sickle-cell anemia. Evidently there must be some advantage in the sickle-cell condition. Natural mutations do not occur frequently enough to maintain so high a percentage of abnormal genes. It has been found that carriers of this trait have a resistance to malaria. The malaria parasites are unable to maintain themselves in the red blood cells of individuals containing heterozygous sickle-cell genes. This more than balances for the loss of the homozygous sickle-cell individuals who die early. Descendants of Negroes brought to North America during the slave days have declined in their incidence of the sickle-cell gene to only 9 per cent at the present time, because carriers of the trait have no advantage over others in areas where there is no malaria. A sickle-cell gene does, then, confer an advantage to an individual in a malaria environment.

Chromosomal Mutations

The explanation of speciation has been further facilitated by facts gained from experimentation with chromosomal mutations. A chromosomal mutation is a chromosomal deviation from the normal. Such abnormal chromosomes can cause changes of various kinds large enough to produce new variations and species.

Let us examine the classic organism *Drosophila,* the fruit fly. It is found that in two species, *D. pseudoobscura* and *D. miranda,* the somatic characteristics are strikingly similar. Although these flies hybridize, their offspring are sterile, and therefore they should be designated as separate species (much like a horse and a donkey producing a mule). The similarity of these two species and their inability to produce fertile offspring aroused the curiosity of researchers. It was found that both contained very similar gene assortments; however, they were arranged in different orders. These changes probably had developed by chromosomal mutations through rearrangement of the chromosomal material. This rearrangement made synapsis (pairing of similar chromosomes) during development of male and female reproductive cells very difficult or impossible, thus inhibiting reproduction by the offspring (Snyder and David, 1957, pp. 319-322).

Another example of rearrangement of the chromatin material is manifest in "waltzing mice," so named because of their inability to walk in a straight direction. This defect results from a hereditary maldevelopment of the semicircular canals in the ear. Transmission usually occurs as a homozygous recessive, but on occasion it was noted that when, in the laboratory, a homozygous normal mouse was crossed with a "waltzer," nothing but "waltzers" was produced. Upon examination it was found that in the normal mouse the portion of the chromosome containing the normal genetic information was missing. This deletion left the one recessive waltzing trait free to be expressed (Winchester, 1958).

Occasionally a piece of one chromosome breaks off and becomes attached to another without a reciprocal exchange. A trait in *Drosophila* was unexpectedly making its appearance as a characteristic linked to the sex of the fly. Examination revealed that a segment from an autosome (not one of the two sex chromosomes) had broken off and had become attached to the X chromosome (one of the sex chromosomes), thus explaining the reason for the change to sex-linked inheritance (Snyder and David, 1957, p. 305).

In discussing the rearrangement of the chromatin material we have only presented half the story. Not only can the material become rearranged but it can also duplicate itself without a corresponding duplication of the cell either by single chromosomes (heteroploidy) or by complete sets of chromosomes (polyploidy). Let us consider some examples.

American cultivated cotton was found to have 26 pairs of chromosomes; 13 large pairs and 13 small pairs. European cotton was found to have only 13 pairs of large ones. This placed American cultivated cotton under suspicion of being a hybrid of European cotton and another cotton possessing 13 pairs of small chromosomes. The cotton that fulfilled this latter requirement was American wild cotton. From this information it was hypothesized that cultivated American cotton had arisen from the hybridization of Old World cotton and wild American cotton, with subsequent natural duplication of both sets of chromosomes. Experiments were made crossing these two. Colchicine treatment increased the number of chromosomes, producing the same chromosomal complement found in American cultivated cotton, thus helping to prove the hypothesis (Snyder and David, 1957, pp. 298-300).

Attempts at synthesizing polyploids have been successful, and this has opened up a means of improving plants. Large fruits (McIntosh apples) have been grown and fiber strength (cotton) has been increased. A cross between the radish and cabbage had considerable potential as an economic success, since both tops and roots of a polyploid of these two might be useful. The tetraploid condition was successfully achieved. This is a condition where there are four complete sets of chromosomes rather than two, as is found in the normal cell. Although the tetraploid condition was successfully achieved, the results were anything but economically successful. The hardy plants had tops of the radish and roots of the cabbage!

"The polyploids frequently have more vigorous vegetative growth and larger and more intensely colored flowers, and hence are especially desired as new horticultural varieties. . . . More than one third of all species of higher plants, the angiosperms, are polyploid, and thus polyploidy has been of considerable importance to plant evolution" (Merrell, 1962, pp. 204-205).

Since polyploidy is the duplication of complete sets of existing chromosomes, it causes accentuation of existing characteristics but is not likely to develop basically different plants. The polyploid plants may classify as new species, however, because they will not cross with other plant species. There is little doubt that polyploidy has been important in the production of plant species.

Can the production of extra chromosomes take place in human beings? There is now definite information that this is the situation with the mongoloid condition. The mongoloid has one extra chromosome, or a trisomic condition (heteroploidy). In human beings the extra chromosomes prove to be detrimental. The addition or deletion of human sex-chromosomes is also found to exist. These conditions are always found to cause nervous disorders, sexual malformation or lack of development, and even death (Bonner, 1961, pp. 76-78).

Recombinations of Genes

The second driving force of evolution is declared to be recombinations of genes owing to hybridization between genetically different individuals or populations. Again it becomes obvious that although many different combinations can result, even as the few keys of the piano can produce many tunes, nothing truly new can be produced. The variations are limited to the extremes within the genes or populations involved in the recombinations. Again, also, we fall back to the gene mutation as the primary drive that could bring about any really fundamental change. Note this example from the plant kingdom. In the Southern States there are two species of iris growing in two types of habitats. One lives in semi-shaded areas along the edges of streams and rivers. It is a slender plant with brick-red flowers. The other species is more stout, lives in marshes, and has the typical violet-purple flower. In recent years man has disrupted the habitats of these flowers by draining the swamps and cutting down trees. This change in the environment gave the two species opportunity to interbreed and also created a new type of habitat, the meadow or pasture. The first result was a swarm of hybrids between the two species springing up in the pastures. Later a stable situation developed, so that a variety of iris developed in the new ecological niche that was like neither parent, but had characteristics from both parents, although the traits of the swamp-growing, violet-purple-flowered iris predominated (Anderson, 1949, pp. 1-11).

In animal and plant populations, increase in numbers will cause migration and spreading of the species into new territories that may be slightly different in some aspect of ecology. Adaptations arising through mutations or recombinations that may better fit these organisms to their new environment will also make them slightly different from the original population. In the example of the white- and normal-eyed flies we saw that it may not require much to make an individual unacceptable to the opposite sex. A minor adaptation of a segment of a population may psychologically separate it from the rest of the society. Other isolating mechanisms that may be more obvious are physical barriers such as mountain ranges, oceans, deserts, et cetera; anatomical barriers such as unusual differences in sizes or modifications in sex organs; and physiological incompatibility. Changes in the genes and the arrangement of chromosomes may also produce genetic incompatibility that would be a major step in the change into a new species. Most of the changes mentioned above would not come about until a time of isolation from the rest of the population had occurred.

Examples of gradual adaptation to the environment through the methods of mutation and recombination are numerous.

Some of these are within our lifetimes, or at least within the past 100 years.

The English sparrow, *Passer domesticus,* was introduced into North America from Europe in 1852. It became established in the East and slowly spread westward until it had reached British Columbia by 1900, Death Valley in 1914, and Mexico City in 1933. Apparently the sparrows did not reach the Hawaiian Islands from the West Coast of North America, because they have been known there since 1870. These islands are well isolated from any continent, and the nearly 100 years since sparrows were introduced there has been long enough to permit them to change and adapt sufficiently to make marked changes in anatomy, behavior, and color (Johnston and Selander, 1964).

The example of the sparrow is probably due to gene mutations in an isolated population. It is readily recognizable, on the other hand, that the new variety of iris is a recombination situation resulting from the hybridization of two species. It becomes apparent, then, that animals and plants are both able to adapt themselves to changing environments in a number of different ways.

It is also apparent that the changes involved in speciation are small; hardly even changes from one species into another. This is microevolution. The major "proof" for evolution falls into the realm of microevolution, and consists of examples similar to those given thus far in this discussion. But evolutionists are eagerly searching for mechanisms that will provide for macroevolution or megaevolution of organisms from one basic type into another basic kind, or from a common ancestor. Savage (1963, p. 94) has set forth this serious problem in the following words:

"The essential features of microevolution and speciation are now fairly well worked out by biologists, but the complex processes that lead to evolution on a grander scale remain an area inviting investigation. At the present time we have only the most shadowy impressions of the forces contributing to the adaptive radiation and diversification of life. For example, can the evolution and diversity of the flowering plants be explained simply on the basis of microevolutionary change, or are other forces contributing to macro- and megaevolution?"

Examples of Speciation

A statement such as this is significant, but we must not make too much of it, because, as we look at the examples of speciation out of the past, there are also questions that a creationist cannot answer and that indicate a level of speciation (at least in some instances) beyond what most of us have previously thought.

A classic example is Charles Darwin's study of finches on the Galápagos Islands, where he was impressed with their great variety. Each island seemed to have its own peculiar finch. These finches filled the various ecological niches that other families of birds, missing from these islands, would normally fill. There are small differences in color, pattern, and size. There are major differences in behavior, in habitat, and in food habits. Birds with different food preferences have bills adapted to the gathering of that kind of food. Some have large finchlike bills for seed cracking. Others have slender bills for insect gathering. The ecological position normally occupied by woodpeckers was taken by a species of finch that, because of lack of a barbed tongue for extracting grubs and worms from holes, took to using a cactus spine for snaring its elusive food. This is one of the few instances of animals resorting to the use of a tool. It is not reasonable to entertain the suggestion that God created all these kinds originally. Modifications in this situation are quite noticeable, although the changes are not sufficiently great to lie outside the concept of variation within the original created kind.

The seas of the world harbor many species of hermit crabs. These amusing fellows run about along the seashores carrying with them a snail shell. These crabs, of the family Paguridae, have conspicuously coiled abdomens, and the tailfan (uropods and telson) is asymmetrical. The coiled abdomen and irregular

Fig. 27.5 A hermit crab. This animal is adapted in many ways to life in an empty snail shell.

tailfan are adaptations that help the animal to live in a snail shell. The fourth and fifth pairs of walking legs are much reduced in size, which permits them to be pulled down into the shell when danger causes the animal to retreat. These small legs also help push the crab back out to the entrance when danger is past. At least two other families also have coiled abdomens and asymmetrical tailfans and at least one pair of rudimentary legs. They do not occupy shells or other objects, and these adaptations do not appear to be needed, although they are not disadvantageous to the animals. These unique features suggest some possible relationship between the families. Did these characteristics develop independently in each family, or did microevolution in the original hermit crab result in these several families with common characteristics? The latter is the more reasonable possibility.

Several species of hermit crabs with straight abdomens inhabit worm tubes, hollow sticks, and other straight tubes. In all other respects they look similar to other hermit crabs. Thus they occupy a small and different ecological niche. At some time in the unknown past they evidently found the scarcity of shells so great that they were forced to use worm tubes and hollow sticks for housing. Their abdomens changed to the uncoiled condition after they took up the new homes, or the new homes were used because of a change in the abdomen. A definite determination of cause and effect here would be difficult. My observations of the difficulties that hermit crabs have in finding suitable shells incline me to favor the hypothesis that environmental pressure forced them to use something other than a shell, and that this led to anatomical changes in the abdomen.

Fig. 27.6   A South American marsupial.

No other part of the world has nearly the varieties of marsupials that Australia has. Here, the habitats occupied by the wolf, the mole, the mouse, the anteater, et cetera, of North or South America are occupied by marsupial animals that resemble rather closely their counterparts in the Western Hemisphere. Did only marsupial mammals migrate to Australia after the Flood, or did these different types originate from some ancestral pouched mammal? Both these suggestions are extreme. Another alternative, one that is more reasonable and more in keeping with the creationist's philosophy, is that several basic types of marsupials were originally present in Australia (perhaps before it was isolated from Asia), and that the many varieties have developed by adaptation and microevolution from these original representatives. Marsupials were present on other continents also, but competition with placental mammals for available habitats prevented the speciation of marsupials as in Australia.

Insects and parasites impress a person with what appears to be a tremendous amount of speciation, some of which may be speciation beyond the lower levels. The original created kind may be represented on the species level by mankind; it may be represented on the family level by the Galápagos finches; it may have been on the order level with some insects; and it may have been on the phylum level with the Acanthocephala, which are entirely parasitic.

The mechanisms described earlier in this chapter are satisfactory for the explanation of microevolution, but they fall short of providing a completely satisfactory explanation of changes that might lead to new families or higher taxa. As creationists we are also left without an answer to this problem The creationist has one additional factor of significance—he is limited in the amount of time available to him to account for microevolutionary changes so great as to bring about new families, orders, et cetera, if indeed such has occurred. The currently understood mechanisms for speciation through gene and chromosomal changes are slow and uncertain. May there not be some other process, presently not known or not well understood, that is also involved in speciation?

Yes, new species of plants and animals are being formed today, though at a slow rate. Adam gave names to all of the mammals and birds during the course of a few hours on the sixth day. Noah took representatives of the original created forms of all of the major land animals and birds into the ark, with sufficient food for all on board. The almost endless intergradations of animals and plants in the world today, the fantastic degeneration among parasites, and the repulsive adaptations of offense and defense, which were not necessary in Eden, lead to the inevitable conclusion that much change has occurred, and that the science of genetics has thus far provided only a partial answer. The problem of rapid speciation of organisms since the Flood is one of the most pressing unanswered questions facing the creationist.

REFERENCES

Allison, Anthony C. 1956. Sickle cells and evolution. Scientific American 195 (2): 87-94, 5 figs.

Anderson, Edgar. 1949. Introgressive hybridization. John Wiley & Sons, Inc., New York. 109 pp.

Blair, W. Frank (ed.). 1961. Vertebrate speciation. Univ. Texas Press, Austin. 642 pp.

Bonner, David M. 1961. Heredity. Prentice-Hall, Inc., Englewood Cliffs, New Jersey. 112 pp.

Clark, Harold W. 1940. Genes and Genesis. Pacific Press Pub. Assn., Mountain View, California. 155 pp.

Dobzhansky, Th. 1951. Genetics and the origin of species. 3d ed. Columbia Univ. Press, New York. 364 pp.

————. 1955. Evolution, genetics, and man. John Wiley & Sons, Inc., New York. 398 pp.

Dowdeswell, W. H. 1960. The mechanism of evolution. Harper & Brothers, New York. 115 pp.

Jepsen, Glenn L., George Gaylord Simpson, and Ernst Mayr. 1949. Genetics, paleontology, and evolution. Atheneum, New York. Reprint 1963. 474 pp.

Johnston, R. F. and R. K. Selander. 1964. House sparrows: rapid evolution of races in North America. Science 144 (3618):548, 5 figs.

Klotz, John W. 1955. Genes, Genesis, and evolution. Concordia Pub. House, St. Louis, Missouri, pp. 266-340.

Marsh, Frank L. 1944. Evolution, creation, and science. Review and Herald Pub. Assn., Washington, D.C., pp. 89-180.

————. 1967. Life, man, and time. 2d ed. Outdoor Pictures, Escondido, California, pp. 162-191.

Mayr, Ernst. 1942. Systematics and the origin of species. Dover Pub. Inc., New York. Reprint 1964. 334 pp.

————. 1963. Animal species and evolution. Harvard Univ. Press, Cambridge, Mass. 797 pp.

Merrell, David J. 1962. Evolution and genetics. Holt, Rinehart & Winston, New York. 420 pp.

Savage, Jay M. 1963. Evolution. Holt, Rinehart & Winston, New York. 126 pp.

Snyder, Laurence H. and Paul R. David. 1957. The principles of heredity. D. C. Heath & Co., Boston. 507 pp.

Srb, Adrian M. and Ray D. Owen. 1952. General genetics. W. H. Freeman and Co., San Francisco, California. 561 pp.

Winchester, A. M. 1958. Genetics, a survey of the principles of heredity. Houghton Mifflin Co., Boston.

CHAPTER TWENTY-EIGHT

Speciation on Oceanic Islands

The Galápagos Islands

IN 1831 CHARLES DARWIN BOARDED the *Beagle* and set sail on a momentous voyage that started a new train of thought in his mind. This eventually matured into a theory that profoundly changed the scientific thinking of the world. Suggestions regarding alterations in organisms as a result of the influence of environment had been made prior to Darwin's time, but the general opinion was that God had created each species as it now appeared. Darwin himself was probably of this mind at the start of his trip, as there is no hint of his having any thoughts regarding the origin of species by natural selection before leaving on the journey. But there is much to suggest that the idea developed and ripened in his mind as a result of his studies and the specimens he collected while a naturalist aboard the *Beagle*.

The Galápagos Islands are probably more responsible than any other region Darwin visited on that trip in convincing him that extant species are not exactly as they came forth from the hand of the Creator. Unable to correlate his observations with his previous theological beliefs, he gradually discarded the Genesis story and substituted in its place the concept of great lengths of time and a gradual development of living things from simple to complex. On this trip Darwin read Charles Lyell's newly published volumes, *Principles of Geology,* and these volumes were doubtless responsible in part for the unfortunate drift in his thinking away from the Biblical account of creation. Lyell's books convinced him of the reality of long ages, and his observations on the Galápagos Islands and elsewhere persuaded him of the progressive evolution of organisms. These two concepts merged into the theory that now circumscribes the thinking of most of the educated world as completely as certain mistaken theological dogmas had done for previous centuries.

The Galápagos Islands consist of ten main islands with a number of small volcanoes and rocky islets. The volcanic origin is obvious—craters, cones, and lava flows are everywhere to be seen. A small amount of thermal activity is still present. The islands do not impress the visitor with their beauty. They are not the idyllic, palm-lined isles with dazzling beaches one might expect for islands at this latitude (nearly under the equator). The black lava and brown ash support a weedy, desertlike growth including large prickly-pear cactus trees up to 30 feet tall. The rainfall is scarce and confined to a small portion of the year. In the higher elevations (some islands reach up to 4,000 feet) rain and fog have nourished luxuriant growths not unlike the tropical jungles. Large open meadows or downs carpeted with mosses, lichens, ferns, and grasses are also found in the interior portions of the larger islands.

In this unpromising archipelago Darwin came upon a strange and puzzling array of living things. It was not the great numbers of species that caught his attention; other sites he visited were far richer in diversity of species. It was not the colorful birds or gaudy insects that appealed to him; they were actually drab, small, and scarce when compared with those of many other locations, even in temperate areas. In fact, at first he was not greatly impressed with any aspect of the fauna and flora of the islands, with the exception of the reptiles, but slowly he began to realize the significance of what he saw, though he did not feel its full impact for several years. A high per cent of the species of terrestrial animals and the plants were native to the islands. Furthermore, animals and plants from one island to another not more than 50 miles apart were different enough to qualify for separation into distinct species.

Of the 185 flowering plants Darwin collected from the islands he visited 100 were indigenous, and many of these were confined to specific islands. Twenty-five of the 26 land birds were new species found only in the Galápagos. Even the seashells, which are usually widely distributed, were half endemic to the shores of these rocky islands. The 15 species of sea fish he caught were all new.

The most striking animals of the islands are the reptiles. More than 100 years ago when Darwin stopped there they were extremely abundant, although sailors, Ecuadorian political prisoners, and buccaneers had already begun the process that has led to the extinction of some varieties of turtles and lizards. The Galápagos tortoise is a living wonder among reptiles. Some specimens have been known to weigh up to 500 pounds, and they are thought to live for more than 100 years. Although able to live in the dry, parched lowlands, they will travel several miles to reach water in the uplands of the larger islands. Darwin noted their well-traveled trails, which lead from all over an island to the few

Fig. 28.1 A large reptile peculiar to the Galápagos Islands.

sources of water. Striking differences are noticeable in the form of the carapace of the tortoises inhabiting different islands.

Two kinds of iguana lizards are also unusual attractions. One of these is the only species of truly marine lizard in the world. That in itself is remarkable, but their exclusive seaweed diet is unique. These ugly reptiles, which reach a length of three feet, are quite at home in the water, though they spend most of their time basking on the rocks in the hot sun. The second species, which is confined to land, subsists on vegetation that includes cactus pads. Numbers of this species are slightly larger than their amphibious relatives, but also torpid, ugly, and stupid. The most striking thing about these three species of reptiles is that they are confined to these islands; none similar to them are found anywhere else in the world. Furthermore it would appear that nascent species were developing on separate islands of the group.

The animals most generally associated with Charles Darwin and the Galápagos Islands are the finches. The full significance of the finches in illustrating speciation did not become apparent to Darwin until after he had left the islands and had opportunity to examine his collections and reflect on the data. He found 13 species of finches (Lack, 1947, p. 18, claims there are 14) with different groupings of the 13 on each island. Although there was not a marked variation in plumage, the birds differed in size and, most remarkable of all, in the shapes of the bills. On the continents different species of the same genus usually have similar bills and different plumage, but the reverse is true on these islands. The beaks are adapted to the type of food the birds take—small, somewhat slender bills for insects, and broad, massive mandibles for seeds, with many gradational steps between the extremes. Habitats normally occupied by other birds on the continents are filled by finches whose bills are adapted to procuring the kinds of foods available in these island habitats. The tool-using finch that functions in the role of the woodpecker has already been mentioned.

Although these islands, which are 600 miles from the nearest

Fig. 28.2　This Darwin finch occupies the ecological niche of a woodpecker.

continental land (Ecuador), have an endemic fauna and flora, the broader relationship to the biota of America is not difficult to see. Darwin puzzled over this fact. If all species were created as they are now and placed where they presently live, why did the animals and plants of the Galápagos Islands resemble those of South America? Why would they not be distinctly unique to the islands or related to genera and families found on continents other than South America? If they were somehow able to reach the islands from South America, why are there now no similar species in South America? Thus it was almost impossible for him to escape the thought that some changes have occurred since the organisms came from South America. This thought was reinforced by his observation that variations were detectable from island to island. Instead of making allowance for variation or speciation to occur in God's original creation, Darwin let down the barriers completely and proposed unlimited change.

Creationists are confronted with the problem of determining how extensive a change has taken place since creation. This is a difficult problem that calls for a great deal more research. Another island archipelago, the Hawaiian Islands, provides a second unique laboratory for the study of speciation.

The Hawaiian Islands*

No group of islands anywhere in the world is so far removed from the continents as the Hawaiian chain. Since speciation occurs more rapidly on oceanic islands that are far removed from continents, we can expect to find more speciation here than in any other group of islands.

The unique nature of the plants and animals of Hawaii is striking. Even though I have studied plants in the American tropics for 20 years, I found no plants in Hawaii that I had seen before, except introduced species. About 1,700 species of plants are native to the islands, of which 1,600 are endemic, that is, not found elsewhere in the world. There are more than 100 endemic species of Pteridophytes (ferns and allies), plus many endemic species of lichens, fungi, mosses, orchids, herbs of other types, shrubs, and trees. Perhaps the most widely publicized native plant is the silver-sword, which grows on the rim of the crater of Haleakala on the island of Maui. This plant looks like a yucca, but it is not a lily. It belongs to the family Compositae, the sunflower family. It lives only on the crater of Haleakala on Maui, and on the island of Hawaii. Many other species of plants are similarly restricted.

Botanists have concluded that about half of the endemic plants came from the South Pacific, about 15 per cent from Central America, 3 or 4 per cent from the Arctic, and the rest from various other regions.

There is an apparent scarcity of insects. In several hours of driving along the highway few insects would be plastered to the windshield. Although insects do not appear to be common in Hawaii, there are nearly 4,000 endemic species representing all the common orders. Coleoptera (beetles), Lepidoptera (butter-

---

* The section on the Hawaiian Islands was written by Ernest S. Booth.

flies and moths), and Hymenoptera (bees, ants, and wasps) are far ahead of the other orders in numbers of species. Only ten species of butterflies occur in Hawaii, and eight of these have been introduced. Only two or three species are at all common.

Except for birds, vertebrates are definitely uncommon in Hawaii. There are eight species of lizards, and just one species of snake. It is so rare that most people claim there are no snakes in Hawaii. Of three species of mammals, only one is native—the Hawaiian bat (*Lasiurus cinereus semotus*). The Hawaiian rat could be classed as native, for it was in Hawaii before the coming of the white man, but it belongs to the genus *Rattus,* which is clearly Asiatic in origin. The third mammal is the mongoose, introduced from India and now a wild animal, especially on the island of Hawaii.

It is not difficult to determine the origin of the two native species of mammals. The bat is the same species as the one found on the mainland of North America. We can safely assume that the original ancestor of the Hawaiian bat reached Hawaii from the West Coast, though we do not know how it got there. It could have clung to driftwood, been blown by a hurricane, or come as a stowaway on a boat, but since it is a mainland species it certainly came from the mainland. The rat is not so easily placed in a sure category. It does belong to the genus *Rattus,* a common Old World genus. We can be sure it did not come from America, for the Hawaiian rat was in Hawaii when the first white man arrived, and it was probably there a long time before that. The ancestors of the Hawaiian rat may have arrived with the Polynesian people from the South Pacific as stowaways in the cargo on their outrigger canoes. They might have drifted to the islands on debris, but this suggestion seems less reasonable.

Animal life is therefore not abundant, but the few animals that do occur are nearly all endemic species. Plant life is abundant in specimens, but far more species occur in most areas of similar size on the continents.

When we examine the birds we find them occurring in four

distinct groups: (1) endemic species, (2) immigrant species obviously having come rather recently from the mainland of America, Asia, or the islands of the South Pacific, (3) species introduced by man, and (4) species regularly migrating to Hawaii from other regions, or oceanic birds normally occurring in Hawaii. We need not discuss number three, because man has been directly responsible here, and number four is a normal phenomenon not peculiar to Hawaii. The second group is recent emigrants such as the night heron, Hawaiian duck, Laysan teal, Hawaiian coot, Hawaiian gallinule, Hawaiian stilt, and the Hawaiian short-eared owl. The ancestors of these birds reached Hawaii from other areas, probably in more recent times, and changes occurring subsequently have produced these endemic subspecies. All are enough like mainland species to be given the same species names as their relatives on the mainland. The migration of these birds probably took place not long ago, because the changes have not been great. On the other hand, if these birds have been in Hawaii for a long time, for unknown reasons they have changed but little.

About 39 species (77 forms) of birds are endemic to Hawaii. Some of these are extinct, leaving about 27 species, some of which are facing extinction. Twenty of these species belong to the family Drepanidae, which we will consider in more detail below. The Moho, or Oo, and the Kauai Moho, belong to the family Meliphagidae, the honey eaters. They probably came from the South Pacific, possibly from Southern Asia. They have undergone so much change that we can only guess at their origin, as we do with the honeycreepers. They are extinct on all islands except Molokai (they may be extinct there, too) and Kauai, where a few are thought to live today.

The family Sylviidae, Old World warblers, is represented by one living species, the Nihoa miller bird, thought to occur sparingly on the tiny island of Nihoa. Its nearest relatives occur on Guam and Christmas Island. The Elepaio, family Muscicapidae, Old World flycatchers, which occurs on Kauai, Oahu, and Hawaii,

Fig. 28.3 Speciation among Hawaiian honeycreepers.

apparently originated from the South Pacific and Southern Asia. There are near relatives on a number of the South Pacific Islands. The Hawaiian thrush, family Turdidae, occurs on most of the islands; its nearest relatives are on islands of the South Pacific. The Hawaiian crow, family Corvidae, appears to be most closely related to crows of Southern Asia, and not those of America.

The remaining two living endemic species are the Hawaiian hawk, a close relative to the North American Swainson's hawk, and the nene or Hawaiian goose, related to the Canada goose of North America. A number of endemic birds have become extinct in recent years, including three subspecies of rail. One shearwater, one petrel, and one storm petrel are endemic. These three are obviously closely related to more wide-ranging species of shearwaters and petrels, and therefore pose no problems of origin.

The Hawaiian Honeycreepers

Among the native birds of Hawaii is the family Drepanidae, known commonly as the Hawaiian honeycreepers. This is the only native family of birds in Hawaii, although it appears to be related to the Central and South American honeycreepers of the family Coerebidae. It may also be related to the honey eaters,

347

family Meliphagidae, a common family in the South Pacific islands and with two or three rare species still occurring in Hawaii.

Hawaiian honeycreepers are insect-eating and nectar-eating birds of small size and often bright colors. In Hawaii nine species are common enough to be found without difficulty if one looks in the right places. Several other species are either rare or extinct, and still others have become extinct within the past 50 or 75 years. Four of the present species seem to be on the road to extinction, for no apparent reason. In the days of the Hawaiian kings the bright red feathers of honeycreepers were used for making royal robes. This practice took a heavy toll of these colorful birds. Now there is no practical use for the birds; consequently, they should fare well. Since they live mainly on the upper slopes of the high mountains in dense forests, they have few enemies. Disease and lack of insects could be factors. The cutting away of the forests is perhaps the most probable cause for the dwindling numbers of these unique birds. The problem is further complicated by the unusual abundance of four species.

The Apapane (ah-pah-pah-nay) (*Himatione sanguinea*) is probably the most abundant species. At Bird Park and the Lava Tube in Hawaii National Park on Hawaii Island, and at Kalalau Lookout on Kauai, one can see 25 to 100 of these colorful birds at one time from one spot. They fill the forests with their songs. The Amakihi (ah-mah-kee-hee; *Loxops virens*) is also abundant, but many species and subspecies are becoming rare or perhaps extinct.

Honeycreepers are found throughout the islands, but some species are extremely limited in distribution. The bright red or reddish-orange Akepa (ah-kay-pah; *Loxops coccinea*) occurs only on the slopes of the mountains Mauna Kea and Haulalai on the island of Hawaii. The Laysan finch (*Psittirostra cantans*) lives only on the tiny islands of Laysan and Nihoa.

These honeycreepers are not large birds; they range between 4½ and 6½ inches. Their most distinctive and interesting features are the unusual colors and the variation in bill types.

The colors range from almost all red (Akepa mentioned above) to entirely black (Black Mamo, *Drepanis funerea*) except for white outer webs of primary wing feathers that can be seen only in flight. Yellow, orange, and yellow-green are common hues. The Iiwi (ee-ee-vee) (*Vestiaria coccinea*) is considered the most beautiful, but the crested honeycreeper (*Palmeria dolei*) is one of the most unusual. In the latter the plumage is mostly black, but the feathers are tipped with gray on throat and breast, with white on the tips of wing and tail feathers and bright orange on the tips of the body feathers. Orange tips on the neck feathers form an orange collar around the neck. The head has a conspicuous grayish-white crest.

From the standpoint of speciation the bills are most unusual. They range from a short, heavy finchlike bill (*Psittirostra kona*) to the long, slender, strongly down-curved beak (Akiapolaau, ah-kee-ah-po-law-ou; *Hemignathus wilsoni*). In the latter case the lower mandible is much shorter than the upper. The bird fills an ecological niche somewhat similar to a woodpecker. Another honeycreeper looks like a parrot or parakeet (Ou, oh-oo; *Psittirostra psittacea*). Still another has twisted mandibles (Akepa).

The foods of these unique birds are mainly insects and nectar. The habit of taking nectar from blossoms gave them the name "honeycreeper." They are, as a rule, not shy, and many of them are excellent singers. It is unfortunate that some species are disappearing. The birds on Laysan were exterminated a few years ago when rabbits, which were introduced to the island, consumed all the vegetation that produced food for the birds. A few individuals were taken to Midway Islands to prevent extinction and returned to Laysan after the rabbits were killed.

One can only marvel at the honeycreepers of Hawaii, with their many species, their amazing variations, their remarkable bills, their bright colors, and their strange food habits. Where did they come from? Why do they not occur elsewhere in the world? Did they originate in Hawaii or did they emigrate from another area, perhaps from the South Pacific or from Central America?

349

Why are their relatives not now living in these other areas? How is it possible for a family of birds to have such different bills, such striking plumage variations, and food habits varying from nectar to insects?

There can be little doubt that the ancestors of the Hawaiian honeycreepers reached the islands from some other area. There remains, then, the task of deciding upon the point of origin for these hypothetical ancestors. Dean Amadon, who has written an extensive treatise on Hawaiian honeycreepers, thinks they came from the Central American honeycreepers, family Coerebidae. The fact that both families have tubular tongues is the best evidence for this, and since even the finchlike Hawaiian honeycreepers have the tubular tongue, we can perhaps agree with Amadon. This seems to be the best theory.

When we want to find out how the birds reached Hawaii we will have to do some guessing. However, since many other Hawaiian birds occur also in North America (such as the stilt, night heron, Hawaiian owl, Hawaiian hawk, gallinule, and coot) it is apparently possible for birds from the mainland of North America to reach Hawaii. Migratory birds regularly visit Hawaii (golden plovers, terns, some gulls, other shore and oceanic birds), so it is probable that land birds do at times reach such remote islands. It may be that storms transported the original ancestors of the drepaniids.

North America being the nearest land area to Hawaii, some consider this a major factor in favor of the coerebid origin of the drepaniids. However, Central America is almost twice as far from Hawaii as Alaska or the West Coast of North America, and there are no direct wind currents from that direction. Central America is much farther removed from Hawaii than are the islands of the South Pacific, but their food habits and anatomical features provide strong evidence that they may have been derived from the coerebids of Central America. The evidence is, of course, far from conclusive.

Tentatively accepting the coerebid theory of the origin of the

Hawaiian honeycreepers, our next question involves the production of the 20 or so species of these unique birds. The great variety of honeycreepers does not necessarily mean that they arose from a single species. However, the numerous minor variations—such as the lengths and curvatures of the bills, whether the lower mandible is long or short, straight or curved, and the degrees of tubular construction of the tongues—all indicate an origin from at least similar ancestors.

Authorities agree that such changes as have occurred in the Hawaiian honeycreepers to produce some 20 species could have taken place quickly. We know that changes producing new species occur more rapidly on small isolated islands than they do on continents, or on large islands. The factors bringing about these changes are the usual genetic ones such as mutations, chromosomal aberrations, recombinations, et cetera, but isolation appears to play the greatest role in the production of species on remote islands.

The adaptive radiation in these birds might have occurred somewhat as follows: When the first honeycreepers reached Hawaii the bird population of the islands was perhaps very limited, and as a consequence there were many empty ecological niches. The original migrants would multiply and fill the niche to which they were adapted. The empty niches would provide survival value to any mutants that were adapted to them. (The adaptation could have been very imperfect at first.) When population pressure developed in the original population the tendency to occupy other niches would be increased. This would result in "explosive speciation."

The same process could account for the multiplication of species after the Flood; adaptive radiation occurring until all of the ecological niches were filled. This ability of organisms to adapt to varying conditions, and thus to occupy the earth, is one of the wonders of God's creative wisdom, and not an evidence for evolution.

We conclude with Amadon that the Hawaiian honeycreepers

351

came from the Central American honeycreepers, even though they are recognized today as distinct but closely related families. We can agree that many changes could occur quickly in a group of islands such as the Hawaiian, over a period of only a few thousand years, where habitats are restricted, where natural enemies are greatly reduced, and where there is little transfer of genetic stock from island to island. We recognize close relationships among the birds of islands that are close to one another, such as Oahu, Molokai, Maui, and Lanai, but the birds on Hawaii and on Kauai differ noticeably from those of the four islands mentioned first. Still greater differences occur on Laysan and Nihoa, for they are still more remote from the others, and are so small that only extremely limited habitats occur.

REFERENCES FOR GALÁPAGOS ISLANDS

Barlow, Nora. 1935. Charles Darwin and the Galápagos Islands. Nature 136:391.
Beebe, William. 1924. Galápagos, world's end. G. P. Putnam's Sons, New York.
Darlington, Philip J. 1957. Zoogeography: the geographical distribution of animals. John Wiley & Sons, Inc., New York, pp. 529-530.
Darwin, Charles. 1845. The voyage of the Beagle. Doubleday & Company, Inc., Garden City, New York. Reprint 1962, pp. 373-401.
————. 1859. The origin of species. The New American Library of World Literature, Inc., New York. Reprint 1958, pp. 370-381.
Eibl-Eibesfeldt, Irenaus. 1961. Galápagos: the Noah's ark of the Pacific. Doubleday & Company, Inc., Garden City, New York.
Lack, David. 1947. Darwin's finches. Harper & Brothers, New York. Reprint 1961. 204 pp. 27 figs., 3 pls., 37 tables.
————. 1949. The significance of ecological isolation. In Glenn L. Jepsen, G. G. Simpson and Ernst Mayr (ed.). Genetics, paleontology and evolution. Atheneum, New York. Reprint 1963, pp. 299-308.
Moore, Ruth. 1962. Evolution. Time Incorporated, New York, pp. 9-31, 24 figs.

REFERENCES FOR HAWAIIAN ISLANDS

Amadon, Dean. 1950. The Hawaiian honeycreepers (Aves, Drepaniidae). Bull. Am. Museum of Nat. Hist. 95:151-262. Text figs. 1-23. pls. 9-15, tables 1-15.
Baldwin, Paul H. 1953. Annual cycle, environment and evolution in the Hawaiian honeycreepers (Aves: Drepaniidae). Univ. Calif. Pub. Zool. 52 (4):285-398, pls. 8-11, 12 figs.
Bryan, E. H., Jr. 1958. Checklist and summary of Hawaiian birds. Books About Hawaii, Honolulu.
Greenway, James C. 1958. Extinct and vanishing birds of the world. Am. Com. for International Wildlife Protection, Spec. Pub. 13.
Mayr, Ernst. 1943. The zoogeographic position of the Hawaiian Islands. Condor 45:45-48.
Munro, George C. 1944. Birds of Hawaii. Reprinted by C. E. Tuttle Co., 1960 and 1964, Honolulu.

CHAPTER TWENTY-NINE

Animal Adaptation

IN EVERY PART OF THE WORLD one finds animals and plants that are adapted for existence in that location. The polar bear wanders over the ice packs; penguins raise their families on the frigid Antarctic; seals, whales, and other marine mammals sport in the chilling waters. A few thousand miles from the poles, reptiles crawl along the dry hot sands of the desert, monkeys swing through the jungle trees, and albatrosses soar over tropic isles.

Hundreds of unique and limited ecological niches have their own specialized animal and plant inhabitants. The little pool in the crotch of the jungle tree, the decaying leaves of a cactus plant, a cold stream in a cave in the depths of the earth, the shifting sands of an ocean beach, the spray-soaked cliffs behind a plunging waterfall, the litter and debris of a packrat's nest, the cracks and crevices in a coral head, the piles of dung below the rookery of a colony of bats, or the furry body of a ground squirrel—each harbors a specialized group of animals that is marvelously adapted for life in that peculiar habitat.

It is natural that, as Creator, God would fit animals to their environment. Animals destined to eat grass and similar herbs were provided with teeth that made it possible for them to obtain that kind of food. Perching birds were provided with a mechanism that locks their toes and claws tightly to the twig when they squat down to roost for the night. Earthworms contain many setae, or bristles, within the body wall, which they are able to push into the sides of their slippery burrows to help them move. Man has opposable fingers and thumb with many

23

Fig. 29.1 Animals and plants must adapt for survival in a desert habitat.

touch receptors that make it possible for him to carry on a multitude of complex and delicate manipulations necessary for survival. Plants have built-in mechanisms that cause the roots to respond negatively to light but positively to gravity; whereas, the shoot reacts the opposite way to the same stimuli. In the jungle many leaves are smooth all around the blade, so that the frequently falling rain will be channeled to the pointed end, where it drops off. On the other hand, plants living in dry places have various adaptations to conserve or prevent the loss of water. The broad flat leaves typical of most plants would permit excessive evaporation in the desert; consequently, many desert plants have small leaves or no leaves at all. It would be possible to continue almost indefinitely with a listing of animal and plant adaptations that fit them for the life for which they were intended. This is what we would expect of God. If it were otherwise, we might have reason to question the wisdom and perhaps the skill of the Creator.

The original perfect nature of created life and the environment in which it lived was lost through the disobedience of the first human beings. Environments and habitats began to change. The temperature of the air, salinity of water, fertility of the soil, humidity of the atmosphere, relative abundance of water, and many other factors all involved in the environment of living organisms became different and variable. To meet those changes nature had to adapt. It could no longer reflect perfectly its Creator or its original perfection.

"Since the fall of man nature can not reveal a perfect knowledge of God; for sin has brought a blight upon it, and has intervened between nature and nature's God. . . . After the fall, the things of nature could not fully teach the lesson of the great and marvelous love of God. Therefore the Father sent His well-beloved Son into the world, and declared Him to be a perfect revelation of Himself to man. In order that the world might not remain in darkness, in eternal, spiritual night, the God of nature met in Jesus Christ" (Gen. Conf. Bull., March 6, 1899, p. 157).

Changing Environments

If an animal or plant was adapted to live in a certain environment that God established originally, what would happen if that environment changed? This problem confronted every living organism when sin upset the original equilibrium in nature. Four things could happen to an animal (Beltz, 1967):

1. It could go about changing the environment to suit itself. At first thought this might seem a difficult feat to perform, but it must be remembered that the entire environment need not be changed—only that immediately around the animal. Honeybees will beat their wings in a cooperative action to cool the hive in excessively warm weather. Human beings heat their homes and wear clothing to make the environments around their bodies suitable to their needs. The spittle bug whips up a froth in which the eggs are laid and the young develop. Beavers build dams to provide sufficient water for their way of life. Thus, frequently, animals change their environment and are thus able to continue their lives.

2. It could change itself to suit the new environment. With the onset of cold weather many animals and plants change into a different form or state of existence until the adverse conditions are past. A number of mammal species hibernate. Their physiology is completely altered during this time. Many insects pass the winter in resistant egg stages. Plants have seeds and spores

that survive the winter. Trees lose their leaves and go into a state of dormancy until spring.

3. The animal (or plant) may move to a proper environment. The migrations of birds and some mammals are well-known examples of this type of solution to the problem of environmental change. As a general rule plants are unable to make such a change within one generation, but in the course of several generations the transportation of seeds and other propagative structures by wind, water, and animals will bring about migration of plants from an area of adverse conditions to one that is suitable. Non-motile animals are also able to move, in time, by the same means.

4. The organism will die; this has happened many times in the past. Even in recent times animals and plants have become extinct, or appear to be nearly so, and this is not always brought about through direct destruction by man. Climatic conditions are changing in many parts of the world. Some of these changes appear to be the result of intrinsic causes unrelated to man in any way, whereas other climatic shifts are resultant upon such things as agriculture, reclamation projects, and logging, which are carried on by man. Extinction may be a direct result of efforts on the part of the force of evil in the world to destroy God's creatures. "Not even a sparrow falls to the ground without the Father's notice. Satan's hatred against God leads him to delight in destroying even the dumb creatures. It is only through God's protecting care that the birds are preserved to gladden us with their songs of joy. But He does not forget even the sparrows" (8T 273).

Many of the adaptations seen in plants and animals today are a direct result of changes that have marred the perfect creation since sin entered the world, especially since the Genesis Flood. It is completely unreasonable and irreverent to suggest that they were part of God's original creation. Should we accuse God of creating the fangs and poison glands of the reptiles, the sting of the wasps and bees, the musk gland of the skunk with its accompanying odor, the large head and jaws of the soldier ants, or the thorns on the rose? The two statements below refer especially to plants, but apply equally well to animals.

"Not one noxious plant was placed in the Lord's great garden, but after Adam and Eve sinned, poisonous herbs sprang up. In the parable of the sower the question was asked the master, 'Didst not thou sow good seed in thy field? from whence then hath it tares?' The master answered, 'An enemy hath done this.' All tares are sown by the evil one. Every noxious herb is of his sowing, and by his ingenious methods of amalgamation he has corrupted the earth with tares" (2SM 288).

"The God of nature is perpetually at work. His infinite power works unseen, but manifestations appear in the effects which the work produces. The same God who guides the planets works in the fruit orchard and in the vegetable garden. He never made a thorn, a thistle, or a tare. These are Satan's work, the result of degeneration, introduced by him among the precious things; but it is through God's immediate agency that every bud bursts into blossom" (6T 186).

The Nature of Change

Let us examine these changes more carefully. How much change has God permitted Satan to work in the natural world? This is a difficult question to answer, but a look at the amazing, fantastic, and frequently repulsive adaptive structures and behaviors leads to the suspicion that change has been considerable. We will now consider anatomical, behavioral, and degenerative adaptations.

Several mammals subsist almost solely on ants. The echidna, the pangolin, and the aardvark have various modifications that aid them in obtaining this type of food. The head is slender and the muzzle elongated. There is a very long sticky tongue. Claws are adapted for digging and tearing apart the nests of ants. It would seem that animals with this kind of diet do not fit into the perfect scheme of Eden, although some speculate that insects were used for food in the original world. Ellen G. White says, "One animal was not to destroy another animal for food" (CD 396). Are insects included in this statement?

No light penetrates the depths of the seas, and no plants are able to carry on photosynthesis. Consequently, all life that exists at these depths can survive only by being predators or scavengers. Many of the deep-sea fishes have great mouths in comparison with the rest of the body and long, sharp, inward-curving teeth. Perhaps the most unusual feature is the stomach, which can stretch to accommodate a much larger animal. To gulp down so large a victim, the *Chiasmodon* fish moves its heart out of the way and turns its gills inside out, while movable teeth in the throat aid in forcing the animal into the stomach (Ommanney, 1963, p. 13).

Arctic foxes, snowshoe rabbits, weasels, and ptarmigan are able to change the color of their fur or feathers to white in winter. The benefit to the animals is obvious, though a midwinter thaw or an early spring may make the white conspicuous against the brown ground. The falling and accumulation of snow over a period of several months involves temperature and climatic conditions that were not present in pre-sin times. This adaptive behavior has no doubt come about since the change in uniform climatic and environmental conditions.

Some lizards and crabs are able to sever the tail or a leg from the rest of the body. Again there is no question concerning the purpose of the adaptation. No doubt many a lizard is alive today because the wiggling tail was left behind with the predator. In both cases mentioned above, the adaptations are more complex than appear on the surface. The first involves complex changes in physiological processes that lead to the replacing of one color of fur, or feathers, with another. In the second case, unique anatomical modifications are needed in the tail or leg: a preformed breakage plane that facilitates the breaking of the tail or limb at a certain point, and the sealing off of blood vessels to prevent bleeding.

What is the meaning of adaptations such as these? The first two mentioned are for the destruction of life, that of another animal, and the second two are for the preservation of the animal's own life. Ellen G. White recognized this play and counterplay of good and evil. She wrote: "Even the child, as he comes in contact with nature, will see cause for perplexity. He cannot but recognize the working of antagonistic forces. It is here that nature needs an interpreter. Looking upon the evil manifest even in the natural world, all have the same sorrowful lesson to learn—'An enemy hath done this' " (Ed 101).

Let us look at still further examples, in an attempt to understand what sin has done to our world. As in the case of ant-eating mammals, many creatures are marvelously adapted for obtaining and eating other animals. An African snake, *Dasypeltis scaber,* subsists on bird eggs. Although it is only two feet long and correspondingly small in girth, it can eat an egg that is more than twice its own diameter. To accomplish this, it must have very loosely connected jaws, special teeth to keep the egg from slipping, and sharp projections from the vertebrae in the back of its throat to puncture the egg and cause its collapse. Furthermore, the shell is bundled up with the sharp edges in and regurgitated (Carr, 1963, pp. 66, 67). Another reptile, the caiman lizard of South America, has mouth and teeth especially adapted to eating snails, which it breaks up and swallows after spitting out the broken shell fragments (Carr, 1963, p. 52). The parrot fish has massive, strong, platelike teeth with which it breaks off chunks of coral and crushes them. The angler fishes dangle a lure above their big mouths to attract curious fish, which they gulp down. Fish living below the level of sunlight may have a bioluminescent light at the end of the lure. The vampire bat uses the two sharp teeth in the front of its mouth to make a clean cut in the skin of mammals. It then laps up the blood that trickles out.

It would be nearly impossible to exhaust the list of ways in which the diets of animals have been modified, and obviously, also their mouthparts, digestive systems, and appendages. This phenomenon is not confined to animals. Insectivorous plants such as the pitcher plant, the venus flytrap, and the sundew have remarkable devices for catching insects and other small creatures, which they apparently digest and utilize in their metabolism.

Modification of structures used in hunting, eating, and reproduction must be accompanied with appropriate behavior. An animal formerly vegetarian in habit cannot continue to behave as a vegetarian after it becomes structurally fitted for obtaining and utilizing animal food, if it is going to survive. Consequently, the behavior of animals has become equally specialized.

A digger wasp will find a caterpillar, paralyze it, drag it to its nest, lay an egg on it, and seal it into the nest. When the egg hatches, the larva will have live food on which to feed until it pupates. This is a complex chain of instinctive events that probably did not exist originally. Did the original digger wasp, or ancestor of the digger wasp, have a paralyzing stinger and produce larvae that fed on living caterpillars?

Some hermit crabs cannot perpetuate their species without using the shell in which they live. The shell helps the female transfer the eggs, which are released from the genital pores on the underside of the thorax, to the pleopods, which are in a dorsal position on the abdomen (Coffin, 1959). How was a hermit crab able to accomplish this feat before empty seashells were available? How was it able to adapt its reproductive behavior after it began to live in a seashell? We cannot answer these questions, but it is rather obvious that behavior such as this must have developed after death entered the world.

Certain examples of reproductive behavior are not in harmony with the original perfection of Eden. Cuckoo birds lay their eggs in the nests of other birds. This is also true with the North American cowbird. Many birds do not seem to show much discrimination. Objects of various shapes, sizes, and markings may be accepted by the brooding bird in place of her own eggs if the differences are not too great. Some cuckoo birds lay eggs that do not have the same color or pattern as the eggs of the bird to whom the nest belongs. Surprisingly, other cuckoos lay eggs that have a remarkable resemblance (mimicry) to the original eggs. It is difficult to understand how this type of mimicry can be achieved (Welty, 1962, pp. 500-501). In this case both behavioral and structural adaptations are in evidence.

Mimicry often involves behavior also. The geometrid moth caterpillar not only looks like a twig, but it must also assume the correct motionless stance of a twig in order to perfect its mimicry. The moth with large eyespots that resemble the eyes of an owl has more perfect imitation when it is in an upside-down position. It is frequently seen resting on a twig or branch in that orientation. Tree hoppers that look like thorns would be out of place on leaves or flowers. But they are not found in those positions; they remain on stems and branches where their mimicry is nearly perfect. Some caterpillars enhance their grotesque eyespots by arching their bodies or bending their heads down.

Many creatures have developed defensive and detracting tactics to preserve themselves or their offspring. The opossum

Fig. 29.2 Mimicry of the monarch butterfly (upper left), whose milkweed diet makes it unpalatable to birds, by the viceroy (below) supposedly gives the latter a measure of protection. The robber fly (lower right) mimics the bumblebee (above), thereby presumably securing protection from predators.

will feign death to discourage its enemies. The bird with the ostensibly crippled leg or wing, leading a potential predator away from the nest, is a well-known decoy. Some moths are able to perceive the high-pitched sound emissions of bats, and to initiate avoiding erratic flight patterns when a bat approaches.

A list such as this could be extended to great length. The important consideration is the fact that animals have not only been changed in the form of their bodies but have also undergone changes in behavior.

Degeneration

Many of the examples mentioned thus far would not be classed as degenerative, nor would they be examples of major progressive evolutionary changes. The animals may have been profoundly altered, but is it possible to say they are more complex or more simple now than they were originally? The next series of illustrations is intended to reveal the degree of degeneration that has occurred. This interesting study will help us to arrive at a correct philosophy of change and adaptation.

In God's original plan, beneficial relationships between living organisms were no doubt intended. Cooperation for mutual benefit is in keeping with God's character. A number of such examples are known, and perhaps many more are unknown at the present time. Ciliate protozoans in the stomachs of cows and other ruminants aid them in digesting their food. Presumably, the cow reciprocates by providing a satisfactory environment for the protozoans and by bringing to them the grass and straw necessary for the nourishment of both organisms. A similar situation is seen in termites, which have flagellate protozoans in their guts. Vitamin-synthesizing bacteria are known to function in man. Most persons have heard of the symbiotic relationship (mutualism) that exists between algae and fungi in the form of the lichen. Nitrogen-fixing bacteria live in nodules on the roots of legumes. Nitrogen obtained from the air by the bacteria is utilized by the legume to produce its protein-rich seed or fruit.

Fig. 29.3 *Sacculina* is a bizarre barnacle parasite on crabs.

Parasitic barnacle

No doubt this kind of association was much more common in the first-created creatures, but today we see many relationships that are far from beneficial. How has this situation developed? There are two possible routes whereby a parasite may have arisen: (1) A previously beneficial or cooperative existence became changed to one of harm and destruction. (2) A free-living organism became adapted to life on, or within, another organism to its harm.

It is not overly difficult to visualize the possibility of the change of a beneficial symbiont into a parasite. Mention was made above of beneficial protozoans and bacteria. On the other hand, many known species of protozoans and bacteria are disease-producing. Originally, some of these may have been beneficial also.

There is evidence that free-living organisms have changed to a parasitic existence and have undergone great degenerative changes in structure and physiology. Several genera of animals have species that reveal progressive parasitism from those that are completely free-living to others that depend entirely on host organisms. The nematode genus *Athelencoides* (small roundworms that exist abundantly in soil and on plants and animals) is represented by some species that are entirely ecto-parasitic (live on the surface of the plant). Other species of the genus are partially ectoparasitic and partially endoparasitic (living within the plant). Still others are entirely endoparasitic (Winslow, 1960). There seems to be a gradation in this genus from one extreme to the other.

Marine snails parasitic on echinoderms show a series of progressively more degenerate and more parasitic forms. The species at the parasitic end of the scale are hardly more than reproduc-

363

tive sacs. Degeneration has been phenomenal, and the only way the creature can be determined to be a snail is by an examination of the larvae, which are typical for a snail.

Barnacles of the genus *Sacculina* are among the most unusual parasites in the animal kingdom (Fig. 29.3). One stage of barnacle development is called a cypris larva. The typical cypris larva of *Sacculina* attaches itself to a crab and penetrates the chitinous exoskeleton just after the crab has molted and before the skeleton has hardened. It develops inside the crab, but the only external manifestation of the parasite is a formless sac that grows in the region of the crab's abdomen. The reproductive system is within this sac and eggs are formed there. The calcareous plates, appendages, or segmentation typical of normal adult barnacles are completely absent. Inside the crab, rootlike or funguslike processes invade the tissues throughout the host— even to the claws.

In the thorax the creeping, spreading growths of the parasite invade the reproductive organs. Many organisms—even man— have either in their early development or throughout their lives, organs of both sexes represented. The sex that predominates causes the reproductive system of the other sex to remain inactive, dormant, or undeveloped. This is true of crabs, but when the barnacle destroys the testes of the host, for instance, organs of the other sex begin to develop and produce female reproductive hormones. These hormones will initiate the growth of secondary sexual characteristics such as a wider abdomen and female genital pores. Thus, as a result of parasitism, there is almost a complete sex reversal. This situation is sometimes referred to as parasitic castration. It is not yet known how great an injury is done to the crab, but the animal is at least able to survive for a considerable time after infection by the parasite (MacGinitie, 1949, pp. 261-263).

Prior to the creation of this earth and the living things upon it, God had already determined upon a course of action—the plan of salvation—should man lose his perfect righteous nature.

Fig. 29.4 God did not create thorns.

An all-wise God would no doubt also have made provision for plants and animals to survive the drastic changes brought about through sin. The plan of salvation may have involved the physical world, as well as the spiritual, because man's survival as a physical being on this earth was linked to the survival of the plants and animals. If the earth became a desolate, barren waste, man also would vanish from the face of the earth. The great controversy between Christ and Satan has its ramifications, not only in man but throughout the world of living things.

"In brier and thorn, in thistle and tare, is represented the evil that blights and mars. In singing bird and opening blossom, in rain and sunshine, in summer breeze and gentle dew, in ten thousand objects in nature, from the oak of the forest to the violet that blossoms at its root, is seen the love that restores" (Ed 101).

Although we cannot explain all the details seen in what appear to be changes resulting from sin, we do know that there are, throughout nature, two conflicting forces, one tending toward beauty and perfection and the other toward degeneration and death. It is Satan's desire to bring discredit upon the Creator, to cause discomfort to man, and to support his counterfeit of the creation story by working through the laws of genetics to bring about thorns on roses, stingers on nettles, parasites, predators, and the host of other ugly and degenerative changes. The Creator, on the other hand, has given plants and animals the capacity to adapt to the crisis brought on by sin, thus counteracting in part the power of the great destroyer.

CREATION—ACCIDENT OR DESIGN?

REFERENCES

Allee, W. C. *et al.* 1949. Principles of animal ecology. W. B. Saunders Co., Philadelphia. 837 pp. 263 figs.

Baer, J. G. 1951. Ecology of animal parasites. Univ. of Illinois Press, Urbana. 224 pp. 102 figs.

Beltz, Joan D. 1967. Evidences of adaptation. The Naturalist 27 (1):8-16.

Carr, Archie. 1963. The reptiles. Time Inc., N.Y. 192 pp.

Caullery, Maurice. 1952. Parasitism and symbiosis. Sedgwick and Jackson, Ltd., London. 340 pp. 80 figs.

Coffin, Harold G. 1959. The ovulation, embryology, and developmental stages of the hermit crab *Pagurus samuelis* (Stimpson). Walla Walla College Publications of the Department of Biological Sciences and the Biological Station, No. 25.

Dobzhansky, Theodosius. 1951. Genetics and the origin of species. 3d ed. Columbia Univ. Press, New York. 364 pp.

Grant, Verne. 1963. The origin of adaptations. Columbia Univ. Press, New York. 606 pp.

Jepsen, Glenn L., George Gaylord Simpson, and Ernst Mayr. 1949. Genetics, paleontology, and evolution. Atheneum, New York. Reprint 1963. 474 pp.

Klotz, John W. 1955. Genes, genesis and evolution. Concordia Pub. House, St. Louis. 575 pp. 73 figs.

Lack, David. 1961. Darwin's finches. Harper & Brothers, New York. 204 pp. 27 figs. 32 tables.

Lane, Frank W. 1954. Nature on parade. Sheridan House, New York. 333 pp.

MacGinitie, G. E. and Nettie MacGinitie. 1949. Natural history of marine animals. McGraw-Hill Book Co., New York. 471 pp. 282 figs.

Mayr, Ernst. 1963. Animal species and evolution. Harvard Univ. Press, Cambridge. 797 pp. 43 tables. 66 figs.

Moore, Hilary B. 1958. Marine ecology. John Wiley & Sons, Inc., New York. 493 pp. many figs.

Nicholas, G. 1955. Life in caves. Sci. Am. 192 (5):98-106. 8 figs.

Ommanney, Francis D. 1963. Fishes. Silver Burdett Co., Morristown, N.J.

Rensch, Bernhard. 1960. Evolution above the species level. Columbia Univ. Press, New York. 419 pp. 113 figs.

Roe, Ann and George Gaylord Simpson (eds.). 1958. Behavior and evolution. Yale Univ. Press, New Haven. 557 pp.

Scott, John Paul. 1958. Animal behavior. Doubleday and Co., Inc. Garden City, New York. Reprint 1963. 331 pp. 26 figs. 27 plates.

Skaife, S. H. 1961. Dwellers in darkness. Doubleday and Co., Inc., Garden City, New York. 180 pp. 26 figs. 16 plates.

Street, Philip. 1961. Vanishing animals. The Science Book Club, London. 232 pp.

Tax, Sol (ed.). 1960. The evolution of life. Univ. of Chicago Press. 629 pp.

Tinbergen, Niko. 1960. The herring gull's world. Basic Books, Inc. Pub., New York. 255 pp.

Welty, Joel Carl. 1962. The life of birds. W. B. Saunders Co., Philadelphia. 546 pp. many figs.

Wendt, Herbert. 1959. Out of Noah's ark. Reader's Union. Weidenfeld and Nicolson, London. 464 pp. many figs.

Weyer, Edward M., Jr. (ed.). 1953. Strangest creatures on earth. Sheridan House, New York. 255 pp.

Winslow, R. D. 1960. Some aspects of the ecology of free-living and plant-parasitic nematodes. *In* Nematology, fundamentals and recent advances . . . J. N. Sasser and W. R. Jenkins (eds.). Univ. North Carolina Press, Chapel Hill, pp. 341-419, 39 figs. 37 tables.

Zeuner, F. E. 1963. A history of domesticated animals. Harper & Row, Pub., New York. 560 pp. many figs.

SCIENCE AND GOD

" 'Can you find out the deep things of God?
Can you find out the limit of the Almighty?' "
                                        Job 11:7, R.S.V.

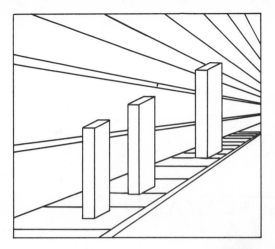

Fig. 30.1 The mind does not always interpret accurately what the eye sees. How does the more distant upright block (left) compare in size with the nearer block? Do the white cube surfaces (center) face up or down? Are the two horizontal lines (below) parallel or bowed?

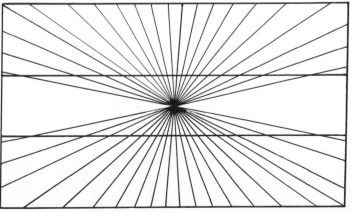

CHAPTER THIRTY

Limitations of the Scientific Method

Ariel A. Roth

SCIENTIFIC METHODOLOGY is highly respected. A scientific answer is frequently referred to as an undebatable statement of fact. Other methods of inquiry are considered inferior. Scientists are regarded by many as being "cold, calculating appraisers of data, who reason logically without emotion or bias" (Ingle, 1954), "who practice the art of infallibility" (Standen, 1950, p. 13), and who presumably "make all wrong answers impossible" (Schilling, 1958).

Scientific technology has been successful in elucidating a number of the mysteries associated with life. Bonner (1965) suggests that after biologists solve the genetic code, man will next be able to control the development of organisms and thus produce the types of life he prefers. This step would be followed by an understanding of the workings of the mind. Control of the development of that faculty would permit the production of super-intelligent beings whose brains might be so large they would have to be detached from the sensory portion of the organism!

Past accomplishments of scientists have given cause for undue confidence in scientific inference, so much so that recently several scientists have expressed concern over the possibility of a return to the attitude of authoritarianism that prevailed in the Dark

Ages, and for which religion is frequently criticized by the scientific community. Speaking of Galileo's intellectual integrity, R. E. Gibson (1964), director of the Johns Hopkins University Applied Physics Laboratory, states:

"This ideal shines through the career of the first great modern scientist, but it is not fashionable now; the present tendency is for the scientific community, now grown powerful, to behave much as the church did in Galileo's time—that is, it permits religious belief and the findings of scholarship to be treated as hypotheses but does not attempt to assimilate them with its own theories. And theologians and scholars regard science in the same way."

M. K. Hubbert (1963), consultant, Shell Development Company, makes this statement:

"Despite the large amount of superficial evidence to the contrary, the present state of science in the United States is one of considerable confusion. In large measure we appear to have lost sight of our intellectual foundations and to have reverted to authoritarianism."

G. A. Kerkut (1960, p. viii), of the department of physiology and biochemistry of the University of Southampton, states:

"It is very depressing to find that many subjects are becoming encased in scientific dogmatism. The basic information is frequently overlooked or ignored and opinions become repeated so often and so loudly that they take on the tone of Laws."

Since the prevalent contemporary attitude is one of general admiration for the accomplishments of science, a proper evaluation of scientific information can be most efficiently approached from the standpoint of an analysis of its limitations. This must be done if a proper perspective is to be maintained. René Dubos (1963), of the Rockefeller Institute, expresses his concern as follows: "But in my opinion, the worst form of anti-intellectualism is the unwillingness to acknowledge the present limitations of science in both its conceptual and experimental structure."

Scientists have discovered an amazing array of facts and principles related to the natural world. Nevertheless, science covers only a limited area of human experience and has been referred to as a closed system. The noted mathematician and philosopher J. W. N. Sullivan (1933, p. 147) illustrates this point by describing the dictionary compiler who defined a violin as a small violoncello, and a violoncello as a large violin. Many scientific philosophers have testified to their belief that science gives an incomplete view of experience. Dryden (1954) points out that "science gives a partial view of life, in many respects a narrow view." He also quotes Eddington on emotions, purposes, and values: "You can no more analyze these imponderables by scientific methods than you can extract the square root of a sonnet." Some of the areas of experience to which science contributes little include art, literature, philosophy, theology, and many subdivisions of these disciplines. Because of this, a rift occasionally develops between science and the rest of the cultural world. This rift testifies to the incompleteness of science.

It is commonly accepted, though often not appreciated, that reality is not identical with observation. A few common examples will illustrate this (Fig. 30.1). White figures appear larger than black ones; two plumb lines side by side are not parallel; we commonly think the earth rotates on its axis every twenty-four hours; we cannot measure the size of anything (Furth, 1950); the edge of a piece of paper appears straight, while under the microscope it appears wavy. Current concepts of atomic physics would indicate that this edge is made up of trillions of miniature motile universes, including electrons, which may be moving at the rate of several thousand miles per second. We assume that our bodies are made of substantial matter, while they are mostly empty space. If all the particles in the human body could be packed together, it would be no larger than a speck barely visible under a magnifying glass. These examples make it proper to ask the question: How much of what we actually believe to be true is false, and only our concept of reality? These matters can be of great significance when one is probing into the unknown.

Inadequate sampling further limits the accuracy of scientific conclusions. Coincidences and exceptions do occur, and one should bear these possibilities in mind before making definite statements. For instance, a person no longer says that birds do not hibernate, for this phenomenon has been observed. The coincidence that, on a twenty-year cycle, the past seven Presidents of the United States have all died in office could also lead one to a wrong conclusion. It is essential that scientific investigation be submitted to statistical analysis before conclusions are drawn. Unfortunately, this is not done as frequently as it should be.

The current emphasis on statistics as a tool for scientific investigation has served to emphasize the tentative nature of many scientific conclusions. The fact that information is statistical means that in science we are dealing with probabilities and not with certainties. These factors must be carefully kept in mind and properly evaluated by the seeker for truth. The statistical nature of scientific information has been corroborated in recent years by the changes that scientists have had to make in a number of fundamental concepts, including the following: the determinacy principle, the law of the conservation of energy, the concept of parity of space, and the chemical inactivity of the so-called inert gases. Since man has studied but a minute portion of the universe evident to him, it is obvious that final conclusions are not at present warranted. Sullivan (1933, p. 158) states: "It is highly probable that all our scientific theories are wrong. Those that we accept are verifiable within our present limits of observation."

Our scale of observation can materially influence our conclusions. As an example, a thinking mite crawling on a wall painted with a mixture of red and white pigment particles would conclude that the wall was red and white, while we would

Fig. 30.2 A mite's-eye view of a colored wall.

unhesitatingly conclude that it was pink (Fig. 30.2). A microbe provided with our patterns of thought, living at the bottom of a fold in the skin of an elephant, might think that when the fold is closed it is night and when it is open it is day. When the elephant washes himself it is a flood; if the elephant has fever, this could mean a heat wave. The lack of sufficient information can lead to wrong conclusions, and in terms of actual truth, it is obvious that at present science cannot provide us with all the answers we want.

In the known universe millions of galaxies containing billions of suns still await investigating, and it seems strange to hear of some scientists who deny the existence of a Creator because His presence has not been directly observed in a minute part of the universe during a short period of time. This type of thinking would be similar to that of an individual who, going into one of the rooms of the Empire State Building and there looking around and not finding the architect, would state categorically that the building had no architect. We cannot use the known as an excuse to deny the existence of the unknown.

The Problem of Bias

Also very significant to adequate observation is the problem of bias in the selection of a sample, or of evidence related to a particular conclusion. If this could be avoided, many of the current controversies, such as the ones over the use of pesticides or the matter of organic material in carbonaceous chondrites, could be settled. No matter what area of knowledge one is investigating, careful scrutiny and integrity to prevent bias is demanded, and investigators in all areas of knowledge could well afford to pay much additional attention to this. Even in the physical sciences, where definition is more easily achieved, the problems listed above are as real as ever. Whyte (1963) points out:

"Today the objectivity of basic physics is less certain (observations are selected and some laws provisional), its mathematics less reliable (quantum divergences), its precision conditional (statistical character), and its primary expressions (abstract operators) lack visual significance. The scope of theory has been immensely enlarged, but its foundations are less satisfactory."

Scientific inference is arrived at largely through a logical process. This process is generally divided into deductive and inductive types of logic. Deductive logic involves making basic assumptions and drawing conclusions therefrom. Inductive logic involves the analysis of evidence with subsequent generalization. It is not always possible to analyze the type of logic pursued in scientific work. Deductive logic can be only as valid as its basic assumptions. The process of generalization in inductive logic is dangerous when one is seeking accuracy. Just because certain generalizations are demonstrably consistent is no sound reason for extrapolating the conclusion to the unknown. Alternatives should be kept under consideration.

In the book *The Logic of Scientific Discovery* the eminent scientific philosopher Karl R. Popper (1959, p. 11) states:

"The empirical basis of objective science has thus nothing 'absolute' about it. Science does not rest upon rock-bottom. The bold structure of its theories rises, as it were, above a swamp. It is like a building erected on piles. The piles are driven down from above into the swamp, but not down to any natural or 'given' base; and when we cease our attempts to drive our piles into a deeper layer, it is not because we have reached firm ground. We simply stop when we are satisfied that they are firm enough to carry the structure, at least for the time being."

The often-quoted statement by Dr. Charles F. Kettering seems appropriate here: "Beware of logic. It is an organized way of going wrong with confidence." It is no doubt somewhat disturbing to a scientist to find that his discipline has such weak foundations. Some comfort can be obtained in the fact that other areas of man's experience do not fare any better. The significant principle that can be concluded from this is the need for caution in approaching truth.

Science does not consist simply in the factual reporting of

information. A considerable amount of interpretation is part of the scientific process, and is necessary for efficiency. This process of interpretation can at times become quite subjective, and is one of the inherent weaknesses of the practice of science. Preconceived ideas and social pressures can greatly influence conclusions. At times these have actually caused the scientist to deliberately falsify information in order to bring forth significant or popular conclusions. The deliberate altering of the now-famous Piltdown skull, probably by Dawson, is an example of the extremes to which a scientist can go. The famous archaeologist Petrie reports that he once caught a pyramidologist secretly filing down a projecting stone to make it conform to one of his theories. Fortunately, such activities are rare in science and are not very significant to the topic under discussion. The manipulation of information to emphasize one aspect or another is a much more significant human characteristic—of this Darrell Huff (1954) gives examples in his book *How to Lie With Statistics*.

All too often preconceived ideas influence conclusions. Numerous tests have demonstrated this, and scientists are in no way free from this fault. As an example, two independent investigators observed by chance the phenomenon of floppiness in rabbit ears after the injection of the enzyme papain. Because of preconceived ideas, both scientists selected the hypothesis that the cartilage of the ear is inert and would not respond to this enzyme. Their conclusions were later proved to be wrong, the floppiness being due to this enzyme. Seventy-five per cent of second-year college students majoring in psychology reported receiving an electric shock from an instrument after the electrodes had been secretly disconnected. A few of the subjects (all female) responded to the imaginary stimulus by screaming or tearing the electrodes from their hands. One subject reported that several toes were paralyzed from the imaginary stimulus. When given placebos, 42 per cent of 500 students at the University of Minnesota reported that their colds were much milder than usual.

It is a sobering thought to realize that the human mind is so easily influenced. Scientists do not appear to be free from this influence. One might say that the mind is somewhat like a jellyfish, and that it tends to take the shape of the container that molds it. The influence of preconceived ideas in science is all the more significant since a hypothesis is part of the scientific method and can readily influence observations and conclusions. This matter deserves much more attention than it has received thus far from scientists. Burtt (1954, p. 28) points out that the various problems we encounter are inevitably stated in terms of inherited notions that should themselves be considered part of a larger problem.

A further encumbrance to scientific objectivity is man's reluctance to change his ideas and opinions. In an article entitled "Resistance by Scientists to Scientific Discovery," Barber (1961) emphasizes the significance of this point. He quotes Planck's well-known statement: "A new scientific truth does not triumph by convincing its opponents and making them see the light, but rather because its opponents eventually die, and a new generation grows up that is familiar with it." Anne Roe (1961) states that the matter of personal commitment of a scientist to a hypothesis deserves more consideration. A hypothesis is a scientist's "baby," and he will not give it up readily. If the scientist comes up with a new hypothesis of his own devising it will be easier to discard the old one. She goes on to say: "I think many scientists are genuinely unaware of the extent, or even of the fact, of this personal involvement, and themselves accept the myth of impersonal objectivity."

Not least among the factors inducing bias in interpretation is the effect of social pressure on the conclusions drawn. A study conducted by Asch (1955) on 123 college students shows that group pressure caused the number of errors in judging the length of various lines to increase from 1 to 36.8 per cent. Only one-quarter of the individuals in this experiment remained free from social pressure. Some went with the majority, which purposefully made errors, nearly all the time, even when there were seven inches difference between lines a few feet away from the observers. Asch states:

"That we have found the tendency to conformity in our society so strong that reasonably intelligent and well meaning young people are willing to call white black is a matter of concern. It raises questions about our ways of education and about the values that guide our conduct."

A proper evaluation of the scientific method is necessary if we are to make maximum use of it as a tool for greater accomplishments. The more accurate our evaluation, the more useful it will be to us.

Science is a "human enterprise" (Schilling, 1958) which has made impressive strides in recent years. Its accomplishments are especially significant where concrete and quantitative aspects of experience are concerned, but it is inadequate in many other areas of experience, and offers few answers to basic philosophical questions. "He who follows science blindly, and who follows it alone, comes to a barrier beyond which he cannot see," states Bush (1965). Ellen G. White emphasizes this point in saying:

"He who studies most deeply into the mysteries of nature will realize most fully his own ignorance and weakness. He will realize that there are depths and heights which he cannot reach, secrets which he cannot penetrate, vast fields of truth lying before him unentered. He will be ready to say, with Newton, 'I seem to myself to have been like a child on the seashore finding pebbles and shells, while the great ocean of truth lay undiscovered before me' " (Ed 133).

Alfred Korzybski says: "There are two ways to slide easily through life: to believe everything or to doubt everything. Both ways save us from thinking." These two extremes are equally applicable in our relationship to science. We must avoid the extremes of complete confidence or of complete disdain for science. We must also avoid the facile tendency of placing an average value on all scientific conclusions. Scientific information varies from true to false, and only by laboriously analyzing the basic premises and evidence available can some degree of accuracy in evaluation be obtained.

The fundamental problems of scientific methodology should teach us tolerance toward those whose opinions differ from ours, and humility about our own opinions. We need to be more thorough in our investigation and less dogmatic in our conclusions. What we glibly call "the frontiers of knowledge" could be more cautiously labeled "the edge of ignorance." Finally, the limitations of science point out that empiricism unaided by other areas of experience is incomplete and prone to error.

REFERENCES

Asch, Solomon E. 1955. Opinions and social pressure. Sci. Am. 193 (5):31-35.
Barber, Bernard. 1961. Resistance by scientists to scientific discovery. Science 134: 596-602.
Bonner, James. 1965. The next new biology. Address given at the annual meeting of the Pacific Division of the American Association for the Advancement of Science, Riverside, California.
Burtt, Edwin A. 1954. Metaphysical foundations of modern science. Anchor Books, New York.
Bush, Vannevar. 1965. Science pauses. Fortune 71:116, 118, 119, 167, 168, 172.
Dryden, Hugh L. 1954. The scientist in contemporary life. Science 120:1052-1055.
Dubos, René. 1963. Logic and choices in science. Proc. Am. Phil. Soc. 107: 365-374.
Furth, R. 1950. The limits of measurement. Sci. Am. 183 (1):48-51.
Gibson, R. E. 1964. Our heritage from Galileo Galilei. Science 145:1271-1276.
Hubbert, M. King. 1963. Are we retrogressing in science? Science 139:884-890.
Huff, Darrell. 1954. How to lie with statistics. Norton, New York.
Ingle, Dwight J. 1954. Psychological barriers in research. Am. Sci. 42:283-293.
Kerkut, G. A. 1960. Implications of evolution. Pergamon, New York.
Popper, K. R. 1959. The logic of scientific discovery. Hutchinson, London.
Roe, Anne. 1961. The psychology of the scientist. Science 134:456-459.
Schilling, H. K. 1958. A human enterprise. Science 127:1324-1327.
Standen, Anthony. 1950. Science is a sacred cow. Dutton, New York.
Sullivan, J. W. N. 1933. The limitations of science. Mentor, New York. Reprint 1961. 192 pp.
White, Ellen G. 1903. Education. Pacific Press Pub. Assn., Mountain View, California, p. 133.
Whyte, Lancelot. 1963. Some thoughts on certainty in physical science. Brit. Jour. Phil. Sci. 14:32-38.

CHAPTER THIRTY-ONE

God in a Test Tube

IN THIS SCIENTIFIC AGE man attempts to reduce to facts and laws all the phenomena of nature. But the scientific method is not adequate for study of God and the elements of religious belief. In large measure the civilized world is atheistic because it believes that there is no evidence that God exists. Others, equally intelligent and educated, are convinced of God's reality. It is a paradox that a cosmonaut can return from a space trip claiming not to have found God, and so denying His existence; whereas a little later an astronaut said that orbital flight confirmed and strengthened his belief in God.

This question of the existence of God needs further consideration. Can we expect to see Him hovering one or two hundred miles above the earth? Can we put Him into a test tube? Can we prove His existence?

To answer these questions let us first consider a few of the many aspects of the environment around us. Life must exist within a relatively narrow range of temperature, let us say, minus 60° to plus 180° Fahrenheit. Temperature, however, can range all the way from —459° Fahrenheit, absolute zero on the Kelvin scale, to millions of degrees Fahrenheit. If our atmosphere were a little less dense we would be bombarded with meteorites, and cosmic radiation would have a strong effect upon life. If water were not abundant in our environment, life would be very difficult, because we are so completely dependent upon water. Water itself has many remarkable properties. Gravity is another important factor to consider. If it were a little less or a little more we would have difficulty walking and getting around. The distance from the moon affects our tides. If we were a little closer to the moon high tides would inundate the land. The size of the continents influences the climate in the interior. If they were much larger the cold would be too severe. The distance from the sun controls our heat, which is just right. If the length of the day were shorter we would not be ready to sleep when night came; if longer, we would be weary before bedtime arrived. The amount of oxygen in our atmosphere, the size of the earth, and its movements around the sun, all have an effect upon life. These are only ten factors; many more could be enumerated.

If ten pennies were marked from one to ten, put into a bag, shaken, and taken from the bag, what are the chances of getting penny number one first: "It is simple," you say; "one chance in ten." What are the chances of getting the pennies numbered one and two in that order? The answer is one chance in one hundred. What are the chances of obtaining pennies one to ten in order if the pennies are put back after each drawing so that there are always ten pennies to draw from? It seems incredible, but mathematically the chances are one in ten billion. On the basis of this little exercise in mathematics it is difficult to conceive of all the factors mentioned above (and the many others not mentioned) being the result of mere chance (Morrison, 1944, pp. 98-100).

Today much is said about the universe, our earth, and our environment being the result of blind chance. Do we realize what this means, and how reasonable or unreasonable it may be? The most impressive area of study to convince one of the existence of a Guiding Force is that of life and living things. This we will now examine in more detail.

Growth and Design

The prevailing skepticism of our time blinds us so that we fail to see evidences of God in the natural world. As biologists work with living things they find that organisms are constantly striving toward the goal of becoming what they are destined to become. Every animal has a goal of being the organism it is supposed to be, and when something blocks the animal from reaching that goal it has many alternatives by which to reach the desired end. A few examples will illustrate.

More than fifty years ago Dr. H. V. Wilson performed a classic experiment with a simple organism, the sponge. Many of the simpler organisms have the ability to regenerate missing parts. They can be cut into two or more pieces, and each piece may develop into a complete organism. Dr. Wilson wondered to what extent this could be carried. He concluded that the smallest unit into which a sponge could be divided would be the individual cell. He took a piece of bolting cloth, of fine mesh, and squeezed the sponge through it. The pores in the cloth were just big enough to let the cells pass through and drop into a jar of sea water. He then examined these isolated cells under the microscope. The cells had the tendency to be attracted to one another, to join when they came close together. Two cells would join to two more cells, small groups to small groups, until finally all the cells were joined together into a ball of cells. Then in a relatively short time, to his surprise, he found that this ball of cells was actually beginning to form itself into a small sponge colony.

A sponge is actually not simple. Many different kinds of cells are involved in a sponge colony. The ball of cells Dr. Wilson observed—which resulted from the combining of all the cells that were squeezed through the bolting cloth—had been completely disrupted. Nevertheless, the cells began to arrange themselves into, or to produce, all the various types of cells necessary to form a sponge colony. Somehow each one had the information, the guidance, whatever you may wish to call it, that controlled them toward reaching their goal of becoming a sponge (Sinnott, 1955, pp. 32-36).

Let us think of another, more familiar, example. Perhaps you have cut a shoot from a geranium plant and placed it in a pot so that it would grow into another geranium plant. This took little time or thought. Yet the piece of stem will develop roots at one end and buds at the other end. The roots develop from large undifferentiated cells that make up the stem but that have the information, the "knowledge," to become root cells. The cells at the other end of the cut stem, which appear just the same, do not initiate the development of roots. They have the information necessary to develop into cells that lead to the formation of buds.

Here is yet another example. Crabs are usually a familiar sight along the seashores. One of these is the hermit crab; a comical little animal that lives in an empty seashell. The larval crab does not look like an adult (Fig. 31.1). It passes through four stages that do not resemble the hermit crab. But a dramatic change to the form of the adult takes place in the fifth stage. This change is somewhat similar to the metamorphosis undertaken by some insects, from the chrysalis to the butterfly for instance. Previous to this fifth stage the crab has

Fig. 31.1 A larval hermit crab.

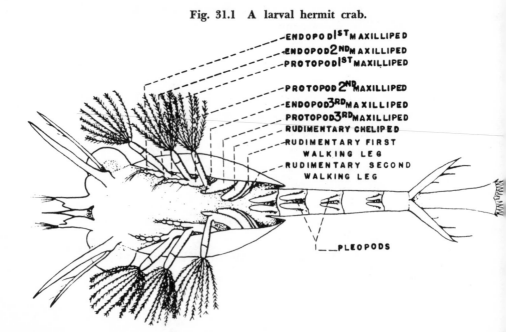

ENDOPOD 1ST MAXILLIPED
ENDOPOD 2ND MAXILLIPED
PROTOPOD 1ST MAXILLIPED
PROTOPOD 2ND MAXILLIPED
ENDOPOD 3RD MAXILLIPED
PROTOPOD 3RD MAXILLIPED
RUDIMENTARY CHELIPED
RUDIMENTARY FIRST WALKING LEG
RUDIMENTARY SECOND WALKING LEG
PLEOPODS

Fig. 31.2 Ground squirrels hibernate during the winter.

absolutely no interest in a seashell. A small seashell dropped into the bottle is no stimulus at all to the crab. But soon after the crab larva changes to a young adult—a very quick change that takes only a few minutes—a shell suddenly becomes very attractive to it. The crab will look the shell over to see whether there is already an occupant. If there is none it will empty the sand, then back into the shell to determine how well it fits. It has never seen a shell before, and only minutes before it had no interest in shells—a dramatic change in the behavior of the animal. Some signal has "turned on," something that guides the creature to enable it to become what it is destined to become.

Many warm-blooded mammals hibernate in winter. During hibernation the animal's heartbeat slows down, sometimes to as low as two or three beats a minute. The respiration of the animal is equally slow, and its temperature drops. It may be curled up, apparently asleep, and feel cold to the touch. The heart beats so slowly that the blood is circulating very sluggishly through the body. Normally under such circumstances the blood would clot and the animal would die quickly. But when the mammal goes into hibernation something triggers the formation of an anticoagulant in its blood, so that all the time it is hibernating its blood, which is moving slowly through its body, will not clot. If the situation did not change when spring came a little injury might cause it to bleed to death. When spring arrives the anticoagulant is no longer secreted into the blood, and the clotting ability returns to normal. Many other examples might be given of the marvelous ability of animals to adapt to circumstances so they can survive.

Animal Navigation

Animal navigation has held the attention of scientists for many years. Because of its usefulness to man, the honeybee has been studied more than most other insects. A few years ago a German biologist discovered that honeybees are able to navigate by the sun, and that they are able to communicate information to one another. Let us set up a hypothetical situation. A honeybee discovers a rose garden in someone's back yard. As the bee flies back to the hive, the relationship of that flower garden to the hive and to the sun is impressed upon its brain. The bee enters the hive and performs a dance on the vertical cone that hangs in the hive. The crucial part of this dance, which is roughly in the form of a figure 8, seems to be the waist of the eight. The bee will perform that part of the dance at an angle the same number of degrees from vertical that the angle of the flower garden is from the point on the horizon that is nearest the sun. If it dances on a horizontal plane it will not be able to use the vertical as the sun's position. The waist of the figure 8 will, in this case, point directly toward the rose garden. The other bees watch, and determine the direction, approximate distance, and kind of flower (von Frisch, 1950, pp. 53-96).

Man has always been interested in the migration of birds. Some birds also migrate by the sun. In their brains they have a

Fig. 31.3 A migrating bird, the red-breasted merganser, caught in a late spring snowstorm.

built-in clock that makes allowance for the movement of the sun, so that they are able to keep traveling in one general direction. A few years ago a student of birds became curious to know whether night-migrating birds would use the stars for navigational aids. He took some European warblers, put them in cages, and noticed that during the normal migration time these birds would flutter and face toward the direction in which they would normally travel if they were free. When he took them inside a room where they could not see the sky, they were disoriented and did not face predominantly in any one direction. He next took these birds and placed them in a planetarium. Projected on the dome was a star pattern similar to that in the sky at that moment. The birds then faced, and fluttered against the cage, in the normal direction of migration. When the star pattern was changed to that of Lake Bikal in Siberia, the birds changed to a direction that would have taken them back to Germany, had they actually been in Siberia. He brought another species of warbler into the planetarium. These normally flew in a southeasterly direction until they were north of Egypt, where they would follow the Nile River southward. In the planetarium they fluttered toward the southeast as expected. Gradually the star pattern on the dome of the planetarium was changed to resemble the night sky north of Egypt. Again the birds changed their orientation as expected (Welty, 1962, pp. 475-476). It is extremely difficult to understand how this impression of the sky pattern on the mind of a bird could have arisen by any chance evolutionary development.

The Human Body

The most marvelous of all creations is the human body. Let us consider a few aspects of it. We originate from one cell, which is the result of the union of male and female reproductive cells. This one cell has within it 46 chromosomes and many genes. In this one cell the entire information and control necessary to guide the complete development of the organism is

25   385

found. It has been said that one could put all the chromosomes of all the people in the world into a thimble. Yet there are no two persons exactly alike. The information, the guidance system, that is stored in these chromosomes and genes is simply fantastic.

We might say that the ability of the hereditary material in the chromosome to duplicate itself, and to keep duplicating and thus eventually develop into an adult human, is something like the ability of a printing press to print, not a picture of itself, but to print another press like itself, which has the ability in turn to print another press like itself *ad infinitum*. This is not an accurate illustration, however, because the complexity of the chromosomes and genes is so much greater than the parts of a printing press. Some students of the cell say that the evolution necessary to form the first living cell would have to be greater than the evolution of life from a cell to a human being. There is no simple living organism, although we may use that term to distinguish some organisms from others of greater complexity.

In an adult the senses and the brain are among the most complex structures. The eye can detect green light with a duration of one eight-millionth of a second, which represents energy equivalent to one three-hundred billionth of an ounce falling one twenty-fifth of an inch. These figures are beyond comprehension. We do not usually think of our noses as being sensitive. Man would not show up well compared with dogs or some insects that have a tremendous ability to smell. But even with human smell, poor as it is, the ability is good enough to detect one thirteenth of a trillionth of an ounce of mercaptan in a nose full of air. No chemical tests known come near to being that sensitive (Zoethout and Tuttle, 1958, pp. 531, 532).

One aspect of the human brain, among many, must suffice as an illustration of its amazing capacity. Dr. Wilder Penfield, a brain surgeon at the Montreal Neurological Institute, has made some interesting discoveries in this area. Because certain discrete parts of the brain are involved in sight, in hearing, and in control of the parts of the body, it is important for him to discover the functions of these various parts in order that in his surgery he will not cut into the vital areas. He takes an electric probe, an electrode, and gently excites certain parts of the brain with a slight electrical stimulus. The individual is under local anesthesia, and thus is able to talk and tell the surgeon the result. In this experiment Dr. Penfield discovered that two relatively small areas on the sides of the brain are involved in the memory of experiences an individual has had during his lifetime. In part, one report of this experiment reads as follows:

"The first patient in which stimulated recollection was observed lived an episode of early childhood with such naturalness that she felt fear again as she had at the time of the original event. Another early patient seemed to see herself as she was while giving birth to her child, and in the surroundings of that original event. One young man saw himself with his cousins at their home in South Africa. It seemed to him that he could hear them laughing and talking. The scene was at least as clear to him as it would have been had he closed his eyes and ears moments after the event, even though it had occurred years earlier.

"One woman heard the voice of her small son in the yard outside her kitchen, accompanied by the neighborhood sounds of honking autos, barking dogs, and shouting youngsters. One patient listened to an orchestra in the operating room, playing a number that she did not herself know how to sing or play, and that she only vaguely recalled having heard before. Another patient heard the singing of a Christmas song in her church at home in Holland. She seemed to be there in the church and was moved again by the beauty of the occasion, just as she had been on that Christmas Eve years earlier" (Wooldridge, 1963, p. 166).

When the electrode is removed, these experience-recalls cease. When the electrode is again placed in position, the experience may be repeated, or the stimulus may elicit a new experience. This experiment is significant. It apparently means that there is a complete sequence of all of life's awarenesses and experiences stored in the brain. Once again we are overcome by the magnitude of such a capacity. It is as though a tape recorder has made a permanent recording of all of life's conscious experiences, and when the electric stimulus is applied some small portion of it is recalled, something that may have been mostly forgotten. One cannot help wondering whether God's original plan for man included total recall. Dr. Penfield himself makes the following statement and question:

"Consideration of the basic mechanism responsible for electrical recall of past experience brings one face to face with the ultimate mystery of the brain: How is the passage of potentials through nerve cells and fibres reflected by, or converted into, human awareness?" (Penfield, 1962).

As you read this article you are aware of your surroundings—the lights, the people that may be near you, the general arrangement of the room. There are many things that are coming into your mind at this moment, and apparently all are being recorded. You will not be able to recall all of it later, but you will be able to remember some of it. But it is all still there, a complete record. It is very difficult to visualize how so small an area of the brain can retain so tremendous a mass of information.

Dr. Edward Kessel, famous biologist at the University of California at Berkeley, writes: "If only all scientists would consider the evidence of science here described with the same honesty and lack of prejudice with which they evaluate the results of their own research; if only they would let their intellects rule their emotions: then they would be compelled to acknowledge that there is a God. This is the only conclusion that will fit the facts. To study science with an open mind will bring one to the necessity of a First Cause, whom we call God" (Kessel, 1958, p. 52).

The Evidence of God

Although strong evidence has been presented, we have not conclusively demonstrated the presence of God. God has not been put into a test tube. God is too great for man to comprehend. You may recall the story of four blind men who touched four different parts of an elephant and came to as many different conclusions of what an elephant is. Why? Because they could not see the whole. This is man's problem. Our knowledge and comprehension are too narrow to encompass the whole that is God. Why, then, does God not make Himself demonstrable to man? Why does God not permit Himself to be put into a test tube, figuratively speaking, and His existence to be proved?

But wait! Before we turn away, hopefully wishing that God would reveal Himself, let us ask ourselves a few questions. Is this the best way that God could devise to convince man of His existence? Is man capable of understanding any scientific revelation of God he might be given? If the reality of God were proved scientifically, would only scientists have the opportunity of knowing God?

In the original creation man had direct communion with God. There was no question in Adam's mind regarding the reality of God. After sin cut off man's direct access to God, his concept of God became blurred or was obliterated entirely. What man then needed was a revelation of God on his own level that he could understand—one that all men could understand.

The marvelous fact to which the whole Bible testifies is that God *did* demonstrate Himself to man, and that He did so in a way every person can understand. He took upon Himself human nature and lived among men. For more than 30 years this exhibition of God in the test tube of human existence revealed God to man. This was God's supreme gift. This "plan of salvation," charted for just such an emergency before the world was created, proved the existence of God. It demonstrated in the most marvelous way possible the attitude of God toward His created beings, and made sure the restoration of direct communion of man with God that was lost.

But we who do not have opportunity to see and associate with God on earth, how can we be convinced? God has not left us without evidence. Several books of the Bible were written by eyewitnesses who worked, lived, and ate with this demonstration of God to man. One of them later wrote: "So the Word became flesh; he came to dwell among us, and we saw his glory, such glory as befits the Father's only Son, full of grace and truth" (John 1:14, *New English Bible*).* God placed Himself where man could see, and feel, and hear Him, and be able to comprehend with his limited capacity what God is. Many who saw and heard His magnificent revelation of that perfect life refused to believe. God's character does not permit Him to force men to believe, either then or now. It is up to each individual to accept or reject the evidence of God in the natural world and in the Holy Scriptures.

REFERENCES

Clark, Harold W. 1940. Genes and Genesis. Pacific Press Pub. Assn., Mountain View, California, pp. 107-147.
————. 1964. Wonders of creation. Pacific Press Pub. Assn., Mountain View, California. 143 pp.
Henderson, Lawrence J. 1913. The fitness of the environment. Beacon Press, Boston. Reprint 1958. 317 pp.
Hoen, Reu E. 1951. The Creator and His workshop. Pacific Press Pub. Assn., Mountain View, California, pp. 140-148.
Howey, Walter (ed.). 1950. The faith of great scientists. The American Weekly, Hearst Publishing Co., Inc., New York. 63 pp.
Kessel, Edward. 1958. Let's look at facts, without bent or bias. *In* The evidence of God in an expanding universe. John Clover Monsma (ed.). G. P. Putnam's Sons, New York, pp. 49-54.
Monsma, John Clover (ed.). 1958. The evidence of God in an expanding universe. G. P. Putnam's Sons, New York. 250 pp.
Morrison, A. Cressy. 1944. Man does not stand alone. Fleming H. Revell Co., Westwood, New Jersey. 107 pp.
Penfield, Wilder. 1962. The thread of experience. What's News, Summer.
Sherrington, Charles. 1940. Man on his nature. The New American Library of World Literature, Inc., New York. Reprint 1964. 287 pp.
Sinnott, Edmund W. 1955. The biology of the spirit. The Viking Press, New York. Reprint 1957. 180 pp.
von Frisch, Karl. 1950. Bees: their vision, chemical senses, and language. Cornell Univ. Press, Ithaca, New York. 119 pp., 61 figs.
Welty, Joel Carl. 1962. The life of birds. W. B. Saunders Co., Philadelphia. 540 pp.
Wooldridge, Dean E. 1963. The machinery of the brain. McGraw-Hill Book Company, Inc., New York. 252 pp.
Zoethout, William D. and W. W. Tuttle. 1958. Textbook of physiology. C. V. Mosby Co., St. Louis. 712 pp., 305 figs.

* *The New English Bible*, New Testament. © The Delegates of the Oxford University Press and the Syndics of the Cambridge University Press 1961.

CHAPTER THIRTY-TWO

Can Man Create Life?

THE PROBLEM OF LIFE and its origin has intrigued man from the beginning. The Bible answers the question, but men who do not choose to believe it have formulated their own theories.

Spontaneous Generation

From ancient times to the present day, people in backward countries have held the idea of spontaneous generation. Frogs rising from river mud, flies coming from rotting meat, and similar phenomena were—and are—used as proof. Redi (1626-1697) and Spallanzani (1729-1799) of Italy, and Pasteur (1822-1895) of France helped to dispel this ignorant notion, but the old belief was slow to die.

In one important aspect the concept of spontaneous generation has not died. It has been rephrased in scientific language and incorporated into mechanistic evolution as the probable method for the origin of life. Significantly, mechanistic evolution requires for its survival as a theory, exceptions to two of the best substantiated laws of life—life begets life, and like begets like!

In 1903 Arrhenius suggested that life came from a source outside our earth. It was soon realized, however, that a spore or other small spark of life on a meteorite would be most unlikely to survive the rigors of space travel and passage through the atmosphere. Furthermore, this theory does not answer the question of how life originated elsewhere.

In recent years the book *The Origin of Life* by the Russian scientist A. I. Oparin has received considerable attention. J. B. S. Haldane, of Great Britain, has also contributed significantly to this subject. Oparin gave a detailed argument for a spontaneous origin of life in the ancient seas, which are thought to have harbored large quantities of organic substances usable in amino acid formation. According to Oparin, an organic molecule would increase in complexity without the necessity of synthetic ability, by the chance combining of substances available in its environment. The possibilities of a chance combination of molecules to become amino acids, and the subsequent chance joining of amino acids to become proteins with the properties of life, are unrealistic. Jacobson (1955, p. 125) reports in the *American Scientist:* "From the probability standpoint, the ordering of the present environment into a single amino acid molecule would be utterly improbable in all the time and space available for the origin of terrestrial life."

What type of environment would be needed for the chance production of a simple protein? He answers that question also (p. 125): "Only the very simplest of these proteins (salmine) could possibly arise, even if the earth were blanketed with a thickness of half a mile of amino acids for a billion years! And by no stretch of the imagination does it seem as though the present environment could give even one molecule of amino acid, let alone be able to order by accident this molecule into a protoplasmic array of self-reproducing, metabolizing parts fitting into an organism."

Another scientist who has been impressed with the odds against the chance formation of proteins has expressed his opinion as follows:

"Proteins are the essential constituents of all living cells, and they consist of the five elements, carbon, hydrogen, nitrogen, oxygen and sulphur, with possibly 40,000 atoms in the ponderous molecule. . . . The chance that these five elements may come together to form the molecule, the quantity of matter that must be continually shaken up, and the length of time nec-

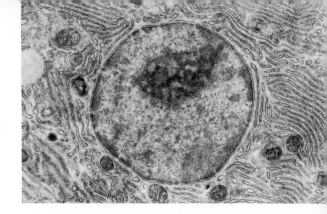

Fig. 32.1 A cell is a complex structure. This cell electron photomicrograph shows the nucleus and part of the surrounding cytoplasm.

essary to finish the task, can all be calculated. A Swiss mathematician, Charles Eugene Guye, has made the computation and finds that the odds against such an occurrence are 10^{160} to 1, or only one chance in 10^{160}, that is 10 multiplied by itself 160 times, a number far too large to be expressed in words. The amount of matter to be shaken together to produce a single molecule of protein would be millions of times greater than that in the whole universe. For it to occur on the earth alone would require many, almost endless billions (10^{243}) of years" (Allen, 1958, p. 23).

George Wald, of Harvard University, while recognizing the improbability of spontaneous generation, states his personal belief as follows: "One has only to contemplate the magnitude of this task to concede that the spontaneous generation of a living organism is impossible. Yet here we are—as a result, I believe, of spontaneous generation" (Wald, 1954, p. 46). It is obvious that the faith required by a believer in the spontaneous generation of living matter is more than that required of a believer in a Creator-God!

God and Life

Even if the conditions stated above were present, life would not necessarily form if given time. An assumption is made here that should be questioned. That life will result when certain complex proportions and organizations of organic matters are achieved either by chance or design is a questionable assumption. Is life merely the fortuitous arrangement of elements and compounds in such a way that life is the natural outcome? If scientists could put together the constituents of a cell in exactly the right proportions and arrangements, would it become a living cell?

Research in the field of virology has produced results that would almost suggest a Yes answer to the above questions. Viruses have been a perplexing group. Some viruses behave like crystals and ought not to be classed as living organisms. Others may be living entities. It is possible in some cases to break the components (protein cover and nucleic acid center) apart and recombine them into functioning viruses. It even may become possible, eventually, to produce viruses or viruslike particles from nonliving organic materials, but there would be a big question as to whether or not these would truly be living organisms.

Crystals grow by the attraction of atoms or molecules to form an exact pattern or lattice. A similar situation may be seen in the more detailed aspects of biological growth. One example would be the reproduction of new strands of DNA (deoxyribonucleic acid) in the nucleus of a cell by the matching of components in the nucleoplasm with corresponding parts in the DNA chain. In other words, the type of growth seen in inorganic situations (crystals) may also be seen in living cells, but this does not mean that living growth consists merely of a vast expansion of this system. It is a great step from a relatively simple and static virus to an extremely complex and dynamic living cell. It is one thing for a printing press to print its own de-

Fig. 32.2 Model of a DNA molecule, with scientist holding a tiny diffraction camera used to photograph biologically fibrous materials.

sign, but it is another thing for the press to "print" another press like itself. Only living things possess the latter ability.

Man may be able at some time in the future to produce what he will venture to call a living object, but it must be remembered that the adjective *living* is subject to various definitions. It is unlikely that man will ever be able to bestow life to a mass of matter in a way that meets God's definition of life. The following references indicate that God is the source of life.

"Not all the wisdom and skill of man can produce life in the smallest object in nature. It is only through the life which God Himself has imparted that either plant or animal can live" (SC 67).

"The prince of evil, though possessing all the wisdom and might of an angel fallen, has not power to create, or to give life; this is the prerogative of God alone" (PP 264).

"The youth need to understand the deep truth underlying the Bible statement that with God 'is the fountain of life.' Ps. 36:9. Not only is He the originator of all, but He is the life of everything that lives" (Ed 197).

"For with thee is the fountain of life" (Ps. 36:9).

"Jesus said unto her, I am the resurrection, and the life" (John 11:25).

"Neither is worshipped with men's hands, as though he needed any thing, seeing he giveth to all life, and breath, and all things" (Acts 17:25).

It is possible that someday the mass media of communication may proclaim that man has created life. But such a claim will certainly require close scrutiny. The assertion will undoubtedly be either questionable, or a case in which the synthesis process has incorporated some previously living material. When man throws his leftover food to the chickens he is merely aiding nature in the process of producing living protoplasm out of nonliving organic and inorganic matter. On the level of the virus this well-known ability of living protoplasm is not so clear or so obvious.

CREATION—ACCIDENT OR DESIGN?

Pharaoh's wise men produced deceptively lifelike serpents, but they were not actually alive (PP 264). It would have been difficult to tell the difference, however. Modern man may be able to produce substances with some characteristics of living organisms. Will they be truly living creations from totally non-living matter? They may be difficult to distinguish from a truly living entity.

The ability to produce true life is an ability of God alone, an ability that even Satan does not have, and one that man certainly will never possess. If man ever obtained this ability he would become as God, and it is fearful to think of the possible results. We can be thankful that the power of creation will always reside in the hands of an all-wise and loving Creator.

REFERENCES

Allen, Frank. 1958. The origin of the world—by chance or design? *In* The evidence of God in an expanding universe. John Clover Monsma (ed.). G. P. Putnam's Sons, New York, pp. 19-24.

Clark, F. and R. L. M. Synge (ed.). 1959. The origin of life on the earth. Pergamon Press, New York. 691 pp.

Clark, Robert E. D. 1961. The universe: plan or accident? Muhlenberg Press, Philadelphia. 240 pp.

Evans, Earl A., Jr. 1960. Viruses and evolution. *In* The evolution of life. Sol Tax (ed.). Univ. of Chicago Press, pp. 85-94.

Gaffron, Hans. 1960. The origin of life. *In* The evolution of life. Sol Tax (ed.). Univ. of Chicago Press, pp. 39-84.

Henderson, Lawrence J. 1958. The fitness of the environment. Beacon Press, Inc., Beacon Hill, Boston. 317 pp.

Jackson, Francis and Patrick Moore. 1962. Life in the universe. The Scientific Book Club, London, pp. 17-65.

Jacobson, Homer. 1955. Information, reproduction and the origin of life. Am. Sci. 43 (1):119-127.

Morrison, A. Cressy. 1944. Man does not stand alone. Fleming H. Revell Co., New York, pp. 31-44.

Oparin, Aleksandr Ivanovich. 1938. The origin of life. 2d ed. Dover Publications, Inc., New York. Reprint 1953. 270 pp.

Ritland, Richard M. 1966. Meaning in nature. General Conference Dept. of Education, Washington, D.C.

Wald, George. 1954. The origin of life. Sci. Am. 191 (2):44-53.

Weisz, Paul B. 1963. The science of biology. 2d ed. McGraw-Hill Book Co., Inc., New York, pp. 39-64.

White, Ellen G. 1903. Education. Pacific Press Pub. Assn., Mountain View, California, pp. 102-112.

————. 1890. Patriarchs and prophets. Pacific Press Pub. Assn., Mountain View, California. 805 pp.

Zimmerman, Paul A. 1959. The evidence for creation. *In* Darwin, evolution and creation. Paul A. Zimmerman (ed.). Concordia Pub. House, St. Louis, Missouri. pp. 96-102.

SECTION 9

THE THEORY OF
EVOLUTION

"O Lord, how manifold are thy works! in wisdom hast thou made them all."

Psalm 104:24

Fig. 33.1 The alternatives: Accident or design, evolution or creation?

CHAPTER THIRTY-THREE

The Theory of Evolution

By Edward E. White

EVOLUTION IS a comparatively modern philosophy based on deductions from certain facts discovered in various branches of science, but in its unrefined state it is also a very old philosophy based on ancient speculations not too closely related to facts. By the term *evolution* we mean the continuous development of living creatures from less complex to more complex organisms, with development not necessarily always in the same direction. Nevertheless, the implication is that by selecting from the complete range of the animate kingdom, living and fossil, it would be possible to present a continuous series of creatures, each one more highly developed than its predecessor, the end of the series being man himself. The evolutionary philosophy states that this process is one of the inevitable laws of nature, a viewpoint diametrically opposed to the doctrine of creation, which is affirmed in the Scriptures to be an immediate act that produced a wide variety of living forms virtually instantaneously.

Early Development of Evolutionary Thought

The nature-philosophers of the fifth and sixth centuries B.C. were aware of the obvious changes that take place in common phenomena. Rain washes and gouges out channels, building stones crumble, wood rots, boys grow into men, rivers produce deltas, water turns into steam or mist, and so on. Indeed, this somewhat vague idea of change was accepted as a fundamental principle of nature, and with the unproved fallacy of spontaneous generation, it led to the speculative conclusion that lowly creatures were continually being produced, and were slowly developing into more complex and more highly organized forms of life.

This idea was modified by the famous Greek philosopher and naturalist Aristotle (384-322 B.C.), who, though recognizing these continual changes, saw the many differences between, and the apparent fixity of, living creatures. He was the greatest authority of his time on natural science, and his authority, owing to the waning interest in nature study and the rise of scholasticism in the Middle Ages, held sway for two millenniums after his death. Aristotle arranged animals into fixed classifications or groups, and recognized, for example, that dog was still dog and remained dog even though it had undergone some change from puppyhood.

The Renaissance, the revival of learning, the foundation of scientific academies, voyages of exploration, and the discovery of the New World were all factors that led to the shedding of the authoritarian teaching of the Middle Ages, and led to the increase of the spirit of inquiry and curiosity that made an appeal to the facts of nature rather than to what antiquarians had said about it. The Bible was still regarded as the Word of God, and this restrained somewhat those speculative philosophers who did not believe that "in the beginning God created the heaven and the earth" (Gen. 1:1) or that in creation week "he spake, and it was done" (Ps. 33:9). In the early eighteenth century, however, divergent views that gained adherents started the cleavage between Biblical teaching and scientific theory.

The French essayist, philosopher, and naturalist, Comte de Buffon (1707-1788) speculated concerning the origin of the solar system and performed a crude experiment to justify his conclusions regarding the immense age of the earth. He also resurrected the old idea of change from one form to another, by concentrating on the similarities between living things and glossing over the rather obvious differences. This was a completely different viewpoint from that of his famous contemporary, the Swedish taxonomist Carl Linnaeus (1707-1778), who went to the other extreme and claimed that the genera and species of his classification were identical with those created in the Garden of Eden, and that since that time they had been fixed and had not varied.

Buffon's travel companion, Jean Baptiste Lamarck (1744-1829), found it easy in the climate of the godless French Revolution to pursue evolutionary ideas. His *Philosophie Zoologique* of 1809 described a ladder of life with living creatures arranged in progressive stages of greater complexity of organization. Further, he outlined his famous but fallacious principle of the inheritance of acquired characteristics, as a necessary evidence of the evolutionary change that he claimed had taken place.

At this time the discovery of many extinct fossils provided more facts that needed interpretation, and the great French anatomist Cuvier (1769-1832) and some of his students suggested that these were remnants of previous catastrophes, each being followed by a successive new creation of different species or types. His influence, great as it was, did not cross the English Channel, where other theories had been and were being devised. Although dissociated at the time from biological science, these theories were ultimately to cause a revolution in this branch of knowledge, as they did in geology. The chief exponent was the Scottish naturalist James Hutton (1726-1797), who unintentionally initiated a controversy regarding the origin of the rocks of the earth's crust. His idea of Plutonism (molten underground magma) differed from the concept of Neptunism (precipitation within a primeval ocean) promulgated by the German mineralogist Werner (1750-1817). Many of Hutton's views on geology in general were further developed by Sir Charles Lyell (1797-1875), who set out to show that all past changes in geology were the result of a long—very long—period during which present causes of denudation, delta formation, and land rise and fall were acting

Fig. 33.2 James Hutton (left), who unintentionally initiated a controversy regarding the origin of the rocks of the earth's crust. William Smith (right), an English canal and drainage engineer, who learned to identify rock formations by their fossils. Charles Lyell (far right), who proposed the theory that all past geological change has taken place at the same rate as it is going on today.

at the same rate as now. His plausible writings attracted the general public, as well as the men of science, and his theory of uniformitarianism became the fundamental philosophy of the newly emerging science of geology. This science now became more than a study of inanimate rocks and minerals, for many strata were found to contain the remains of once-living creatures, and these fossils demanded a special study all on their own. An English canal engineer, William Smith (1769-1839), had noticed in his work that he could identify layers of rock of different composition in various areas of England by the characteristic fossils they contained. This idea was developed into another fundamental concept in paleontology, which became a special branch of geology—stratigraphy and its use of index fossils.

The scientific soil was now fertile for the rapid development and establishment of the theory of evolution. Hutton and Lyell had provided limitless time, variations in living creatures had been noted by numerous biologists, theological opposition had been weakened by higher criticism of the Scriptures and a liberal interpretation of the book of Genesis generally, although the way was not entirely open for a reception of Darwin's theory of the mechanics of evolution.

Charles Darwin (1809-1882) waited 15 years before publishing his *Origin of Species by the Process of Natural Selection,* and even then the book met a hostile reception from church leaders, though it was hailed as a masterpiece by many biologists. By this theory man was deprived of his origin in the Garden of Eden and made out to be a descendant of the brute beasts through a constant struggle for survival. The theological implications of this upward urge were tremendous, for it implied a denial of human degeneracy and fall, and of man's need for salvation.

The new idea was completely contrary to church teaching. The climax came in the great debate of 1860 at Oxford University when Bishop Wilberforce, representing popular theology of the day with its liberal interpretation of the Scriptures, was utterly and convincingly defeated by Thomas Huxley. Theology then became the bondmaid of science, and the goddess of reason, which the French Revolution had first set up in the latter part of the eighteenth century, now became tacitly accepted in other countries as an object of worship. Science became the great god of learned and unlearned alike, its authority superseding even that of Sacred Writ. From this time on, the facts of science have been increasingly interpreted in terms of the evolutionary hy-

403

pothesis. Geology and biology in particular have become permeated with this idea, which is accepted virtually as a fact requiring only more research to establish its final truth.

Evolution and the Church

What is the place of the Seventh-day Adventist Church in this conflict between the evolutionary hypothesis and the simple account of creation given in the Bible? The apostle Peter makes a remarkable prediction in 2 Peter 3, of a last-day conflict between scientists and the Bible. He names three areas of debate that are of supreme importance to Seventh-day Adventists. He says that latter-day philosophers, appealing to evidences from the natural world to support their contentions, will be scornful of three beliefs held by those who accept Bible authority. The three points specified are:

1. The second advent of Christ, verse 4.
2. The creation, verse 5.
3. The Flood, verse 6.

Objections to these three beliefs are comprehended in the principle of uniformity, a fundamental geological assumption that the apostle, a nonscientist, states in almost the language of the inventor of the hypothesis—"all things continue as they were from the beginning" (verse 4).

It will be of interest to trace some steps preceding and following the establishment of the theory of uniformity, and to note parallel movements that offset its influence and its implications.

The Scottish geologist, James Hutton, who overthrew the Neptunist theory and replaced it with the Plutonist theory, declared in 1785, "We see no vestige of a beginning, no prospect of an end." For him the earth had no creation, neither did he foresee a catastrophic climax when "the heavens being on fire shall be dissolved." Hutton was accused of infidelity and atheism, but he blandly refuted the charge by disclaiming any statement about creation; he did not see one, and if there were one, it was at a time infinitely remote. Surely it was more than a coincidence that at this very time Bible students were preaching the time of the end, the very antithesis to "no prospect of an end."

A little later, in 1804, came an oft-quoted statement from the eloquent Thomas Chalmers, a noted Presbyterian theologian and scientist, which attempted to bridge the slowly widening gap between a literal interpretation of Genesis and a liberal reading. At a chemical lecture at St. Andrews he defended the science of geology and certain attacks made upon it by saying: "The writings of Moses do not fix the antiquity of the globe." This dictum has been a refuge for theologians, who, seeing the long eons required by geological speculation, have bowed to the new scientific authoritarianism and meekly allowed higher critics to extract whatever meaning they wish from the words of Scripture. Significantly, in this same year, 1804, came the founding of the British and Foreign Bible Society, which set as its goal the placing of the Word of God without note or comment in the hands of the people of all countries at a price each could afford. The undermining influence of liberalizing the Word of God was counteracted by the devoted action of a group who were determined to place this Word of Life within easy access to earth's millions.

The science of geology received probably its greatest impetus from the careful investigations of Sir Charles Lyell, who, setting out with the theory of uniformity in his mind, summarized his findings in his *Principles of Geology,* 1830-1833. The book was a best seller, plausibly written, and read even by ladies in their drawing rooms. It was this book which influenced Charles Darwin during his voyage around the world on the *Beagle.* A main thesis of this volume was to demand an enormous length of time in ages past in order to produce the present geological changes that were so manifestly slow and gradual. Again we find a counterbalance, this time on the North American continent, in the person of William Miller, who in 1831 began to preach the approaching end of the age and a cataclysmic destruction of the earth in a unique, nonuniformitarian catastrophe. Was it entirely by chance that in 1833 when uniformity was on the lips of the scientists that there should have occurred the most outstanding meteoric display of all time, a display that the Seventh-day Adventist Church, while recognizing other occasions when "the stars fell," has understandably marked as fulfilling the prophecy of Matthew 24:29?

Miller's prediction of our Lord's return in 1844 was to fail, but out of the chaos and disorder that followed this tremendous disappointment there arose a group of Sabbathkeeping Adventists, small in numbers, without financial resources, but with a dedicated program of proclaiming the good news of our Lord's soon return to "many peoples, and nations, and tongues, and kings" (Rev. 10:11). This same year—1844—marked the culmination of the work of Charles Darwin, for his theory of the origin of species by the processes of natural selection was then ready. He feared to publish it, however, because it was against the teachings of the church. Describing his feelings as akin to those of a person having committed a murder, he wrote to a friend, who counseled him to go slowly.

Darwin's book was ultimately published in 1859 and reviewed favorably by Thomas Henry Huxley, who undertook to defend the new hypothesis at the famous Oxford debate of 1860. The theologians were represented by the capable debater Bishop Samuel Wilberforce, who came confessedly to smash Darwin. But he proved to be a dismal failure, as a result of insufficient knowledge of science, of liberal interpretation of the Scriptures that ignores their evident meaning, and of descending to invective against his opponent. Thereafter theologians began to abdicate their faith in the literal Word of God, and for it, substituted faith in the inerrancy of the new god of science.

It was also in the year 1860 that the name Seventh-day Adventists was chosen. The phrase *Seventh-day* implies belief in creation, and the word *Adventist,* in the promise of Christ's return. The denominational name stands as a witness against all who scoff at the Bible account of creation at the beginning of the world, and at our Lord's promised return at the end of the world. The name envisions both a divine beginning and a divine end to earth's history, the exact opposite of Hutton's "no vestige of a beginning, no prospect of an end." Seventh-day Adventists "came to the kingdom for such a time," and are still here for the same purpose. Their very existence as a denomination testifies against the uniformity idea.

The fact that Seventh-day Adventists are opposed to evolution does not mean that they are opposed to science. They believe in scientific investigation and the careful collection of data. Further, they explain current biological and geological phenomena in terms of the Biblical creation and Flood—as a considered and reasonable alternative to the evolutionary concept.

REFERENCES

Clark, Harold W. 1940. Genes and Genesis. Pacific Press Pub. Assn., Mountain View, California, pp. 9-35.
Clark, Robert E. D. 1958. Darwin: before and after. Grand Rapids International Publications, Grand Rapids, Michigan. 192 pp.
Darwin, Charles. 1859. On the origin of species by means of natural selection. The New American Library of World Literature, Inc., New York. Reprint 1958. 524 pp.
————. 1860. The voyage of the Beagle. Doubleday & Company, Inc., Garden City, New York. Reprint 1962. 524 pp.
Draper, John William. 1875. History of the conflict between religion and science. D. Appleton and Co., New York. 373 pp.
Eiseley, Loren. 1958. Darwin's century. Doubleday & Company, Inc. Garden City, New York. 378 pp.
Glass, Bentley, Owsei Temkin, and William L. Straus, Jr. 1959. Forerunners of Darwin: 1745-1859. The Johns Hopkins Press, Baltimore. 471 pp.
Himmelfarb, Gertrude. 1959. Darwin and the Darwinian revolution. Doubleday & Company, Inc., Garden City, New York. 480 pp.
Irvine, William. 1956. Apes, angels, and victorians. Readers Union, Weidenfeld & Nicolson, London. 278 pp.
Locy, William A. 1953. Biology and its makers. Henry Holt and Co., New York. 477 pp.
Marsh, Frank L. 1950. Studies in creationism. Review and Herald Pub. Assn., Washington, D.C., pp. 7-112.
Moore, Ruth. 1961. Man, time, and fossils. Alfred A. Knopf, New York. 436 pp.
Nordenskiöld, Erik. 1928. The history of biology. Tudor Publishing Co., New York. 629 pp.
Osborn, Henry Fairfield. 1913. From the Greeks to Darwin. The Macmillan Co., New York. 259 pp.
Romanes, George John. 1892. Darwin, and after Darwin. The Open Court Pub. Co., Chicago. Vol. I, 460 pp.; Vol. II, 344 pp.
Taylor, Gordon Rattray. 1963. The science of life. McGraw-Hill Book Co., Inc., New York. 368 pp.
White, A. D. 1896. A history of the warfare of science with theology. Dover Publications, Inc., New York. Reprint 1960. Vol. I, 415 pp.; Vol. II, 474 pp.

CHAPTER THIRTY-FOUR

The Form of
Living Things

COMPARATIVE MORPHOLOGY or anatomy is, as the term implies, a comparison of the forms and structures of various plants and animals. In the late nineteenth century comparative morphology was, with embryology, considered the most productive avenue of approach to the study of evolution.

Comparative morphology has been thought most useful in showing phylogenetic (evolutionary) development. For instance, the flipper of the whale, the foreleg of the frog, the wing of a bird, the foreleg of a dog, and the arm and hand of man have basically the same structure and therefore are said to have the same common ancestry. Each has essentially the same bones, although in certain instances some are fused. Each limb bears adaptations enabling the organism to cope with its particular environment.

In addition, the presence of vestigial structures is used as evidence for dynamic evolution. For instance, it is known that whales and snakes exhibit what are thought to be traces of hind leg skeletal elements and musculature. Young hoatzins (a South American bird) are born with workable fingers and claws on featherless wings, which they use for moving about in the trees. In our own bodies vestigial structures have shrunk from the scores first listed by militant evolutionists to a few such as the vermiform appendix, muscles to move the ears, and caudal vertebrae. Creationists generally believe that living organisms have undergone some degeneration since their original creation. It would not be surprising, therefore, if some structures were actually degenerated and rudimentary (vestigial, if you please). This might be expected, and would be as good evidence for degeneration as for evolution. It is interesting to notice, however, that the great majority of the so-called vestigial organs have been shown to be necessary and functioning parts of the human body.

With the advent of the experimental sciences, proofs of a more quantitative nature were sought for evolution. Comparative morphology, a descriptive science, declined as the spearhead of evolution and was replaced by genetics. Evolutionists interpret the findings of comparative morphology as evidence of phylogenetic relationships, while special creationists feel they indicate creation by a God with a master plan. Comparative morphology is useful for showing the differences and similarities of animals and plants, and their possible taxonomic relationships, but it is not useful in determining phylogeny. It is significant that more recent publications on evolution are brief in their discussion of comparative morphology as it relates to evolution (Merrell, 1962; Dowdeswell, 1960; Savage, 1963).

Although many classic examples could be cited because the old literature on vertebrate comparative morphology (anatomy) is voluminous, only one more will be given. The number of cervical (neck) vertebrae in mammals is usually seven. These seven may differ considerably in size and shape, but the number of vertebrae is rather consistently seven. Giraffes, mice, elephants, and even porpoises have seven cervical vertebrae, but their necks may be long and slender as in the giraffe, or fused so that the head cannot be turned as in the porpoise. Although there are some exceptions, what does this general consistency of cervical vertebrae mean? More than one interpretation is possible from this type of circumstantial evidence. To the evolutionist it may show phylogenetic relationships; to a creationist it will show conservation of design and a plan in the mind of a

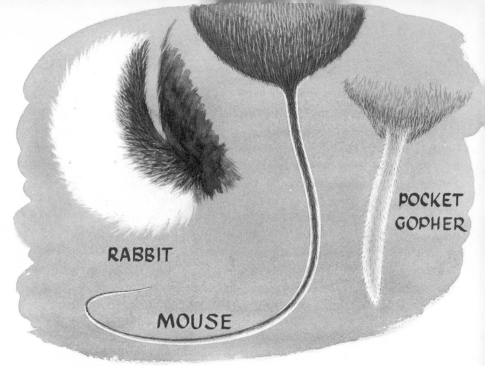

POCKET
GOPHER

RABBIT

MOUSE

Fig. 34.1 These mammals have different numbers of tail vertebrae.

Master Creator. Why have cervical vertebrae been used to illustrate phylogeny and not some of the other groups of vertebrae such as the lumbar (back), or caudal (tail) vertebrae? The reason is the variation in numbers of these vertebrae in different mammals. No good phylogenetic relationship could be shown by the use of these bones. Yet evolutionists do not seem to be concerned about this problem when they use the cervical vertebrae in support of evolution (Fig. 34.1).

Convergence

A problem for the theory of evolution is the presence of many examples of animals and plants from widely different taxa that cannot be said to have common ancestry, yet which show striking similarities in their morphology, physiology, and behavior. Convergent evolution, as this is called, supposes that organisms from widely different backgrounds develop similarities because they live in the same kind of environment and have had the same selective pressures influencing their heredity. This

410

may be partly true in some situations, but this explanation cannot apply to all cases. The phenomenon of bipolarity could possibly be explained by similar environment. For example, marine invertebrates living roughly equal distances north and south of the equator often have morphological similarities. Hermit crabs from the Puget Sound of Washington State are matched by hermit crabs approximately an equal distance from the equator along the coast of Chile. Presumably such factors as temperature, length of daylight, shelter, oxygen, and food supply are similar in the two areas, and the crabs have adapted themselves to the two separate environments with remarkably similar results.

In other types of convergent evolution no such environmental factors are in operation, and the evolutionist must find some other solution to the problem. The vertebrate and the cephalopod both have the same type of eye for instance, yet no one suggests that there is any phylogenetic relationship. Furthermore, the other classes of mollusks are not so well equipped. Neither are the arthropods and echinoderms which are considered higher on the evolutionary tree. Fish, toothless anteaters, and birds all have gizzards, but obviously no evolutionary significance can be attached to this fact. If evolution has been in operation, gizzards must have arisen independently in these animals. The gray mullet, *Mugil olivaceus,* and the herring, *Chatoessus nasus,* are in widely different families, but they have nearly identical gizzards. The evolutionist is forced to conclude that these two species evolved similar structures independently (Willey, 1911, pp. 109-112).

Convergence is also well illustrated by the social insects. Is it not remarkable that two different orders of insects such as the Isoptera (termites) and the Hymenoptera (bees, wasps, and ants) should develop a social order with similar morphological types? Both have workers, soldiers, kings, and queens. The separation of these insects by so large a taxonomic unit as an order precludes any possibility of there being a common relationship between the two. The evolutionist must explain this

411

by "converging evolution," though the chance of such a thing happening is fantastically remote.

Preadaptation

The modern concept of morphology is dynamic; that is, the structure of the animal is the result of adaptive pressures exerted by its environment. Morphology is therefore not static, but constantly changing as environments change and as pressures such as competition for food and scarcity of ecological niches are felt. Within certain limits this is undoubtedly a correct concept. Animals and plants do have the ability to adapt, and environments are changing. It stands to reason, therefore, that any morphological type may be only a transient step in the constant adaptation of organisms. But can this go indefinitely in any one direction? Is there no limit to the amount of change that can occur to an animal or plant in its constant struggle to adjust? The science of taxonomy both for living and fossil organisms replies to these questions with an emphatic No. If no limit to the amount of morphological change existed there would not now be the distinct discontinuities between kinds found in the world today and in the paleontological record.

Preadaptation is declared to be involved in the ability of animals to move into and populate a new environment. Undoubtedly this is a correct appraisal of some speciation that has occurred and is still occurring. Seals related to the Weddell seal have enlarged canine teeth. The Weddell seal has this feature most strongly developed. As a result, it can forage farther south under the Antarctic ice, where there are no natural breaks for breathing, by using its canines for cutting breathing holes in the ice (Davis, 1963, p. 83). Did the Weddell have a preadaptation of long canines that made it possible for the animal to move into what would normally be an unfavorable environment? This is entirely possible.

Briefly, other similar examples are the flying lizard (*Draco*) and the blind cave fish of Yucatan (Davis, 1963, pp. 84-85). Cave fish of the Yucatan Peninsula belong to four families and show varying degrees of loss of sight and eyes. Each has closely related forms outside of caves that have weakened vision and show nocturnal, burrowing, or crevice-seeking habits. It is logical to assume that the blind species in the caves may have been derived from these non-cave dwellers that were preadapted to existence in an unlighted environment.

Flying lizards (actually only able to glide) are able to flatten and laterally expand the thoracic ribs and supporting membrane. Other types of lizards are only able to flatten themselves against a branch while resting. The supposition is made that *Draco* may have evolved its present adaptation for gliding from a preadaptation of being able to mold itself to a branch. This type of reasoning is based more on circumstantial evidence than the other two examples just given, but it is not beyond acceptance by creationists if it should turn out to be correct. These are examples of relatively minor changes that do no more than support microevolution.

Preadaptation as an evolutionary mechanism has been derived from the study of the anatomy of related forms, and is one result of the modern approach to comparative anatomy. The idea of preadaptation has recently experienced some revival, as it has been combined with genetics to interpret mechanisms involved in microevolution.

Evolution of the Invertebrate Animals

In 1960 there appeared a little book by G. A. Kerkut entitled, *Implications of Evolution*. It is perhaps the most penetrating book on this topic to appear in print. Although the author is an evolutionist, he attempts to show that there is more than one way to interpret the evidence concerning the evolution of the invertebrate phyla. The reader is urged to refer directly to this work, as only a few statements can be included here. The evolutionary and phylogenetic affinities of organisms from the viruses to the Metazoa are critically analyzed.

After reviewing the evidence for the origin of the multicellular animals (Metazoa) he concludes as follows: "What conclusion then can be drawn concerning the possible relationship between the Protozoa and the Metazoa? The only thing that is certain is that at present we do not know this relationship. Almost every possible (as well as many impossible) relationship has been suggested, but the information available to us is insufficient to allow us to come to any scientific conclusion regarding the relationship. We can, if we like, *believe* that one or other of the various theories is the more correct but we have no real evidence" (Kerkut, 1960, p. 49).

After making this statement he deals with the question of simple and complex characteristics. Animals are categorized as "primitive" or "advanced," but the characteristics upon which these designations are based are quite subjective. The evolutionary bias of the investigator greatly influences what he considers to be "primitive" and what is "advanced." Kerkut (1960, pp. 55, 56) lists 11 simple or primitive characteristics of the sponges. Sponges are often classed among the most primitive of animals, intermediate between the Protozoa and the Metazoa. Many of their features, however, are not simple. The author himself then proceeds to list 11 characteristics that are not primitive, or are less primitive than phyla of animals such as the coelenterates and ctenophorans, which have usually been placed higher up on the phylogenetic scale. He summarizes the search for the most primitive metazoan with this pointed confession:

"What can one conclude about the most primitive of the Metazoa? There are, as we have seen, five contestants, Porifera, Mesozoa, Coelenterata, Ctenophora and the Platyhelminthia, for this title. These groups are almost completely isolated from each other though a few tenuous connexions can be made. It is quite clear that the available evidence is insufficient to allow us to come to any satisfactory conclusion regarding their interrelationships" (Kerkut, 1960, p. 99).

The book review by Bonner (1961) on *Implications of*

Evolution was almost as startling as the book itself. Only the first paragraph can be quoted here.

"This is a book with a disturbing message; it points to some unseemly cracks in the foundations. One is disturbed because what is said gives us the uneasy feeling that we knew it for a long time deep down but were never willing to admit this even to ourselves. It is another one of those cold and uncompromising situations where the naked truth and human nature travel in different directions."

REFERENCES

Bonner, J. T. 1961. Book review on *Implications of Evolution* by G. A. Kerkut. Am. Sci. 49 (2):240-244.

Colbert, Edwin H. 1961. Evolution of the vertebrates. John Wiley & Sons., Inc., New York. 479 pp.

Davis, D. Dwight. 1963. Comparative anatomy and the evolution of vertebrates. *In* Genetics, paleontology, and evolution. Glenn L. Jepson, George G. Simpson, and Ernst Mayr (eds.). Atheneum, New York, pp. 64-89.

Dowdeswell, W. H. 1960. The mechanism of evolution. Harper & Brothers, New York. 115 pp.

Downs, Lloyd E. 1945. Evolution or creation. Published by the author. La Sierra College, Arlington, California. 96 pp.

Kelly, Peter. 1962. Evolution and its implications. The Scientific Book Club, London, pp. 52-58.

Kerkut, G. A. 1960. Implications of evolution. Pergamon Press, New York. 174 pp.

Klotz, John W. 1955. Genes, genesis, and evolution. Concordia Pub. House, St. Louis, Missouri. 575 pp.

Marsh, Frank L. 1944. Evolution, creation, and science. Review and Herald Pub. Assn., Washington, D.C., pp. 181-200.

Merrell, David J. 1962. Evolution and genetics. Holt, Rinehart and Winston, Inc., New York. 420 pp.

Nelson, Byron C. 1952. After its kind. Augsburg Pub. House, Minneapolis, Minnesota, pp. 18-32.

Olson, Everett C. 1960. Morphology, paleontology and evolution. *In* The evolution of life. Sol Tax (ed.). Univ. of Chicago Press, pp. 523-546.

Savage, Jay M. 1963. Evolution. Holt, Rinehart and Winston, Inc., New York. 126 pp.

von Frisch, Karl. 1950. Bees: their vision, chemical senses, and language. Cornell Univ. Press, Ithaca, New York. 119 pp., 61 figs.

Willey, Arthur. 1911. Convergence in evolution. E. P. Dutton and Co., New York.

CHAPTER THIRTY-FIVE

Like Begets Like

THE IMPACT made on the educated world by the appearance of Darwin's *Origin of Species* was profound. It seemed to be the key that would completely open the door to the acceptance of evolution. With the wide acclaim given the book, it was to be expected that a veritable flood of opposition from the clergy and other religiously oriented persons should be poured upon the book and its author. Darwin was naturally a rather retiring person who had no heart to be at the forefront of the battle. He retreated into his studies, and others of a more aggressive nature took up the fight for him. One of the most vociferous and effective was Ernst Haeckel, who championed the cause of Darwin and evolution so persistently and tenaciously that he became known as Darwin's bulldog.

Biogenetic Law

Recently I picked up Haeckel's four volumes on *The History of Creation* and *The Evolution of Man* and thumbed through them. A tremendous amount of convincing material is marshaled together here. To a reader of the times these volumes must have seemed to contain most telling arguments for evolution. Now, after more than three quarters of a century, even an evolutionist looks at these volumes from a vastly different perspective. Yet it is saddening to think of the great numbers who probably lost their faith in Holy Scripture as a result of Haeckel's forceful presentation. This sadness is not lessened by the realization that these persons lost their way because of arguments most of which are now recognized as unfounded and erroneous—based as they were on insufficient data and false premises.

On page 418 are illustrations of embryos of man, rabbit, calf, hog, chick, tortoise, salamander, and fish shown in several stages of development (Fig. 35.1). Their resemblances, especially in the early stages, are remarkable. Perhaps no other picture has been reproduced more often, or has exerted more influence for evolution than this one. Haeckel is probably best known today as the author of the theory called the biogenetic law, but which is better known as recapitulation. Briefly, this concept envisioned that the past evolutionary history of an animal was condensed into the animal's short embryonic development. The phrase "ontogeny recapitulates phylogeny" was thrown around for many years with obvious relish by proponents of progressive evolution. It means that the development of an animal from conception to adulthood (ontogeny) goes back over (recapitulates) its evolutionary history (phylogeny).

The resemblance of embryos of various animals in early stages had been noticed by Von Baer, Louis Agassiz, Fritz Müller, and other pioneer embryologists, some of whom remarked pointedly about it. But it was left to Haeckel to make the most sweeping applications that have had a profound effect on subsequent biological investigations, especially in embryology. It must stand as one of the most persistent and hard-dying theories of modern times, because for 30 or more years now it has been under serious attack by geneticists and embryologists themselves, who have presented devastating evidence of its fallacious character. It has been used in elementary biology and zoology textbooks until recent years as an evidence of evolution. This intriguing theory appears so convincing to the uninitiated that there has been widespread reluctance to give it up.

In brief, Haeckel's biogenetic law was supported by such observations as these: The embryo begins life as a one-celled organism reminiscent of the beginning of life on the earth. Later it becomes a hollow ball of cells, which Haeckel said illustrates

27 417

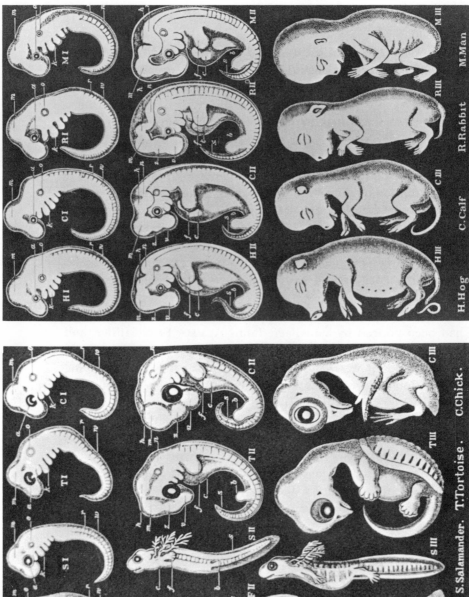

F.Fish.   S.Salamander.   T.Tortoise.   C.Chick.

H.Hog   C.Calf   R.Rabbit   M.Man

Fig. 25.1 Ernst Haeckel's illustration supporting his recapitulation concept.

that step in evolutionary history when the highest form of life was a similar ball of cells that lived in the primordial seas. He named this hypothetical creature a blastea. When the ball of cells of the embryo folded inward (the usual next step in embryology of many animals), to become thimble-shaped, he compared it to the jellyfish and anemones of today. In reptiles, birds, and mammals the embryo develops within fluid held in by membranes. This is also cited as illustrating the aquatic stage in evolutionary history.

The caterpillar larva was presumed to represent the annelid worm stage in insect evolution, the frog tadpole the fish stage in frog evolution, and the "gill slits" the fish stage in human evolution. This term "gill slits" is a hangover expression from the time of feverish but biased research in embryology that for years followed Haeckel's elaboration of the recapitulation theory and that has become permanently incorporated into embryological terminology. The kidneys, heart, and other organs of vertebrates were said to pass through stages that mirrored their supposed evolutionary progress.

The extent to which this concept pervaded the biological thinking of the times is graphically shown in these quotations taken at random from several old books on evolution and biology.

"The embryologist joins in and shows how the individual development reads like a condensed recapitulation of presumed racial evolution, how the past lives on in the present, how circuitousness in the individual becoming may receive historical interpretation—how, in short, in a general way, the individual animal climbs up its own genealogical tree" (Thomson, 1925, p. 80).

"Out of such considerations as these [a previous discussion of embryology] has come one of the most important and far-reaching laws that the biologists have ever stated. It is as follows: 'Each individual animal, in passing from the egg to the adult, repeats in an abbreviated way, in a few days or years,

419

many of the steps taken by the race to which it belongs, in its evolution from its single-celled ancestors to its present condition.' Put briefly, it reads: *Individual history is a brief* recapitulation of race history" (Galloway & Welch, 1922, p. 490; italics original).

"Embryonic development is a brief and condensed repetition of a series of ancestral stages through which the race has passed" (Haupt, 1940, p. 345).

The Theory Doomed

As early as the turn of the century cracks in this striking edifice began to develop. August Weismann's theory that inheritance comes about through the germ plasm, that is, through the reproductive cells, and that any modification of the adult must first be contained in the germ plasm, suggested that evolution was not an adding, step by step, of new stages onto the old. Modifications occurred in the embryological processes, as well as in the adult morphology. With the rise of the science of genetics, the incorrectness of the biogenetic law became more and more apparent. Thomas H. Morgan, a pioneer in genetics who popularized the use of the *Drosophila* fruitfly for research in genetics, ventured to say back in 1916: "Actual experience with discontinuous variation has taught us that new characters that arise do not add themselves to the end of the line of already existing characters but if they affect the adult characters they change them without, as it were, passing through and beyond them. I venture to think that these new ideas and this new evidence have played havoc with the biogenetic 'law' " (Morgan, 1916, p. 18).

The reasons for discarding recapitulation as a valid support for the theory of evolution, as given by several authors, are here summarized (Weisz, 1963; Shumway, 1932; Courville, 1942; Nelsen, 1953; Ballard, 1964):

1. New types are not formed by the addition of new steps onto the end of the embryological development of an existing

species. This point has been emphasized above. That the developing human heart successively passed through a two-chambered fishlike heart and a three-chambered reptilelike heart before assuming the four-chambered mammalian heart was widely acclaimed. Note what Ballard (1964, p. 509) says:

"No false biological statement has had a longer or more popular life than the one about the ontogeny of the four-chambered mammalian heart recapitulating its phylogeny from the two-chambered fish heart and the three-chambered amphibian or reptilian heart. Often repeated in the days when Haeckel's so-called biogenetic law was widely and uncritically accepted, it can still be found in some elementary texts, side-by-side with correctly labelled diagrams of the four-chambered fish heart and the five-chambered frog heart."

2. The embryos of different animals are not as much alike as suggested. Haeckel has been accused of schematizing the embryo series both figuratively in his writings and literally in the drawings. The blastula consists of a hollow ball of cells in some organisms, but in many others it is solid or has an entirely different form. The gastrula does arise by invagination in some animals such as the starfish, but most animals produce the gastrula by other processes. "Similarly, the embryos of fish and of man actually resemble each other only in very general, superficial ways. Even the eggs exhibit specific differences unique to the species, and these differences become progressively more pronounced as development proceeds" (Weisz, 1963, p. 733).

3. There is no reason at all why heredity traits should reveal themselves in the same order during embryonic development as they were acquired during their supposed evolutionary history.

4. Experimental embryology has shown that in the development of organs and tissues, cells may be derived from several sources. Furthermore, chemical organizers control the rate and type of cells produced. These organizers, in turn, are produced under the direction of genes inherited through the egg and

sperm. In other words, not only the morphological characteristics of the adult are inherited but even the mechanism by which they are expressed. This is incompatible with the recapitulation theory.

5. Many features are found in embryos that do not fit into the supposed picture of evolutionary development. For instance, what stage in evolutionary history corresponds to that stage of the fish when it has a large yolk sac attached to its abdomen? Why are certain steps completely omitted, as in certain tree-dwelling frogs and land salamanders that have no larval stages? Examples such as these where there are additions, omissions, or falsifications of the supposed ancestral record are extremely numerous.

Despite the problems with the biogenetic law that have shown up because of the rise of the science of genetics and continued research in embryology, current volumes, especially textbooks, still continue to cling to the theory. Textbooks are usually several years behind the leading edge of research, but in this case the reluctance to cast aside the old is especially noticeable. Note the following statements taken from two well-known textbooks of zoology and biology:

"This existence, in the life cycles of complex forms, of developmental stages which resemble those of much simpler animals is considered significant in evolutionary interpretation and is the basis of the so-called Recapitulation Theory. This states, in essence, that in its own developmental sequence each individual organism exhibits transitory stages which represent stages in the evolutionary history of the group to which it belongs. . . . Each individual in its development more or less repeats, in abbreviated form, the long history of evolution of its ancestry" (Guthrie & Anderson, 1957, pp. 225, 429).

"This parallelism between the fossil record [considered to be a record of the evolutionary process] and the regular growth processes in a developing egg is too detailed to be ignored. The obvious inference from embryology is that the seeming inefficiencies and indirections correspond to part-way stages in the history of life on the earth. The embryo retreads much of that historic path—even taking detours that are no longer needed" (Milne & Milne, 1958, p. 424).

Although the recapitulation theory is slowly (too slowly!) dying out, embryology is still used as an area of evidence for evolution. The development of the embryo may not trace its past evolutionary history, but may reveal its more immediate ancestral affinities. *The Science of Biology* by Paul Weisz (1963), although saturated with evolution, is one of the few elementary textbooks in biology or zoology that clearly states the truth concerning Haeckel's biogenetic law. He gives the place of embryology in the interpretation of evolution as follows: "In short, if the development of an egg repeats anything, it merely repeats the development of previous generations of its own species, not the evolutionary development of other animals. . . . It is quite natural that related animals descended from a common ancestor should resemble one another in some of their adult as well as some of their embryonic features. Such resemblances may or may not be pronounced, depending entirely on how widely the evolutionary paths have diverged" (pp. 733, 734).

Those who do not accept the theory of progressive evolution may interpret the general similarities of morphology and function in developing embryos of different kinds in the same way that Nelsen (1953, p. 351) did. Here is his apt way of expressing it: "Nature does not build ten tracks to send ten trains with different destinies out of a station when she can use one track for all for at least part of the way." I would like to call this method in God's operation, "conservation of plan." God did not devise different developmental processes for all the different animals when one plan was suitable for most of them for at least part of their growth.

REFERENCES

Ballard, William W. 1964. Comparative anatomy and embryology. The Ronald Press Company, New York.

Courville, C. B. 1942. The causal significance of 'parallelism': an inquiry into certain fundamental principles of embryonic development. Bull. Deluge Geology and Related Sci. 2 (1):1-35.

Galloway, Thomas Walton and Paul S. Welch. 1922. Zoology. P. Blakiston's Company, Inc., New York.

Guthrie, Mary J. and John M. Anderson. 1957. General zoology. John Wiley & Sons, Inc., New York.

Haeckel, Ernst. 1899. The evolution of man. Vols. I and II. D. Appleton and Company, New York.

———. 1899. The history of creation. Vols. I and II. Kegan Paul, Trench, Trübner & Co., Ltd., London.

Haupt, Arthur W. 1940. Fundamentals of biology. McGraw-Hill Book Company, Inc., New York.

Milne, Lorus J. and Margery J. Milne. 1958. The biotic world and man. Prentice-Hall, Inc., Englewood Cliffs, New Jersey.

Morgan, Thomas Hunt. 1916. A critique of the theory of evolution. Princeton Univ. Press, Princeton.

Nelsen, Olin E. 1953. Comparative embryology of the vertebrates. The Blakiston Company, Inc., New York.

Nelson, Byron C. 1952. After its kind. Augsburg Publishing House, Minneapolis, Minnesota, pp. 33-41.

Shumway, Waldo. 1932. The recapitulation theory. Quart. Rev. Bio. 7:93-99.

Thomson, J. Arthur. 1925. Concerning evolution. Yale Univ. Press, New Haven.

Weisz, Paul B. 1963. The science of biology. 2d ed. McGraw-Hill Book Company, Inc., New York.

CHAPTER THIRTY-SIX

The Physiology and Chemistry of Life

PHYSIOLOGICAL OR BIOCHEMICAL EVOLUTION has gained prominence in recent years. A large and impressive literature is developing, but it will be possible to examine only a few representative examples of the kind of data currently being taken from these fields to support the theory of evolution.

It is not easy to separate physiological evolution from biochemical evolution, and perhaps there is no need to do so. Some of the examples used here could also be listed under the section on biochemistry.

Much use has been made of functional similarities or contrasts to trace possible evolutionary relationships of animals. This physiological evolution is merely a new approach, replacing in part the outdated recapitulation theory (see chapter 35, "Like Begets Like"). In this recent area of investigation the levels of comparison range from such general topics as digestion, excretion, and respiration to such specifics as essential vitamin needs, forms of excretory nitrogen, and respiration abilities.

The following two examples from Storer (1951, p. 209) illustrate how physiological evolution is treated in textbooks: (1) Some of the hormones from the endocrine glands, such as thyroxin, are similar in widely different animals. A thyroid deficiency in one type of animal may be relieved by feeding thyroid or injecting thyroxin from another type of animal. This is true from frogs to man. (2) Many of the digestive enzymes present in different animals are essentially alike in their physiological action. For example, the enzyme trypsin, which acts on proteins, occurs in many animals from protozoans to man, and amylase, which acts on starch, is present from sponges to mammals. It is implied that these widespread occurrences of hormones and enzymes in the animal kingdom indicate common origins or a continuous evolutionary progression for animals. Downs (1945, p. 16) comments as follows: "Since all animals live in the same world, eat similar food, breathe the same air, are composed of the same substance—protoplasm, and carry on the same life functions, it is to be expected that the same hormones and enzymes should function in widely different animals. Why should the Creator be asked to create a new enzyme and a new hormone for each separate function of each species of animal?"

The chicken embryo first excretes ammonia, then urea, and finally uric acid as an adult. Lower animals such as the frog excrete waste nitrogen in various forms, from ammonia through urea, and finally as uric acid. Since ammonia is the form usually excreted by aquatic animals, urea by land animals, and uric acid by birds, the conclusion was drawn that the chick embryo was recapitulating or retracing its evolutionary history in development from some sort of aquatic animal through some land form to the final form and function of the bird.

A closer look into the sources of these excretory products in birds reveals that they are functional changes rather than recapitulation of evolutionary history. The amount of ammonia is small, and does not increase as the embryo grows. Uric acid is formed from the fifth day, and continues as the excretory product throughout life. Urea is from yolk breakdown, and not from the kidney. The kidney excretes only uric acid, the excretory product of an adult bird (Prosser and Brown, 1961, p. 145).

Essential nutrients and vitamins required by many different types of animals have been studied, and various conclusions based on the comparisons have been made. Comparisons of this sort are looked to as a new source of evidence in support of evolutionary development, but the physiological and biochemical evidence is often very weak and ambiguous (see Spector, 1956, p. 199).

Do these requirements prove that all these animal forms evolved from a common ancestor, or are they evidence for a theory of origins that relates all creatures to a common Creator? The answer to this question obviously depends on the reader's preconceptions.

The Creator has used many physiological and biochemical functions in a wide variety of animals. There is little reason to question this situation. If the same function can be used in many different animals why should different means be used? To use several different methods for accomplishing the same purpose would perhaps indicate lack of planning and lack of conservation of design and function. The nervous systems of animals, although very different in organization and structure from animal to animal, are similar regarding the mechanisms for the conduction of nerve impulses and the substances used for bridging the gaps between nerves and between nerves and tissues. Muscle tissue is similar in many different animals, at least in the vertebrates. The energy sources utilized by muscles are also similar through a widely scattered assortment of vertebrates and invertebrates (see section concerning phosphagens). Again it must be said that these points can be made to appear to support evolution only if a person has already chosen to believe evolution.

The process of osmosis is of vital importance to all living organisms. Salt-water bony fishes have blood of less density than the water surrounding them. It is therefore necessary for them to prevent desiccation by taking in large quantities of sea water. The water and salt are both absorbed, but the salt, which is in greater concentration in the sea water than in the blood, is excreted from the body by special cells located in the gills of the fish. The urine that is excreted is isotonic, that is, of the same concentration as the blood.

Fresh-water fishes, on the other hand, live in an environment of much less density than the protoplasm or blood of the animal.

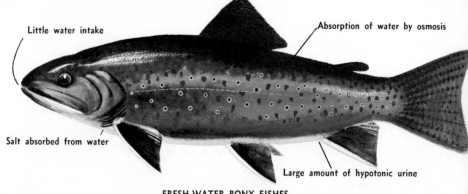

Little water intake

Absorption of water by osmosis

Salt absorbed from water

Large amount of hypotonic urine

FRESH-WATER BONY FISHES

Fig. 36.1 The processes of osmosis and excretion in fresh- and salt-water fishes.

Osmosis is constantly bringing water into the body, and this must be removed. These fish excrete large quantities of hypotonic urine, or urine that is less concentrated than the blood. In excreting large amounts of urine there is danger of loss of salts from the body. This problem is solved by special cells also located in the gills that absorb salt from sea water (Fig. 36.1).

Some interpretations of evolutionary significance have been based on these facts. Since sea water is much nearer the density of protoplasm and blood, it is thought that life originated and developed for some time in the sea. The fishes, however, are said to have developed in fresh water because of the presence of filtering units or renal corpuscles in the kidneys. Such structures would hardly have been necessary in the seas, because the problem there is not that of filtering water from the blood but rather of removing the salt and retaining the water. The presence of a few renal corpuscles in the marine fishes is pointed to as a carry-over from their past fresh-water existence.

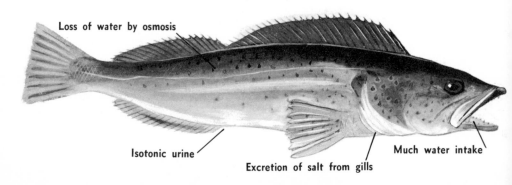

Loss of water by osmosis

Isotonic urine

Excretion of salt from gills

Much water intake

SALT-WATER BONY FISHES

Sharks are also well supplied with filtering units in the kidneys, in contrast to the marine fishes. In addition, enough urea is retained in the blood to bring its concentration to somewhat above that of sea water. The few cases where elasmobranchs (sharks and related fishes) have been found in fresh water are thought to represent a situation where these fishes have moved to a fresh-water environment in more recent times. The urea retained in the blood of these creatures is considerably less than is retained by those in the sea; nevertheless, the density of the blood of these sharks is greater than that of the bony fishes that live in the same environment and that have about the same salt concentration in the blood but do not have the urea. The urine excreted by these sharks is more hypotonic and in greater quantity than the urine of their bony associates.

The theory that some sharks caught in fresh water in more recent times have adapted to it is probably correct, since the few cases known are in large lakes that in some instances are rather clearly shown to have become isolated from the sea in post-Pleistocene times. Other supposition regarding the origin of fishes because of the structure of their kidneys is just that—supposition. A creationist sees in this situation other examples of the design of God, fitting and adapting each creature for its habitat. He has, however, given His creatures a certain amount of latitude for variation and adaptation, so that the organisms may be able to adjust to changing environments. This adaptability is seen in the land-locked sharks.

Immunology

Immunological techniques have been employed from time to time for testing the relationships that exist between the serum proteins of a wide variety of species of animals. When a foreign substance is introduced into the body of an animal, a rabbit, let us say, the rabbit will build up quantities of antibodies against this undesirable invading substance. If the foreign substance is introduced again it will be met by the previously produced antibodies in what is called an antigen-antibody reaction. The rabbit's blood may be drawn into a test tube, and the antigen-antibody reaction can be examined under quantitative conditions.

If rabbit serum containing antihuman antibodies is mixed with chimpanzee serum, a reaction will occur, and the reaction will be more violent than that obtained with the serum of other animals because the serum of the chimpanzee is more like that of human serum. Therefore, the rabbit antihuman antibodies reacted with it almost as they would react with human serum, against which the antibodies were originally produced. The measure of relationship between animals is therefore considered to be determined by the strength of the reaction—the stronger the reaction the closer the relationship, the weaker the reaction the more distant the affinities.

"Some of the earliest studies were conducted by Nuttall. Perhaps the most exciting at the time was the discovery that rabbit serum containing antihuman antibodies reacted almost as strongly with chimpanzee serum as it did with human serum; somewhat less strongly with sera from the other apes; still less with monkey sera; only slightly with carnivore and ungulate sera; and essentially not at all with insectivore, rodent, and marsupial sera" (Merrell, 1962, p. 111).

Results such as these are about what would be expected merely by looking at the animals. Their similarities and dis-similarities to man are apparent. This technique becomes more useful, however, in attempting to determine the affinities of animals with morphological features intermediate or obscure as compared to other animals. The results of this type of testing have shown that the dog and coyote are more closely related to each other than either is to the wolf, and the musk ox turns out to be more of a goat than a cow. Zoologists have pondered over the giant panda. Does it belong to the bear family or to the raccoon family? The serum protein test indicates that it is more closely related to the bear.

Attempts are not only being made to use the serum proteins

as a means of solving some of the existing classification problems, but the technique is also being employed in an endeavor to show phylogenetic relationships in support of evolution. This type of blood testing can be of value to science, but a good deal of caution should be exercised in using the results to indicate phylogenetic relationships. The precipitin reaction that results from this testing is not absolutely specific, and for this reason the cross reaction that occurs does not require the presence of molecules identical with the serum protein molecules.

"It could hardly be maintained that an ostrich and a parrot are more nearly allied than a wolf and a hyena and yet that would be the inference from the blood tests" (Scott, 1917, p. 80). Other results show that some men are more closely related to certain monkeys than to other men, and the closest relation to the whales is the bat (Nuttall, 1904)! Thus it seems obvious that the serum protein tests cannot stand as accurate indices to the phylogenetic relationships of animals in different major taxonomic units, but merely stand along with morphology, physiology, biochemistry, and embryology as indicators of basic differences and similarities originally molded into living organisms by the Creator. It may be useful in determining relationships, or helping with the classification of closely related animals that perhaps are the product of microevolution.

Biochemistry

Two examples will be given of the type of information being used in support of biochemical evolution. There are two main types of photosensitive pigments in vertebrate eyes. These are known as rhodopsin and porphyropsin, which differ but slightly in molecular composition.

Vitamin A, which is derived from orange carotenoid pigments in plants, is involved in the chemical structure of these pigments. In the human eye, rhodopsin is photosensitive, and upon the stimulus of light it breaks down into several transitory substances including vitamin A. This breakdown of rhodopsin excites the receptors in the retina, which pass the stimulus along the optic nerve to the brain, where it is interpreted as a visual image. Rhodopsin is constantly being reconstituted, which makes continuous vision possible. When a person steps into a dark room he may have to wait a few moments for his eyes to adapt to the dark. This is because he must wait for a greater amount of rhodopsin to be built up in the eyes so that they will be sufficiently sensitive to perceive the small amount of light in the room.

Rhodopsin is found in the eyes of marine and land vertebrates, also in the eyes of crustaceans and in the squid. Porphyropsin, on the other hand, occurs in the eyes of fresh-water fishes including the lampreys, which are considered primitive living vertebrates. This fact has also been used to support the theory that fishes first arose in fresh water. A shift from porphyropsin to rhodopsin is postulated for fishes when they invaded the salt water or the land. Salmon and eels, which spend time in both fresh and salt water, have both types of pigments, although the pigment associated with the environment in which they hatched predominates—porphyropsin for the salmon and rhodopsin for the eel.

This type of reasoning is based on extremely circumstantial evidence and an a priori acceptance of evolution. As a matter of fact, several problems confront the evolutionist in this situation. Salt-water and fresh-water fishes are often very similar. Different species in the same genus may occupy both fresh water and salt water, and therefore have different visual pigments. Obviously such a situation is useless in showing phylogenetic distinctions. It is also noteworthy that animals such as a frog, which goes through a metamorphosis from fresh water to land during the course of its development, change from the use of porphyropsin to rhodopsin. This is no evolutionary change, but a direct adjustment to its way of life under the control of heredity.

There are exceptions to the rule, which may become more general as the pigments of more fishes are examined. The wrasse fishes of the family Labridae are exclusively marine, but have only porphyropsin (Merrell, 1962, p. 109). In time, visual pigments may turn out similar to the example next given below —entirely worthless as indicators of evolutionary history.

Phosphagens

Baldwin (1937, p. 70) gives the following table, which has been presented in many biology classrooms. It also appears in the older editions of Prosser's *Comparative Animal Physiology,* as well as in other works.

Phylum and Class	Arginine phosphate	Creatine phosphate
Platyhelminthia	+	----
Annelida	+	----
Arthropoda	+	----
Mollusca		
Lamellibranchiata	+	----
Cephalopoda	+	----
Echinodermata		
Asteroidea	+	----
Holothuroidea	+	----
Echinoidea	+	+
Protochordata		
Tunicata	+	----
Enteropneusta	+	+
Cephalochorda	----	+
Vertebrata	----	+

It is pointed out that as a general rule invertebrates do not have creatine phosphate (CP), and vertebrates do not have arginine phosphate (AP). Both of these substances are energy reserves for muscle contraction. When the muscles are involved in the expenditure of energy, these two phosphagens help re-

Fig. 36.2 Sea urchins contain creatine phosphate, but this fact has no phylogenetic significance.

store ADP (adenosine diphosphate) to ATP (adenosine triphosphate), which is the immediate source of energy for the muscle.

There are some exceptions to the statement above concerning the presence or absence of these substances in invertebrates and vertebrates. It will be noticed that one of the classes (Echinoidea, or sea urchins) of the phylum Echinodermata does contain creatine phosphate (Fig. 36.2). Notice also that the nonvertebrate members of the phylum Chordata (called Protochordata here) have one or the other or both phosphagens. There has been considerable question through the years regarding the invertebrate phylum from which the vertebrates presumably arose. Advocates of the echinoderm origin of vertebrates considered the above information good evidence that they arose from the echinoderms and protochordates. It is obvious that to one inclined to believe in evolution this would appear to be another link in the chain of circumstantial evidences for evolutionary progression.

This example has been rather widely published and used, an unfortunate fact in the light of more recent research, which shows that not only Echinoidea and the Protochordata contained CP but also species in the phyla Mollusca and Annelida. The authors either considered their findings in error or thought the amounts too insignificant to consider. Since that time several investigators have looked into the phosphagens in invertebrates. Using refined techniques, they have shown that creatine phosphate is present in several invertebrate phyla not suspected previously. Furthermore, two new phosphagens, taurocyamine phosphate and glycocyamine phosphate, have been discovered, and these were apparently mistaken for AP in some of the annelids that were shown to have TP, GP, and CP, but no AP at all! The table given earlier would now be amended to read as follows:

Phylum	AP	CP	Other phosphagens
Protozoa	+		+
Sponges	+	+	+
Coelenterata	+	+	+
Platyhelminthia	+		
Nemertina	+		
Nematoda	+		
Annelida	+	+	+
Arthropoda	+		
Mollusca	+	+	
Echinodermata	+	+	
Protochordata	+	+	
Vertebrata		+	

(Kerkut, 1960, p. 129)

In light of this development the following quotation from Kerkut (1960, pp. 127, 128) is well taken: "What conclusion can be drawn with regard to the distribution of phosphagens in the animal kingdom? The first conclusion is that there is certainly no simple cleavage of the animal kingdom into vertebrates with CP and invertebrates with AP. Instead it is clear that both CP and AP are found throughout the invertebrates. The second conclusion is that one cannot base any phylogenetic speculation on the occurrence of CP or AP since related genera within a class can differ widely in their phosphagens. The third conclusion is that it is highly probable that other phosphagens in addition to the recently discovered GP and TP will be found to play a role in tissue metabolism."

Another quotation from the review by James Bonner (1961) of Kerkut's book *Implications of Evolution* will perhaps be a fitting conclusion to this topic: "What we have all accepted as the whole truth, turns out with some mild inspection, to be rather far from it. Apparently, if one reads the original papers instead of relying on some superficial remarks in a textbook, the affinities become extremely clouded indeed. We have all been telling our students for years not to accept any statement on its face value but to examine the evidence, and, therefore, it is rather a shock to discover we have failed to follow our own sound advice."

REFERENCES

Baldwin, E. 1940. An introduction to comparative biochemistry. Cambridge Univ. Press, New York. 112 pp.

Bonner, John T. 1961. Book review on *Implications of evolution* by G. A. Kerkut. Am. Sci. 49 (2):240-244.

Downs, Lloyd E. 1945. Evolution or creation. Pub. by the author. La Sierra College, Arlington, California. 96 pp.

Kerkut, G. A. 1960. Implications of evolution. Pergamon Press, New York. 174 pp.

Merrell, David J. 1962. Evolution and genetics. Holt, Rinehart and Winston, New York. 420 pp.

Nuttall, G. H. F. 1904. Blood immunity and blood relationship. Cambridge Univ. Press, New York.

Prosser, C. Ladd. 1950. Comparative animal physiology. W. B. Saunders, Philadelphia.

Prosser, C. Ladd and Frank A. Brown. 1961. Comparative animal physiology. W. B. Saunders, Philadelphia. 688 pp.

Scott, Berryman William. 1917. The theory of evolution. The Macmillan Co., New York. 183 pp.

Spector, William S. (ed.). 1956. Handbook of biological data. W. B. Saunders Co., Philadelphia.

Storer, Tracy I. and Robert L. Usinger. 1957. General zoology. McGraw-Hill Book Co., Inc., New York.

CHAPTER THIRTY-SEVEN

The Testimony
of the Fossils

PRECEDING CHAPTERS IN THIS SECTION show that most of the evidence used for the support of evolution from the areas of experimental and descriptive biology are facts and interpretations that have little significance and carry little weight except for a person who already believes in evolution. The rest of the evidence falls in the category of microevolution, which is not out of harmony with the creation interpretation. This chapter on paleontology looks briefly at the past, to determine whether the fossil record supports macroevolution, the point where evolutionists and creationists disagree.

Fossils and their bearing on evolution are discussed elsewhere in this book. The reader is referred especially to chapter 16, "Fossils and the Flood," and Section IV, "The Fossils." Inasmuch as this aspect has already been presented, in relation to specific problems, it is not necessary to undertake a lengthy consideration here. The absence of major missing links in the fossil record, and of evidence from living organisms that large changes are presently occurring, pose problems of great difficulty for those who believe in evolutionary progression from a simple organism to the overwhelming complexity of man. These are among evolution's weakest points.

Perhaps the best way to emphasize this situation is to use several statements from well-known paleontologists. In 1930 A. H. Clark, a noted invertebrate zoologist and paleontologist, wrote the book *The New Evolution: Zoogenesis*. Aware of the absence of connecting links, he felt compelled to attempt to explain this situation by introducing a new theory of evolutionary development. He proposed that some type of explosive evolution developed the major categories of animals and plants back in the Cambrian period or earlier, and that they have remained essentially unchanged since. The whole volume is well worth reading. The following statement is indicative of many others scattered throughout the work:

"When we examine a series of fossils of any age we may pick out one and say with confidence, 'This is a crustacean'—or starfish, or a brachiopod, or annelid, or any other type of creature as the case may be. . . .

"Since all the fossils are determinable as members of their respective groups by the application of definitions of those groups drawn up from and based entirely on living types, and since none of these definitions of the phyla or major groups of animals need be in any way altered or expanded to include the fossils, it naturally follows that throughout the fossil record these major groups have remained essentially unchanged. This means that the interrelationships between them likewise have remained unchanged" (Clark, 1930, p. 100).

His theory sounds so much like special creation of all animals and plants at one time in the past that he hastens to explain that this is not what he is proposing. He does not attempt to suggest a cause for a supposed explosive evolution in the past. He is simply attempting to account for the discontinuity that exists between organisms throughout the record, and this is honorable. But how simply this problem could be settled by belief in a Creator who established the major kinds of organisms at creation!

It should be disconcerting to evolutionists to find so few of what they call ancestral types. A search of paleontological literature for these, whether plants or animals, repeatedly turns up admissions by the authors that ancestors are unknown. Very frequently the oldest known fossil representatives of a plant or animal group are remarkably like the living examples seen today.

Note these statements selected at random from several paleontology books. Speaking of liverworts and mosses respectively, Andrews (1961, pp. 398, 401) says: "The oldest authentic liverwort is *Hepaticites kidstoni* Walton from the Yorkian series of the Upper Carboniferous of Shropshire, England. Although its exact affinities are not known it is remarkably similar to some of the modern leafy liverworts and indicates that the group had already enjoyed a long period of evolution."

"The spore-bearing organs of these Permian mosses have not been found, so that more precise comparisons with living forms are not possible. Their importance lies in the fact that they are well preserved, they are unquestionably mosses, and sufficiently similar to modern ones in their vegetative organization as to suggest no major changes in moss evolution since that time."

Darrah (1960, p. 39) comes to a similar conclusion regarding the liverworts. "No fossil representative thus far recognized suggests that ancient bryophytes were very different from living forms."

Beerbower (1960, pp. 424, 467, 469, and 472) has perhaps been more frank than most authors of elementary paleontology textbooks. "All are distinct at their first appearance" (reference is to crinoid echinoderms).

"On the other hand, they [vertebrates] are pretty well diversified on this first appearance."

"Unfortunately most of the connecting forms [fishes] are still listed among the 'missing links.' "

"These two, the sharks and the bony fishes, were distinct at their first appearance in the fossil record."

Statements such as this are tacit admissions of the same fact: "Although Cambrian life was unlike that of the present, it was not as totally primitive as one might suppose, and it ranged from simple spongelike creatures to complex arthropods" (Matthews, 1962, p. 95).

One well-known historical geology textbook (Dunbar, 1960,

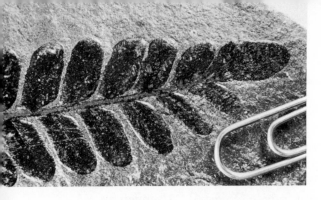

Fig. 37.1 A well-preserved fern fossil from the Carboniferous. Its evolutionary ancestors have not been found.

p. 237) states: "The presence of several hundred species of insects in the Pennsylvanian makes their sudden appearance at this time the more remarkable. The diversity of the forms represented implies a long antecedent evolution whose record may yet be found in Mississippian if not in Devonian rocks." The experience of the past 100 years would indicate that this wistful hope will never be realized.

The Lack of Evidence for Plant Evolution

The problem is just as acute with plant as with animal fossils, as an examination of preserved plant remains proves. Here is a frank summarizing statement from one paleobotanist:

"It has long been hoped that extinct plants will ultimately reveal some of the stages through which existing groups have passed during the course of their development, but it must be freely admitted that this aspiration has been fulfilled to a very slight extent, even though paleobotanical research has been in progress for more than one hundred years. As yet we have not been able to trace the phylogenetic history of a single group of modern plants from its beginning to the present" (Arnold, 1947, p. 7) (Fig. 37.1).

Plants and animals are identified by the use of keys. It is noteworthy that the same keys used for the identification of living plants and animals of larger taxonomic groups such as classes, orders, and families can be used for the identification of fossils. In very many cases they even closely resemble living genera and species. If a key made for use on living things can also be used on fossils, it is obvious that there has been little change in the interrelations between organisms.

440

Speciation has undoubtedly produced variations and new species. It may have produced even greater changes. Many genera have also probably developed since the Flood, and it is possible that the same has been true for some families and perhaps higher categories. The creationist would not expect keys for living species and genera to be entirely satisfactory for fossils, but he does expect keys for the higher taxonomic units to fit, and this is exactly the situation he finds.

In recent years the study of spores and pollen grains (palynology) obtained from sediments and bogs has opened up a new and fascinating area of research. Spores and pollen grains are extremely resistant to decay, and have been sufficiently well preserved in deposits and plant accumulations to make identification possible.

One surprising result is the discovery of the reproductive cells of seed plants in strata classified as Cambrian (Leclercq, 1956; Axelrod, 1959; Burdick, 1966). This has far-reaching implications because it means that evolutionists must consider the evolution of vascular plants (plants that have sap- and water-conducting tissues) to have occurred by Cambrian times or earlier. Thus there is little evidence that can be construed as supporting the progressive development of plants in the sediments that contain fossils. Pushing the evolution of the plants to a time within the Precambrian puts it almost out of the realm of study, because Precambrian sediments are practically devoid of fossils the world around, or are igneous crystalline rocks, which would not be expected to contain recognizable fossils.

Psilophytes, which are usually first seen in Devonian rocks, were thought to be the ancestors of vascular plants. Now that pollen from complex seed plants has been found well below the Devonian, one well-known paleobotanist has suggested that these Psilophytes are the end of an evolutionary line rather than the beginning (Axelrod, 1959, p. 264).

The testimony of the fossils is clear. Major progressive evolution has not occurred. The following statement by G. G. Simpson

(1944) in *Tempo and Mode in Evolution* is an unusual and fitting statement with which to end this short discussion:

"The facts are that many species and genera, indeed the majority, do appear suddenly in the fossil record, differing sharply and in many ways from earlier groups, and that this appearance of discontinuity becomes more common the higher the level, until it is virtually universal as regards orders and all higher steps. . . .

"The face of the record thus does really suggest normal discontinuity at all levels, most particularly at high levels, and some paleontologists . . . insist on taking the record at this face value. Others . . . discount this evidence completely and maintain that the breaks neither prove nor suggest that there is any normal mode of evolution other than that seen in continuously evolving and abundantly recorded groups. This essentially paleontological problem is also of crucial interest for all other biologists, and since there is such a conflict of opinion, nonpaleontologists may choose either to believe the authority who agrees with their prejudices or to discard the evidence as worthless."

REFERENCES

Andrews, Henry N., Jr. 1961. Studies in paleobotany. John Wiley & Sons, Inc., New York. 487 pp.

Arnold, Chester A. 1947. An introduction to paleobotany. McGraw-Hill Book Co., Inc., New York. 433 pp.

Axelrod, Daniel I. 1959. Evolution of the Psilophyte paleoflora. Evolution 13 (2): 264-275.

Beerbower, James R. 1960. Search for the past. Prentice-Hall, Inc., Englewood Cliffs, N.J. 562 pp.

Burdick, Clifford. 1966. Microflora of the Grand Canyon. Creation Research Society Annual.

Clark, A. H. 1930. The new evolution: zoogenesis. The Williams and Wilkins Co., Baltimore. 297 pp.

Darrah, William C. 1960. Principles of paleobotany. The Ronald Press Co., New York. 295 pp.

Dunbar, Carl O. 1960. Historical geology. John Wiley & Sons, Inc., New York. 500 pp.

Leclercq, S. 1956. Evidence of vascular plants in the Cambrian. Evolution 10 (2): 109-114.

Matthews, William H., III. 1962. Fossils, an introduction to prehistoric life. Barnes & Noble, Inc., New York. 337 pp.

Simpson, G. G. 1944. Tempo and mode in evolution. Columbia Univ. Press, New York.

CHAPTER THIRTY-EIGHT

Missing Links and Living Fossils

IF EVOLUTION HAS BEEN in operation for hundreds of millions of years one would expect to find a continuum—a continual series of gradations—from simple to complex. But such is not the case, either in the fossil remains of plants and animals or in the living species. It was this very lack that gave birth to the term "missing link." Most individuals think of an intermediate between man and ape when the expression "missing link" is used, but countless numbers of connecting links are needed to bridge the gaps that exist between every major group of plants or animals and its supposed neighbors. Paleontologists have been engaged in a constant search for these links, but the results of their efforts are extremely meager. Below are listed several so-called connecting links, with a brief evaluation of their qualifications for such positions.

Another interesting category of organisms is the so-called "living fossils," plants and animals that were supposed to have been extinct for at least several millions of years, but which have been found to be alive and thriving somewhere in the world. It is difficult for the evolutionary paleontologist to understand how an animal existing since Paleozoic times could have left no trace of itself in the rocks since, for example, the Devonian period. He is also bothered by the fact that there may be little evidence of evolutionary change between the Devonian specimens and the recent ones. The creationist is not bothered, because he counts no more than a few thousand years since the organism was incorporated into the fossil record.

Peripatus is a small animal that lives in the damp tropical forests of Africa, Asia, Australia, South and Central America, and a few other areas (Fig. 15.3). It prefers moist places under logs and comes out at night, or on days when the humidity is close to 100 per cent. It is described by some as coming closer than any other to being a missing link between two phyla. It looks much like a caterpillar, two or three inches long, with soft velvety skin and many pairs of legs. Some of its structures are similar to the arthropods, others are annelidlike. In turn, certain characteristics unlike either arthropods or annelids are typically its own. *Peripatus* shows no external segmentation. There is a pair of legs for each internal segment of its body, but these legs differ from arthropod legs in that they are not jointed. It has claws on the ends of the legs which resemble those of some arthropods. The outer skin covering is somewhat like that of annelids.

It differs in that it is ridged and covered with microscopic projections that make it feel like velvet. Although it has simple annelid-type eyes, it feels its way about by two sensory projections on the head. The three-segmented head is thought by some to be a condition midway between that of the annelids and the arthropods, since arthropods have a six-segmented head. The internal anatomy shows resemblances to both arthropods and annelids; the circulatory and respiratory systems are similar to the former and the excretory system is like that of the latter. The reproduction system also shows some similarities to annelids, but the nervous system is even more simple.

There has been much discussion as to whether this little animal should be placed in the phylum Annelida or the phylum Arthropoda. The controversy has been solved at least temporarily by placing it in a phylum by itself, Onychophora. If this animal were really a connecting link it seems only logical that it would not show some annelidlike and some arthropodlike characteristics, but would show an intermediate stage of transition from annelid to arthropod. Neither should it show characteristics distinctly not like either of these phyla unless it represented its own branch of the evolutionary tree, a situation that would disqualify it from being a good connecting link.

Monotremata.—This small and unique group of animals lives primarily in Australia and certain surrounding areas. The order Monotremata includes two families represented by the duck-billed platypus and the spiny anteater. The earliest fossil evidence of these animals was discovered in Australian Pleistocene deposits. Monotremes are unique in that they lay eggs, but are classed as mammals because they suckle their young.

The platypus is found at nearly all altitudes in Eastern Australia (Fig. 38.1). Its habitat is in and about streams and lakes, where it makes burrows in the banks. These animals reach a length of approximately two feet and have a flattened head with the jaws projecting forward to form a ducklike bill, which is covered with a sensitive rubbery covering. They possess a beaverlike tail and webbed feet with powerful claws. The eyes and ears are protected by folds of skin when they swim, and the body is well covered with a dense, velvety coat of fur.

The spiny anteater lives in open forest, scrubland, or rocky areas in Australia, Tasmania, and New Guinea. It has a long muzzle with a terminal mouth, within which is a long sticky tongue it uses to lap up ants. The animal is about 20 inches long and is covered with sharp spines interspersed through the fur.

Both the platypuses and the anteaters lay eggs and suckle their young. Their mammary glands terminate in small pits into which milk is secreted and whence it is lapped up by the young.

Fig. 38.1 An Australian curiosity—the egg-laying duck-billed platypus, a supposed connecting link between reptile and mammal.

The platypus lays one to three eggs that hatch in from seven to ten days and are incubated constantly, whereas the anteater lays a single egg and incubates it in a small transitory abdominal pouch which, incidentally, is not considered homologous to the pouch of the marsupials.

These animals are said by evolutionists to be connecting links between reptiles and mammals. The mammalian features include the covering of hair and the mammary glands. The reptilian similarities appear in the skeleton, the urogenital system, the transitory teeth in the anteater and the complete absence of teeth in the platypuses, and the egg laying aspect of both.

These animals are connecting links only if the assumption of evolution is held. In a group of animals as varied as the mammals it is obvious that some species will resemble reptiles more than others. It is not necessary to postulate that forms that depart somewhat from the typical for the group are the result of evolution from another group toward which the departure may be presumed to tend.

Archaeopteryx.—The announcement of the first fossil evidence of birds was made in 1861 when a fossilized bird feather was found in what is called the Upper Jurassic lithographic stone in the quarries at Solenhofen, Bavaria. Later in the same year a nearly complete fossilized bird skeleton was discovered, the *Archaeopteryx*, earliest known bird. Only one other specimen, other than a feather similar to *Archaeopteryx* feathers, has been found.

Archaeopteryx was approximately the size of a small crow, with a stout little head and beak with teeth. This bird exhibits three remarkable features:

1. The jaws are said to have true conical teeth set in sockets like those of many reptiles.

2. The digits in the wings were not completely fused; the first three functioned as claws.

3. The long slender tail was composed of vertebrae, and the

feathers diverged pinnately from its axis, not fanwise as in modern birds.

This animal is understandably a favorite "connecting link" among evolutionary paleontologists. "It would be difficult to find a more perfect 'connecting link' between two groups of animals, or more cogent proof of the reptilian ancestry of the birds" (Schuchert and Dunbar, 1953). But if this bird is really an intermediate between reptiles and birds, why did it not have primitive feathers instead of completely formed feathers such as birds have today? Furthermore, the wings were not rudimentary, but were well developed and capable of use for flight.

Offhand, *Archaeopteryx* does appear to have a remarkable combination of avian and reptilian characteristics. One would be tempted to wonder whether a cross between the classes Reptilia and Aves had actually occurred, but we must admit that hybridization between classes is not seen today. There is no reason why birds with pinnately feathered tails should not have existed in the past. The appearance of some reptilian similarities in the morphology of birds could be merely a coincidence not entirely unexpected, considering the broad variation in morphology that is possible in a class. Although *Archaeopteryx* is extinct and no such bird is known to exist now, the hoatzin has two claws on the front edge of the wing during youth. At least two other orders of birds are known to exhibit one claw.

It therefore seems best, because of the present limited information on *Archaeopteryx,* to consider it an unusual bird, now extinct, that had a position within the diversity of this class, that lay nearer the gulf between reptiles and birds than other members of the class.

Living Fossils

Crinoids.—These flowerlike echinoderms are commonly called sea lilies or feather stars. They are related to the starfish, sea cucumbers, and sea urchins. Most species have jointed stalks by which they are attached to the sea bottom; others have no stalk when adult and are free swimming. There are about 2,100 species of fossil crinoids, and about 800 species of living representatives. Few living specimens exceed eight inches in length, though some reach a length of nearly two feet. Extinct forms had stalks up to 70 feet long.

Crinoids were exceedingly abundant in the ancient seas. Their remains make up crinoidal limestone in Paleozoic strata. Although they were thought to be extinct or rare at one time, living species are now known to be widely distributed but mostly confined to the bottom in deep water. Where conditions are favorable they may make up large aggregations.

Lingula.—This phylum of bivalves, thought for some time to be members of the Mollusca but now classed as a separate phylum Brachiopoda, were abundant Paleozoic marine inhabitants (Fig. 38.2). Within this phylum the genus *Lingula,* which currently lives in the oceans of the world, is found attached to the bottom in mud or sand by a peduncle. This same genus is found in the fossil marine fauna of the Cambrian. The morphology of both brachiopods is practically identical, despite the supposed lapse of time between Recent and Cambrian times. The habitat of the fossil species was apparently similar to that of the living—mud or mud-sand bottoms.

Tuatara.—Most zoology textbooks describe the tuatara as a relic of the past. Although the tuatara looks like a lizard, several anatomical and physiological characteristics distinguish it as the only survivor of the order Rhynchocephalia, or beak-headed reptiles (Fig. 38.3). Living specimens have been found only on

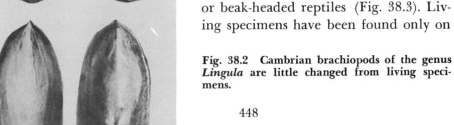

Fig. 38.2 Cambrian brachiopods of the genus *Lingula* are little changed from living specimens.

448

Fig. 38.3   **The tuatara, representative from New Zealand of a nearly extinct reptile order.**

islands off New Zealand, where they live in holes on sandy hills by the shore.

The eggs of tuatara, which are quite small for a reptile that commonly attains a length of two feet—only about one inch in diameter—require 12 to 13 months of development before hatching! It is likely that the eggs, like those of other reptiles, are fertilized internally, but a distinguishing difference in the male is the absence of any means of inseminating the female.

More than a hundred technical papers have been written about tuatara. Why should this reptile be the object of so much intensive study? Scientists believe that in finding out why *Sphenodon* (the generic name) has outlived all the other members of the order, they will find the answer to the extinction of all the giant reptiles of past ages.

The skeleton of one of these reptiles found in the Jurassic deposits of Europe is almost exactly like the living tuatara today. The last fossil evidence is found in the Early Cretaceous, which supposedly leaves a time gap of 135 million years. This similarity

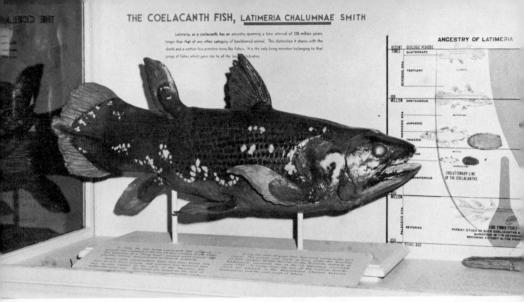

Fig. 38.4 The coelacanth, once thought extinct for 70 million years but recently found alive.

should suggest that only a short time has elapsed, insufficient for evolution to change the morphology of the tuatara. It is much simpler, and in accord with the evidence, to believe that this species has survived a few thousand years since the Flood.

Coelacanth.—Scientists were shocked when, in 1938, a coelacanth was caught alive east of London, Cape Province, South Africa. According to the paleontological record the last coelacanths lived approximately 70 million years ago. Fourteen years later a second specimen was caught near the island of Anjouan in the Comoro group near Madagascar. Six more have since been taken in that same vicinity, the largest one measuring approximately five feet and weighing 150 pounds.

Some of the significant characteristics of coelacanths, which set them apart from other fishes, are overlapping scales that give the body an armour of three layers of scales, a skull consisting of two nearly separate parts, teeth clusters on the upper jaw, a small tail and fin extending beyond the main caudal fin, hollow spines (hence the name coelacanth), and fins located on limblike extensions from the body (Fig. 38.4).

"One of the remarkable characteristics of the Coelacanths is that they have changed very little during the time that they

450

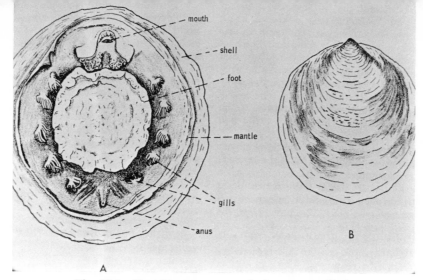

Fig. 38.5 *Neopilina,* an unusual deep-sea mollusk.

have lived. The bony structures of our modern Coelacanths are almost exactly the same as those left by Coelacanths hundreds of millions of years ago" (Smith, 1956, p. 235).

One of the coelacanth fossil skeletons contained two smaller skeletons, and from that it was surmised that they gave birth to live young. However, one of the eight live coelacanths was a gravid female with eggs. The deduction of paleontologists from fossil specimens that coelacanths were live bearers was shown to be questionable by the discovery that modern living coelacanths are egg layers.

Neopilina.—Probably even more unusual than the discovery of living coelacanths is that of a deep-sea mollusk that according to paleontologists became extinct about 280 million years ago during the Devonian period. On May 6, 1952, off the Mexican Coast, ten specimens were dredged from a depth of 3,590 meters. These were the first examples of living segmented mollusks (Fig. 38.5). One of the main characteristics of the phyllum Mollusca is nonsegmentation. On December 7, 1959, four more segmented mollusks were brought up from the north end of the Peru-Chile Trench. These differed in some respects from the ten found in 1952, the most notable differences being five pairs of gills rather than six, a much more prominent periostracum, and a much thinner shell. These differences have

451

been considered sufficient to place the mollusks in different species of the genus *Neopilina.*

"280 million years is a long time and one cannot help but wonder about its reality. Fossils of this class of mollusk were apparently plentiful in the early Paleozoic strata and it is amazing that none have been found in the marine strata of the Mesozoic or Tertiary, if indeed these actually represent the hundreds of millions of years following the Paleozoic that they are supposed to" (Whitcomb and Morris, 1961, p. 178).

One of the basic premises of historical geology is that the absence of fossils of a certain group of organisms from rocks of a supposed geologic age is proof that this group did not exist at the time the sediments of which these rocks are composed were laid down. This assumption is weakened or even disproved by the present-day existence of organisms that are absent from the fossil record for long periods of geologic time. *Neopilina* exists today and is found as fossils in rocks dated 280 million years ago, but is not found in intervening rocks. Since it certainly has existed continuously over the supposed 280 million years, its absence from the intervening layers proves nothing. If the absence of fossils of *Neopilina* from all of these layers proves nothing, what does the absence of *any* group of organisms at any period of geological history prove? The answer is obvious.

King Crab.—*Xiphosura polyphemus,* the king crab, or horseshoe crab, is really not a crab, but a relative of the arachnids, or spiders, ticks, scorpions, et cetera. According to evolutionists it is a "holdover" from past ages. These strange arthropods are abundant along the eastern coast of the United States from Maine to Mexico. Every attempt to establish them permanently on other coasts has been unsuccessful. Structurally the scorpions appear to be their closest relatives, although certain features of the larvae seem to suggest a relationship to the trilobites. Again the question suggests itself—Have these creatures really existed relatively unchanged for millions of years while other animals have undergone evolutionary development, or has there been only a brief time lapse since the fossil king crabs were buried?

Cycads.—One of the best-known representatives of the cycads is *Zamia,* which grows in parts of Florida, the West Indies, and South America. *Zamia* is dioecious (both sexes not on the same plant), and its fernlike fronds are arranged much like those of a palm tree. The East Indian genus *Cycas* attains 67 feet in height and 40 inches in diameter. Fossil cycads or similar forms have been found in England, France, Russia, Wyoming, Kansas, and a number of other areas. The most abundant remains have been located in the Black Hills region of South Dakota. These fossils are quite abundant in Mesozoic formations, but today they constitute a very minor portion of the world flora.

Ginkgo.—*Ginkgo biloba* has been called the maidenhair tree because of the resemblance of its leaf to that of the maidenhair fern (Fig. 38.6). Ginkgo trees may grow to more than 90 feet, with a trunk diameter of three to four feet. Only the one species, *G. biloba,* is in existence today. In comparatively recent times the Ginkgo was found growing on the grounds of temples in China. From there it was carried to many parts of the world, and is now used as an ornamental shade tree. Ginkgo is dioecious, having male and female parts on separate plants.

Fossil remains have been found in East Greenland, France, Japan, Washington State, and many other areas. Fossil findings of reproductive structures have been lacking; consequently, taxonomy has been difficult. However, variations in leaf morphology indicate that several species once existed. It is difficult to determine why this hardy plant nearly became extinct.

Metasequoia.—The most notable of living plant fossils is the genus *Metasequoia.* Fossils with a structure about midway between the giant California tree, *Sequoia sempervirens,* and the swamp cypress *Taxodium distichum* of the southern United States, have been found in a number of locations. In 1941 the genus *Metasequoia* was proposed, and described as including certain species that had previously been assigned to *Sequoia* (Chaney, 1951).

Fig. 38.6   The Ginkgo, or maidenhair tree (left).
Fig. 38.7   The Metasequoia, or dawn redwood (right).

Five years later, in February, 1946, Mr. Wang-chan, a Chinese forester, discovered three living trees representing an undescribed species of the genus in Szechwan, in southeastern China. Later in the year more were found, and eventually many came to be known. The living *Metasequoia* is a large tree, growing as much as 115 feet tall and with a trunk thickness of seven and one-half feet. It sheds its leaves in winter in a manner similar to tamarack or larch.

Metasequoia was apparently on the verge of extinction. Seeds of the tree have been transported to many places in Europe and America, in the hope that it may become firmly established elsewhere. With the foliage and cones of three similar trees—cypress, *Sequoia*, and the newly found *Metasequoia*—available for classification, many fossil specimens that had previously been assigned to *Sequoia* or cypress were moved to *Metasequoia*, making it the most abundant genus of the Taxodiaceae, or cypresslike family, in North America in Upper Cretaceous to Miocene formations (Fig. 38.7).

Chaney (1951) speculates that "Metasequoia probably disappeared from the living forests of North America as a result of changes in the precipitation regime from a summer-wet to a summer-dry [pattern] around the close of the Miocene."

As we have seen, the absence of connecting links and the presence of living fossils both pose enigmas for evolutionists. Although the search for connecting links has gone on for more than a hundred years, the spectacular discoveries of living fossils have been made relatively recently. Those who believe in creation and in a short period of existence for living things on the earth anticipate that continued exploration for missing links will make little more headway than in the past, but may turn up more living fossils.

REFERENCES

Andrews, Henry N., Jr. 1961. Studies in paleobotany. John Wiley & Sons, Inc., New York, pp. 289-346.

Bogert, Charles M. 1953. The tuatara: Why is it a lone survivor? The Scientific Monthly 76:163-170.

Buchsbaum, Ralph. 1948. Animals without backbones. Univ. Chicago Press. 405 pp.

Burton, Maurice. 1954. Living fossils. Thames and Hudson, London. 282 pp.

Chaney, Ralph W. 1951. A revision of fossil *Sequoia* and *Taxodium* in western North America based on the recent discovery of *Metasequoia*. Trans. Am. Phil. Soc. 40 (3):171-263.

Colbert, Edwin H. 1955. Evolution of the vertebrates. John Wiley & Sons., Inc., New York. 479 pp., 122 figs.

de Beer, Sir Gavin. 1954. *Archaeopteryx lithographica.* Jarrold & Sons, Ltd., London.

Lane, Ferdinand C. 1953. The story of trees. Doubleday & Co., Inc., Garden City, New York. 384 pp.

Lemche, Henning. 1957. A new living deep-sea mollusc of the Cambro-Devonian class Monoplacophora. Nature, 179 (4556):413-416.

Merrill, E. D. 1948. A living *Metasequoia* in China. Science 170 (2771):140.

Romer, Alfred Sherwood. 1945. Vertebrate paleontology. Univ. of Chicago Press, Chicago. 687 pp.

Schuchert, Charles and Carl O. Dunbar. 1953. Outlines of historical geology. John Wiley & Sons, Inc., New York.

Seward, A. C. 1963. Fossil plants. Vol. IV. Hafner Pub. Co., New York. 543 pp.

Smith, J. L. B. 1956. The search beneath the sea. Henry Holt and Co., New York. 260 pp.

Welty, Joel Carl. 1962. The life of birds. W. B. Saunders Co., Philadelphia. 546 pp.

Whitcomb, John C., Jr. and Henry M. Morris. 1961. The Genesis flood. The Presbyterian and Reformed Pub. Co., Philadelphia, pp. 176-180.

CHAPTER THIRTY-NINE

Science and Faith

AN AUTOMOBILE SLOWS TO A STOP in front of the church. A child, neatly dressed and with Bible in hand, runs up the steps of the building, turns for a quick wave, and disappears inside for Sunday school. He learns many Bible stories, including that of the creation of the world. In simple faith he accepts this account of the origin of the earth and living things.

As time passes, he enrolls in elementary school. The books he studies describe the origin of matter and life, and the subsequent development of animals and plants in a way much different from what he learned in Sunday school. Innocently he asks questions, but teachers pass them off or say something about the Bible being a book of good morals, but that it is not scientifically accurate. Unless the boy's parents are informed and have clear convictions with respect to Biblical history and evolutionary theory, they can do little if anything to avert the breakdown of their child's faith.

In high school science and social studies classes the theory of evolution is presented in greater detail and as unquestionable fact. His teachers may openly discredit the Bible. Television programs and outside reading all support, with nearly one voice, the evolutionary theory of the origin and development of life. Furthermore, the student may find that his minister—if he has one—accepts nominally, if not openly, the theory of evolution. Upon being questioned, he may explain that the first chapters of Genesis are an allegorical presentation of the evolutionary process. Perhaps he will explain that God created life originally but permitted evolution to operate in its further development. How

can a teen-ager be expected to hold out in conspicuous noncon-
formity to a belief that is disregarded or ridiculed by his peers
and his elders? If there is anything a teen-ager fears, it is to be
different from the crowd.

In college and graduate education the faith that has been
lost is actively replaced by another, with the continued and more
intensive exposure to an evolutionary and atheistic philosophy.
At this level teachers feel quite uninhibited about expressing
their own personal anti-Biblical sentiments. The mass of seeming evidence accumulates to overwhelming proportions, and
never along the educational pathway since Sunday school has
there been opportunity to examine the evidence on the other
side of the question.

A young man thus enters his career, strongly satisfied that the
Bible may be a good book for children, but that evolution is an
undeniable fact, and that if God exists He is not a personal being.
Slowly, unconsciously perhaps, faith in God and His Word has
given way to faith in a theory. A mass of supposedly scientific information has replaced the former belief in the origin of the
earth and of life. In some countries science has in effect become a
religion.

For many years a great number of scientists with a non-
Christian perspective have been doing research in biology and
geology. The amount of literature and the number of facts that
have been amassed are staggering. The volume of supposition and
theory that has been built around these data is equally amazing.
Nearly the whole scientific world is arrayed against many of the
views expressed in this book, especially those that deal with creation, the Flood, and a relatively short time span for the created
world.

On a television panel celebrating the centennial of Charles
Darwin's book *Origin of Species*, Sir Julian Huxley began his
comments by saying: "The first point to make about Darwin's
theory is that it is no longer a theory but a fact. No serious
scientist would deny the fact that evolution has occurred, just as

he would not deny the fact that the earth goes around the sun" (Tax, 1960, p. 41). This is not an isolated statement, but typical. The issue is even more confused by such statements, which over-simplify the problem. To be sure, microevolution is a fact; but the obvious minor changes occurring in living things today are no more a basis for extrapolating that limitless change (macroevolution) has occurred in the past, than the appearance in the sky of a few unidentified flying objects is reason for generalizing that these objects are from Mars and contain small green men!

A majority of the arguments for evolution are taken from biology. By comparing the structure and physiology of living things, relationships and lines of ascent are supposedly revealed. An examination of the embryological development of various animals is said to reveal evolutionary kinships, and even their past evolutionary history. Study of the laws of inheritance shows how living things have changed, and this—it is claimed—supports evolution.

But a comparison of the form, function, and biochemistry of living things is in no way conclusive for evolution. These evidences can with equal ease be used to support belief in a Creator who used basic patterns and processes throughout life. This plan of action makes sense, and is what would be expected of an intelligent Being.

It has been said that the science of genetics proves evolution. But the word *evolution* must be defined. If *evolution* merely means change, genetics definitely does support evolution. But if *evolution* means major change from one basic kind of organism to another basic kind, or progressive change toward ever-increasing complexity, evolution certainly has not been proved by the study of inherited characteristics. This important distinction is usually overlooked completely, and is not mentioned in connection with assertions regarding the evolutionary theory. Mechanistic evolution requires exceptions to two fundamental laws of biology—that living things develop only from living things, and that they produce offspring basically similar to themselves. Thus believers in mechanistic evolution disregard accepted scientific principles, and are actually unscientific.

Where, then, are the major evidences for evolution, a progressive evolution from simple to complex that would bridge major kinds? By the claim of the evolutionists themselves, the fossils within the earth are the major support for the evolutionary theory, because they constitute a record of the past. But what do the fossils reveal? The sudden appearance of complex life forms in the oldest or lowest rocks is opposite to the results expected from the theory of evolution. There could hardly be a more serious problem for adherents of this theory. Furthermore, the absence of connecting links, or the presence of gaps between kinds of organisms, is a related problem that makes the weight of evidence the fossils give against evolution even more crushing.

The very men who call evolution a fact and no longer a theory are aware that the facts of biology may be explained in more than one way. They are not ignorant of the fact that the fossil record poses tremendous problems for the theory of evolution. They know that evolution has no satisfactory explanation of origins, that the pushing of this problem out into space or onto other heavenly bodies does not solve it. They are acquainted with the second law of thermodynamics, which would work against the build-up of amino acids and proteins needed before that original spark of life could develop on the earth. These men who claim the "fact" of evolution are aware of the conspicuous absence of adequate evidence for human evolution. The supposed "fact" of evolution, with its basic principle of the survival of the fittest, does not explain man's ability to appreciate esthetic and spiritual values. What role could evolution have in developing music appreciation, a sense of humor, and emotions of sorrow, joy, and love? The sudden extinction of the dinosaurs is another puzzle they have not solved. "Living fossils"—life forms which supposedly became extinct millions of years ago and whose remains have not been found in the intervening sediments but which are living today—are a mystery to them also.

459

They are aware that the good preservation of the fossils in the rocks, requiring the rapid burial of organisms to prevent decay and disintegration, is favored by catastrophic conditions rather than uniform and gradual accumulations of sediments, and that the explanations given for the origin of coal and oil are unrealistic and unsatisfactory. They should know that erosion would completely wear down all mountains to flat plains little above sea level, not once but many times, if geologic times and erosion rates are correct. They should be cautious about making dogmatic statements, knowing that geology still searches for answers to such basic problems as causes of glaciation, mountain building, and volcanic activity.

The creationist with his belief in a fiat creation, the Flood, and a short earth history, is not without problems. Information regarding speciation rates required in the short span of post-Flood time, radioactive dating results, supposed growth positions of plants and animals in sedimentary beds, the stratification of fossils in the earth, et cetera, is needed. Unfortunately, very few competent scientists with a creationist orientation have been doing research. At the present time probably not more than one out of every hundred geologists questions long geologic ages and continuous, progressive evolution. Likewise, the literature supporting creation and the Biblical account of the earth and its history is not voluminous. There is reason to believe that an equal amount of effort by creationists during the past century would have resulted in a much more satisfactory account of the history of the earth and its living forms than is now afforded by the evolutionary theory.

Militant evolutionists are aware of all or most of the problems for evolution that have been mentioned, but they are caught in a web of circumstances of which they are unaware—circumstances created by the educational process and the intellectual climate of which they are the product. All men have opinions and biases, and are much influenced by social pressure and prevailing concepts. Constant exposure to one theory of origins, and only one, has convinced them that there is no alternative, and that evolution must be the full and complete answer. But their bold pronouncements in favor of evolution are reminiscent of the restrictive declarations on science put forth by religious leaders during the Dark Ages, the Renaissance, and even the Age of Enlightenment. By their dogmatic assertions, which go far beyond the facts of science, they, the evolutionists, have, for practical purposes, fallen into the *same* error and have closed and bolted the door to further fruitful research.

The history of scientific investigation has many examples of pitfalls on the hard road to truth. It is well for all in search of truth to keep in mind the following points:

1. Theories frequently change. That which is now widely accepted may later be shown to be untenable, even by those who may have been strong advocates of the original theory.

2. Theories and reconstructions are often based on fragmentary materials or information. This has been especially true in the field of human evolution.

3. Theories are often supported by facts that may with equal validity be used in support of another theory. Much of the interpretation of paleontological material falls into this category.

4. Basic suppositions that are questionable or invalid may be used in the interpretation of data.

5. Theories may be based on incorrect experimental results or observations.

6. Facts may be interpreted to satisfy a personal bias or presupposition, or to uphold a favorite hypothesis.

7. Deliberate falsification of facts and materials sometimes occurs. This is rare, but cannot be ruled out entirely.

The creationist readily recognizes the role of faith in his beliefs. Faith in Jesus Christ as a personal Saviour from sin is a fundamental Christian belief. Earth's early history as recorded in the Bible cannot be proved, either historically or scientifically, but it is accepted because of faith in the veracity of the Scriptures. Thus compulsive evidence for creationism cannot be

461

claimed. Faith must be called upon to bridge the gap between the evidence and proof.

But this is decidedly true of evolution also. It is obvious from the preceding pages that evolution, as generally understood, is not a fact. Statements of the "fact" of evolution strike one as whistling in the dark. Much faith—more than required of a creationist—is needed by the believer in evolution, unless he blindly accepts what he is told by others. Then he must have faith—misdirected faith—in those who instruct him. How unfortunate it is that most of the millions who pass through the educational process described at the beginning of this chapter have little opportunity to weigh the evidences pro and con, to maintain or develop a faith in God and in His account of world history.

An untruth asserted often enough may, in time, be accepted no matter how wrong it is. This psychological experience, referred to as brainwashing, has happened to many people without their being aware of it. We have been told so often that life came from nonliving material that many now believe it. When medieval man began to emerge from the Dark Ages, the popular belief in spontaneous generation—living things springing from nonliving materials—began to disappear. Scientists such as Louis Pasteur later convinced the world by concrete scientific experimentation that spontaneous generation is not possible. Yet on this point evolutionists are attempting, in effect and in the name of science, to lead man back to the primitive concepts of the Dark Ages.

It is time for modern man to shake himself awake to the brainwashing process that has broken down his ability to use "common sense," and to become aware of the absurdity of a theory that says our boots developed out of nothing (spontaneous generation) and that we can lift ourselves up by pulling on the straps (progressive evolution)! With all the time, technology, and materials available, man has not been able to produce a perpetual motion machine. In fact, the United States Patent

Office has officially decided that such a machine is impossible and will not consider requests for patenting any such contraption. But mechanistic evolution requires that organisms build themselves out of nothing and then continually improve themselves as they maintain their existence!

In this discussion nothing has been said of the abundant archeological evidence for the accuracy of the Bible. No mention has been made of the numerous historical predictions by inspired writers of Scripture that have been fulfilled. Mention has not been made of the fact—most important of all—that millions of human beings have been transformed morally, by the miracle of conversion set forth in the Bible, and have found meaning, purpose, and hope in life they had not known before. These facts, though out of the realm of science as considered in this book, are additional weights that press the scales far down in favor of a divine act of creation, a concept that likewise has its origin in the pages of Holy Writ.

By faith the creationist accepts the Biblical account as a correct history of the earth. By faith men receive the evolutionary theory as a true basis for understanding prehistoric times. A man is circumscribed by his faith. His life, hope, and destiny are determined by the quality of this faith. One faith holds to a theory that permits him to trace his descent "from germs and mollusks and apes," whereas the other entitles him to be a part of the genealogy that traces his ancestry back to "Adam, which was the son of God."

REFERENCES

Tax, Sol (ed.). 1960. The evolution of man. Univ. of Chicago Press. 473 pp.

Postscript: What of the Future?

THERE IS GREAT NEED for men of keen minds and sharp eyes, who are also firmly and strongly grounded in the Bible and on the "Rock of our salvation," to study in the areas of geology, paleontology, and speciation. Only a few are presently attempting to do any thorough investigations here. There is room for many more. These questions are of vital importance to the church because they involve our understanding of creation, the Flood, the time of creation and the Flood, the length of time involved in creation and the Flood, the power and omnipotence of the Creator, the weekly cycle, and the sanctity of the Sabbath. The topic of creation versus evolution also, and necessarily, involves the origin of man, the origin of sin, and the need for salvation. In fact, practically every major belief of Seventh-day Adventists is undermined by the prevailing concepts of geology and evolution.

God has provided us with many evidences, some of which have been recounted in this book. It is not His will that we should be perplexed concerning our beliefs and the statements of Scripture. We can expect His blessing as we study and labor to give to the world's millions a better view of the past and the future of this planet. We should equal and excel the quality of research produced by scientists who support evolution. In all our study and observations it is well to remember and to heed these words of warning and admonition:

"I have been shown that without Bible history, geology can

prove nothing. Relics found in the earth do give evidence of a state of things differing in many respects from the present. But the time of their existence, and how long a period these things have been in the earth, are only to be understood by Bible history. It may be innocent to conjecture beyond Bible history, if our suppositions do not contradict the facts found in the sacred Scriptures. But when men leave the word of God in regard to the history of creation, and seek to account for God's creative works upon natural principles, they are upon a boundless ocean of uncertainty" (3SG 93).

To many problems we do not now have satisfactory answers. Certain observable phenomena presently seem to point toward a great age for life on the earth, or to long-acting geological forces, or to contra-Biblical interpretations. What should be our approach toward these situations? Should we arbitrarily conclude that the first portion of Genesis must be de-emphasized, reinterpreted, or disregarded? Would it not be better to look back at the way the Lord has led us and know that we have not followed cunningly devised fables? Would it not be better to look at the strong evidences of the accuracy of God's Word that are available, and accept by faith—for the present—those truths for which we do not have evidence, knowing that in time facts may be revealed that will vindicate our faith? At the same time, we should also keep our minds open to a better understanding of the Genesis account of earth's early history.

A spirit of humility is an appropriate attitude for a scientist. There is so much we do not know. For instance, if we did not have modern glaciers to demonstrate the effects produced on the surface of the earth by glacial action, how could we correctly interpret the evidences seen in areas far removed from contemporary glaciation? Only by seeing what ice can do was it possible to develop a correct theory of the origin of certain deposits and phenomena that are not now near glaciers. It would have been exceedingly difficult to arrive at a correct conclusion if there had been no opportunity for comparison.

There has been no catastrophe in recent times comparable to a universal flood. In certain cases small local floods may help our understanding of the results of a universal flood, but undoubtedly many phenomena of a worldwide inundation by water are difficult to interpret because there is no basis for comparison. We have no basis of comparison for God's activity of creation in six literal days. We have no basis of comparison by which to know what life was like in a sinless world. These unknowns make the work of the creationist in interpreting the past difficult. But we do have abundant opportunity to verify the accuracy of the Bible, and on the basis of this confidence we accept by faith that which we cannot now verify concerning the past history of the earth.

The following from *Fundamentals of Christian Education* encourages us as we ponder problems and questions of this nature, and sets a standard toward which we can strive:

"When the human agents shall exercise their faculties to acquire knowledge, to become deep-thinking men; when they, as the greatest witnesses for God and the truth, shall have won in the field of investigation of vital doctrines concerning the salvation of the soul, that glory may be given to the God of heaven as supreme, then even judges and kings will be brought to acknowledge, in the courts of justice, in parliaments and councils, that the God who made the heavens and the earth is the only true and living God. . . . All nature will bear testimony, as designed, for the illustration of the word of God. . . .

"The author of nature is the author of the Bible. Creation and Christianity have one God. All who engage in the acquisition of knowledge should aim to reach the highest round of progress. Let them advance as fast and as far as they can; let their field of study be as broad as their powers can compass, making God their wisdom, clinging to Him who is infinite in knowledge, who can reveal the secrets hidden for ages, who can solve the most difficult problems for minds that believe in Him" (FE 374, 375).

I look forward to the future with hope and anticipation because I believe God will reward the efforts of His people to find truth and to raise up a barrier against the error that has engulfed the world. I look for new and powerful evidences that will give even stronger support to the Biblical story of earth's origin and subsequent history. Furthermore, the present direction of events indicates that world history is about to make a dramatic change, a change even more momentous than a world deluge. The Flood left the antediluvian world in partial ruin, but the coming event, when the Creator appears in the clouds of heaven, will result in complete destruction and leave this rebellious planet, which has suffered the ravages of sin, again in utter chaos. Even as Noah and his family were saved by miraculous preservation in the ark, so will God's people be saved from the final destruction of the earth. To this event, and to the subsequent complete restoration of the earth, we direct our attention and on it we base our hope.

Collecting and Preparing Fossils

Hunting fossils and building up a collection is a fascinating activity. Unless specimens are scarce and unusually difficult to find, a day spent in a fossil locality can be a long-remembered experience.

Techniques and procedures for the collecting and preparing of fossils are numerous, and this account is intended to be only a bare outline. The person who desires more information concerning any technique (including many not discussed here) should refer to the references listed at the end of this appendix.

Collecting

The hunting and collecting of fossils is usually dirty work; old clothes should be worn. Shoes are likely to be scuffed. Hiking or climbing boots are helpful because they support the ankles, a factor appreciated when walking on rough terrain. Hat, dark glasses, and work gloves are often needed. Rain, with the subsequent need for waterproof clothing, must be considered a possibility in some areas and during certain seasons.

Below is a list of tools and equipment needed for the field collection of fossils. More detail concerning some of these items used in the more specialized techniques is given under the discussions that follow. Not all of these tools and supplies would probably be used for any one expedition.

Hammers—Pick-end or chisel-end geology hammers are both good,
   depending on the type of rock and the individual's preference.
Shovels
Picks
Crowbars
Chisels—a variety of types and sizes

Paint brushes—several sizes

Hand lens

Steel tape

Glue—Duco or other plastic cements are indispensable

Shellac

Alvar—a plastic preparation that can be dissolved in acetone to any desired viscosity and that has proved useful as a cement in many types of paleontological work

Hydrochloric acid

Tissue paper

Newspaper

Plaster of Paris

Burlap (tow) bags

Scissors

Jackknife

Specimen bags or boxes

Notebook and pencils

Maps

Camera and equipment

Fossils are less common in coarse-grained materials such as conglomerates and breccias (volcanic breccias excepted). Fine-grained rocks—for example, sandstones, siltstones, and shales—are better preserving substances and more likely to reveal the fine detail of fossils. Fossils are seldom found in igneous and metamorphic rocks. Two exceptions are volcanic ash and breccia, abundant in fossils.

Unless one knows from previous experience that fossils can be expected in a particular locality there is little value in haphazard digging. Visual examination of gulleys, rock exposures, stream cuts, talus slopes, badland terrain, quarries, et cetera, may reveal fossils and indicate whether digging is feasible or necessary. Chips and fragments should be followed upstream or uphill to their source if possible. The more experience one has collecting fossils, the more specimens he is likely to find. Do not neglect to split open shale slabs and crack nodules. Don't overlook small fossils, which might prove to be more valuable than large ones. Use the hand lens to scan rocks for foraminifera and other microfossils.

If fossils are numerous the first ones that are picked up will probably be discarded in a short time for better and more perfect specimens. It is always wise to collect several of each kind. If much climbing is necessary refrain from doing most of the collecting until the descent, unless a particularly valuable specimen is found.

A pack sack or carrying bag is most desirable when one is prospecting for smaller specimens such as shells, brachiopods, corals, et cetera. Fragile specimens should not be placed loosely in a bag with other fossils. Small boxes or bottles with cotton or other soft material are desirable for small or fragile fossils.

Specimens without data are practically worthless. Whether one is collecting random fossils over an extended area or dealing with one vertebrate skull, careful data taking is necessary. Some of the points that should be especially noted for each specimen or each new collecting site are:

1. Date (and name of expedition, if any).
2. Position of fossil (upright, upside down, et cetera).
3. Condition of preservation.
4. Type of surrounding material.
5. Impregnating substance (calcium, silicon, et cetera). An acid bottle (HCl) is useful to test for rocks and fossils containing lime.
6. The general geological structure of the area.
7. Kinds of fossils associated together.
8. Types of fossils or sediments in strata above and below.
9. Method of deposition of sediments and fossils, if determinable.
10. Geologic formation in which fossil is found, if known.
11. Detailed geographic location of specimen.
12. Any other information concerning the site, environment, and specimen that appears significant.

Later, in the laboratory, the scientific name of the specimen and the names of the collector and identifier are listed on the slip that accompanies the specimen. To facilitate note-taking a hard-cover notebook small enough to slip into a jacket pocket should be kept available. The hard cover gives support for writing while the notebook is held in the hand.

Although it is impossible to go into detail on specific groups of fossils, a few points relating to some of the more common types will

471

be helpful. In more recent times microfossils have assumed great importance in paleontology and stratigraphy. Many foraminiferans, especially fusulinids, are found in well-indurated rock. No special care is necessary in collecting such rocks. If the microfossils are loose in sand or unconsolidated material they must be placed in small boxes, bottles, or bags that can be tied or that have drawstrings. This prevents the material from being scattered and lost, and protects it from crushing. Identifying labels or numbers should be placed inside the containers, as well as affixed to the outside. Rock specimens may be wrapped in paper sacks or placed in specimen bags along with the data written on a card or slip of paper. It is convenient to throw such fossils loosely into the trunk of the car and plan to record the data later, but this practice should be avoided. It is easy to forget the circumstances associated with the fossils, especially if they roll behind the spare tire and are not discovered until many days later.

Invertebrate fossils such as mollusks, corals, bryozoans, brachiopods, and crinoids may be found free from the matrix or still embedded in the surrounding material. It is a frequent temptation to reduce the matrix greatly to conserve weight, but this can be done more carefully in the laboratory. Taking back larger (not too large, unless you have a mule or a jeep close by!) blocks often results in obtaining specimens that would have been lost if the chipping or trimming of the slab had been done in the field. Isolated free specimens may be fragile and require protection from crushing. Dipping them into a solution of thin plastic cement such as Alvar is sometimes warranted. Wrapping well in newspaper or tissue paper may be sufficient.

Fish specimens are usually found in shale or other fine-grained deposits that may have a good cleavage. Less often they are found in nodules. Vertebrae and other fish bones may sometimes be seen loose in unconsolidated rock.

Excavation of fish remains is best accomplished from above or at right angles to the bedding plane, which is usually also the plane of the fossil. This method permits obtaining large slabs and complete skeletons. Flat chisels (automobile springs provided with chisel edges are excellent for heavy work) are needed to split the shale slabs. Parting along the plane of a fish often leaves an impression on the upper and lower slabs (part and counterpart). Both of these should be saved and numbered or labeled so that they can be matched again later. One impression (or compression) may show detail that the other will not. In some cases it may be desirable to impregnate fragile carbonaceous skeletal remains of fishes with thin Alvar to prevent disintegration. Preparing fish fossils for transportation may involve making a plaster of Paris cast as described below for mammals.

Many people think primarily of mammal or reptile remains when fossils are mentioned. The discovery and excavation of these are exciting, but here patience is especially desirable. The natural inclination is to pull the "find" out of the ground and rush back to show it off to admiring friends. The basic problem with a delicate or valuable fossil is to get the specimen from the site to the laboratory as intact and undisturbed as possible.

If digging is to proceed on private land, an obvious step is to obtain permission from the owner. A claim or permit may be indicated also if the excavating is to be done on government land.

The extent and limit of the find should first be determined for a tetrapod fossil. As with fish fossils, digging is best done from the top

Fig. A.1 Fossil ready to wrap for transportation.

down if possible. Excavation should proceed above and around the fossil until it remains on a pedestal. Expose as little as possible of the actual surface of the bone. The bone that is exposed should be coated with shellac if it is dry. Wet tissue paper or newspaper should then be placed on the shellacked bone as soon as it is dry to prevent the plaster of Paris cover from adhering to the bone. When the exposed part of the bone has thus been treated, the specimen is ready for jacketing with plaster of Paris and strips of burlap. The burlap strips should be one to three inches wide, and long enough to reach down the sides almost to the pedestal. Dip the burlap strips into a rather thin mixture of plaster and lay these over the specimen until it is completely covered, except for the pedestal of soil upon which it rests. Fragile points or projections of bone should be protected and the contours smoothed out somewhat before the burlap strips are laid down. The burlap strips wetted with plaster of Paris must be pushed into all depressions and follow carefully all contours, so that when the cast hardens there will be no air spaces between the cast and the specimen. Damage to the specimen can occur if it is not well supported by the cast at all points. When the jacket or cap has hardened, the whole specimen may be tipped off its pedestal, the excess dirt scraped off the bottom, and the rest of the plaster cast applied. When all the plaster has set and dried, the fossil will be encased in a strong covering that protects it from damage during transportation. It must be kept in mind, however, that whenever the plaster-soaked burlap strips are being applied directly to the bone, they must be preceded by shellac and tissue paper. If the specimen is badly splintered, it may be well to spray or paint it with a thin solution of a plastic cement to hold the numerous little fragments together.

Various modifications of the preceding description can be used depending on the size of the specimen, its condition, and its value. Small specimens may be taken out of the ground and dropped into plaster of Paris, or the plaster may be poured into a small trench

Fig. A.2 A properly encased fossil can be moved with safety.

Fig. A.3 Large fossils are especially vulnerable to damage if not properly protected.

around the fossil. Wherever possible a layer of soil should be left around the fossil to prevent the plaster from coming in direct contact with the bone, otherwise shellac and paper must be used. Experience will teach other methods of using plaster casts. The important considerations that always must be remembered are that the specimen must not be disturbed any more than necessary, and that a hard protective covering must be formed around it to preserve it during transportation. It may be desirable to incorporate sticks or poles into the cast to strengthen it or to facilitate transportation.

Fossil leaves are among the more abundant fossils, and large numbers of leaves may sometimes be found in a small area. If large slabs of leaves are desired, excavation must proceed at right angles to the bedding plane. When slabs are split they should be examined carefully for other evidences of plants such as leaflets still attached to stems, cones, seeds and fruits, flowers or parts of flowers, catkins, and fern leaflets showing fruiting bodies. Counterparts of either impressions or compressions (the part containing the carbon matter) should be saved and given the same number or mark. Varnish, shellac, or plastic preparations should not be used on either parts or counterparts unless fragility of the rock slab requires strengthening.

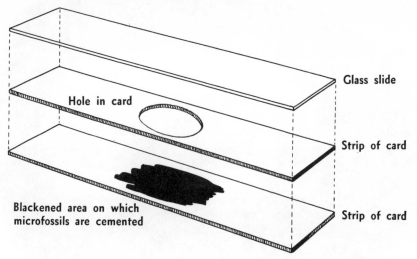

Fig. A.4 A simple microslide for the examination of microfossils.

It is often possible to collect a large number of leaf fossils from one quarry. The slabs should be trimmed and stacked on edge away from the working area. Slabs should be wrapped and packed tightly with newspaper or tissue paper, depending on the size and strength of the specimens. Any vibration or sliding of the rock because of loose packing in the box or crate can lead to breakage or mutilation.

The Cleaning and Preparation of Fossils

Most laboratory preparations on microfossils are for the purpose of preparing them for microscopic examination. This entails the making of thin sections which permit the transmission of light. The pieces are then mounted on microscope slides. The making of thin sections of well-indurated rock containing foraminiferans or other microfossils involves cutting off a thin section with a diamond saw, trimming it to the right size, grinding this section down until it is the desired thickness, and mounting it on a glass slide. Conventional lapidary equipment can be used, but thin-section equipment manufactured for that specific purpose is most satisfactory.

A common procedure especially used with Paleozoic foraminiferans (fusulinids) is simpler and requires less equipment. It is used with free specimens. A foraminifer is selected and placed in the desired orientation in a drop of thermoplastic. When the plastic has hardened and the specimen is cemented to the slide, grinding can begin. This is done by rubbing the slide, fossil down, on emery paper in water. Frequent examination under magnification is necessary to ensure that the grinding does not proceed beyond the plane desired. When this point has been reached the plastic is melted with heat and the specimen is remounted with the ground face against the glass. Proceed again with the grinding as before until the desired thickness is reached. After washing and drying, conventional mounting media can be dropped over the specimen and a cover glass set in place to make a permanent microscope slide.

Whole mounts of microfossils can be made in the following way: Cut out two 1"-by-3" pieces of stiff card (same size as glass microscope slide). With India ink make a black spot about the size of a penny in the center of one of the pieces of card. Cut a hole in the center of the second card slightly smaller than the black spot on the first card. Spread a thin layer of glue over the black spot and quickly transfer to the glue the microfossils you wish to mount. A fine, camel's-hair brush is useful for handling these small specimens. A dissecting microscope or good hand lens is also necessary. When the glue has hardened and the specimens are firmly affixed to the black spot, cement the second strip to the first one in such a way that the hole is right over the black spot. When these two strips have dried, they in turn may be glued to a glass microscope slide so that the hole is covered by the glass. This provides a semi-permanent slide from which the gross external morphology of the microfossils can be examined. Data can be written on the second strip to one side of the hole before it is glued to the glass slide.

Invertebrate slabs frequently need only to be washed and affixed with a number. Free specimens may not even need washing. On the other hand, it is often desirable to break up slabs that are composed of unconsolidated or partly indurated rock to get to the specimens that are bound within it. This can sometimes be accomplished by washing or soaking in water. Agitation and heating of the water may also speed up the breakdown of the matrix and the release of the fossils. One of the most useful methods of obtaining fossils from a hard matrix is by acid. The most common example of this type of situation is fossils impregnated with silicon embedded in limestone or dolomite. Blocks of such rock are placed in a plentiful amount (several times the volume of the rock) of 10 per cent hydrochloric acid. This dissolves away the limestone or dolomite and leaves the silicious fossils. After the blocks have been digested down, the residue should be thoroughly washed (for several hours) and spread out to dry. More fragile specimens released may be hardened by dipping in thin Alvar. Very delicate specimens of great beauty may be obtained by this method.

Ten to 15 per cent acetic or formic acids are useful for calcareous fossils. Since these are weaker acids, the blocks should be broken into smaller fragments (one inch or less if possible). It may be necessary to decant off the old acid, wash out the mud from the residue at the bottom, and replace new acid several times before the rock has been completely broken down. When the rock has disintegrated, the fossiliferous residue must be thoroughly washed and spread out to dry. When rinsing the mud and inorganic matter from the residue, use gentle water action to prevent the loss of small but valuable fossils. Concentrated hydrofluoric acid may be used on rock with a silicious content, but great care must be exercised with this strong acid. Plastic dishes, gloves, and a fume hood are necessary.

Acetic and formic acid may also be used for dissolving or loosening the matrix from around fish skeletal remains. One interesting possibility for smaller specimens is to pour clear embedding plastic over a slab containing a clean and exposed fish skeleton. The rest of the slab is later dissolved from the other side after the plastic has hardened, so that the finished product is a fish skeleton supported by clear plastic on one side but obviously visible from both sides.

The preparation of reptile and mammal fossil remains can be extremely exacting, and demands patience. The specimen may be fractured or splintered so that it is necessary to expose only a small part at a time, and harden and cement together the bones to prevent them from disintegrating. Some of the tools that are useful for this type of work are small chisels, awls, curved scrapers, et cetera (used on leather and for shoe repairs), dental burrs and bits used in a small hand-held electric drill, and the ever-necessary brushes for clearing away sand and dust.

It is best to put the specimen, plaster cast and all, into a shallow box of sand or on a sandbag. This prevents any undue jarring while scraping and drilling is being done. Do not remove the entire plaster cast at once. Remove only enough to permit access to part of the specimen. With a soft brush wipe away the sand and dirt so that one can see clearly. If the fossil is embedded in sandstone or some other hard material, it will be necessary to use hammer and chisel to remove this material from the fossil. A shoemaker's hammer and awls have been found excellent for use in this type of work. The awls are small enough so that they can be used in restricted spots on the fossil. Care must be taken not to break up the fossil with this treatment. If the material surrounding the fossil is soft it can be scraped away with much less difficulty. However, fossils embedded in soft material are often more fragile than those embedded in hard materials, and consequently, more care must be exercised to prevent cracking the fossil.

As bone is exposed it is well to paint it with a thin solution of plastic glue or cement. This may be prepared by diluting commercial plastic glue with acetone until it is thin enough to run freely into the cracks of the bone. If the fossil is badly fractured, as fossils often are, the thin glue will cement the fragments together. Larger pieces of bone can be glued together with a thicker preparation of glue.

Especially useful for plant fossils, but also sometimes for corals, brachiopods, and vertebrate fossils (especially fishes), is the peel technique. Because it is relatively simple, this method will be described in detail below.

The peel technique has found its greatest use with coal balls. A flat surface is made by cutting through the coal ball with a diamond saw. The cut surface must then be brought to a smooth polish. Specimens in calcified or dolomitized rock are placed face down in 5 per cent hydrochloric acid (concentrated hydrofluoric acid for specimens in silicified matrix) and held off the bottom by coarse sand or gravel. Twenty seconds to several minutes will be required to etch the polished surface, depending on the hardness of the rock. The ball is then washed gently and allowed to dry. With the specimen supported, the etched face up and slightly inclined, acetone is poured on the surface. It will run down and collect along the lower edge. One side of a sheet of cellulose acetate previously trimmed to the right size is laid against the lower edge of the face and the rest of the sheet gently lowered so that the acetone that collected on that edge of the face will be forced back up the surface and under the acetate sheet. Too much acetone wrinkles the acetate film and too little allows air spaces to remain between the film and the etched face. Practice will be necessary to perfect the procedure.

The etching of the coal ball surface removes some of the matrix from around the plant materials, which consequently protrude slightly above the surface. The peel, which is pulled off after 30 minutes or longer, will contain within it the plant material that was etched out by the acid. Allow the pulled peels to dry for an hour or more and then store them in envelopes. The most satisfactory cellulose acetate film is about 0.003 inch thick. With slight modifications the same technique can be used with the other kinds of fossils mentioned earlier. The delicate carbonaceous film of a small fish skeleton or a leaf compression can be transferred to a peel.

A variety of materials for embedding or making molds or casts is available. Rubber, latex, plastic, and plaster are used under various conditions and for different purposes. Many interesting and valuable procedures are known for many different kinds of fossils, and anyone interested in more details will find original references valuable. Equipment and supplies mentioned in this section may be obtained from a number of different places, and it would be wise for anyone planning to do fossil collecting and preparing to contact the geology department of the nearest university for information concerning the nearest sources of the various supplies and equipment.

Labeling and Cataloging the Collection

A neat and well-arranged collection of fossils represents much labor and time. The specimens must be cleaned and prepared as described in this chapter. Then they should be identified if possible. This is not for amateurs. If an amateur attempts to identify his specimens he should have them checked by an expert before being satisfied regarding the accuracy of the scientific names. Some specimens are obvious and are not difficult to identify if one has the proper literature, but most fossils are not easily assigned a correct name. This problem is further complicated by broken or poorly preserved material, which so often represents the best a collector can find. Literature for the identification of the many different kinds of animal and plant fossils is scattered throughout many sources and may be difficult to obtain. However, a well-kept collection containing adequate data and field notes is a valuable collection even though the fossils are not identified. This can always be done later if necessary, whereas the data and notes are easily forgotten or lost with time.

Small and loose specimens should be placed in plastic or cardboard trays. Such trays are not readily available and may be expensive, but a telephone call to the local university may provide information concerning the cheapest local source. Plastic or cardboard trays of two or three sizes are indispensable for arranging a neat collection. It may be impractical to number all of the small specimens, especially if there are many of the same species all collected at the same time from the same locality. They may all be placed in the same tray with a numbered label containing the data indicated as necessary earlier in this chapter. Single specimens in a tray, large fossils, blocks, or slabs should be numbered. Assign consecutive numbers to the fossils as you collect them and write this number on the specimen in an inconspicuous place with black India ink. A small dab of clear-drying glue such as Elmer's Glue-All, or thin Alvar spread over the number after it has dried, will protect it from being scratched or rubbed off. If the rock is dark in color and the India ink number will not show on the dark background, first paint a white rectangle and then record the number in the white rectangle. The number given the rock along with other necessary data should be written on a label and kept with the specimen.

Since there is always the possibility of labels being lost, a chronological listing of numbers should be kept in a ledger or notebook. It is a good habit to write a number on a specimen and the same number in the ledger at the first opportunity after obtaining the fossil. All the necessary data and other information that might be worth while keeping should be recorded by that number in the ledger. Later (perhaps years after the collecting details have been forgotten) the number on the fossil can be compared with the number in the ledger, and thus the information necessary for making the label to put in the tray with the fossil, or to make out another label in case the first one is lost, can be obtained.

A collection of fossils can be valuable because of the information it gives about the past. Whoever decides to collect fossils should determine to do it carefully and make a collection of which he will be proud. On several occasions individuals have told me about this or that fossil they once had but that is now lost or misplaced, fossils that would have been valuable. Even more frequently fossils are shown me for which there is no data, and the owners cannot remember where they found them. Such specimens are practically worthless. It is hoped that all who read these pages will resolve to keep their eyes open for interesting fossils and will record the necessary information for the ones they collect. Many people working together in this way will help to solve some of the riddles that confront all students of the past history of the earth.

REFERENCES

Camp, C. L. and G. D. Hanna. 1937. Methods in paleontology. Univ. of Calif. Press, Berkeley. 153 pp., 58 figs.
Grabau, A. W. and H. W. Shimer. 1910. Hints for collecting and preparing fossil invertebrates. *In* North American index fossils. A. G. Seiler, New York, vol. 2, pp. 803-819.
Kummel, Bernhard and David Raup. 1965. Handbook of paleontological techniques. W. H. Freeman and Co., San Francisco. 852 pp. Extensive treatment of paleontological methods with exhaustive bibliographies.
Lacey, W. S. 1953. Methods in paleobotany. N. Western Natur., Abroath, Wales 24:234-249.
Lahee, F. H. 1961. Field geology. McGraw-Hill Book Co., New York. 926 pp.
McKenna, M. C. 1962. Collecting small fossils by washing and screening. Curator 5 (3):221-235.
Ransom, Jay Ellis. 1964. Fossils in America. Harper & Row, Pub., New York. 402 pp.
Toombs, H. A. and A. E. Rixon. 1950. The use of plastics in the transfer method of preparing fossils. Mus. Jour. 50 (5):304-312.
Walton, J. 1928. A method of preparing fossil plants. Nature 122:571.
————. 1930. Improvements in the peel-method of preparing sections of fossil plants. Nature 125:413.

Glossary

Aberration—a mutation involving chromosomes.

Abyssal—referring to ocean depths below 6,000 feet.

Albinism—the absence of pigment in an organism.

Algae—groups of plants without water- or sap-conducting tissues; often single-celled or filamentous, and growing in water. Examples—green scum on ponds and seaweeds in the oceans. Division Thallophyta.

Allochthonous—from elsewhere; not native or indigenous.

Andesite—a type of fine-grained extrusive volcanic rock containing acid plagioclase.

Anemones—a group of flowerlike sea animals belonging to the phylum Coelenterata.

Angiosperms—plants with seeds enclosed in an ovary; the majority of seed-bearing plants.

Antediluvian—before the Genesis Flood; pre-Flood.

Anthracite—a hard, black coal with a high carbon content.

Anthropology—the study of man, particularly as it relates to race and distribution.

Antibodies—substances produced by a living organism to combat invading foreign proteins (antigens).

Anticline—convex- or upward-arched strata.

Antigen—a foreign protein that invades a body and usually initiates the formation of antibodies.

Aquatic—of or pertaining to fresh water.

Archean—usually, what are considered to be oldest-known rocks; Early Precambrian.

Arcuate—curved or arched.

Arenaceous—rock derived from sand; sandy.

Argillaceous—rocks derived from clay; having a large clay content.

Arthropods—a phylum of animals having jointed legs, such as the insects, crabs, and spiders.

Artifact—a man-made object of prehistoric age.

Aseptic—sterile; free of germs.

Atoll—a roughly circular group of coral islands arising from a submerged platform.

Autochthonous—original or native; not foreign or from elsewhere.

Autosome—the chromosomes in the nucleus of a cell, except the sex chromosomes.

Basalt—an extrusive igneous rock, dark in color and usually exhibiting columnar jointing.

Batholith—a great mass of matter that has pushed up toward the surface of the earth.

Belemnites—bullet-shaped fossil remains of extinct squidlike organisms.

Benthonic—concerning the bottom of the sea.

Biogenetic law—a law now proved incorrect, which states that each developing organism recapitulates, or passes through, its past evolutionary history.

Biogeography—the study that deals with the geographic distribution of living things.

Biosphere—the sphere of living things; all living things.

Biotic—pertaining to all living things; to life.

Bipolarity—the similarity of organisms in like habitats located approximately equal distances north and south of the equator.

Blastoids—a group of extinct echinoderms somewhat resembling the crinoids or sea lilies.

Blastula—a stage in embryological development consisting of a hollow ball of cells.

Bog theory—the theory that coal has formed from the burial and compaction of peat bogs.

Brachiopods—a phylum of bivalves somewhat resembling clams—extremely abundant fossils in marine sedimentary deposits.

Breccia—rock consisting of angular broken fragments cemented together.

Browsing—eating the leaves of trees and shrubs.

Bryophytes—mosses and liverworts.

Bryozoan—a phylum of common marine animals sometimes referred to as moss animals.

Calamites—large extinct horsetails or scouring rushes of the division Pteridophyta or Arthrophyta.

Calcareous—consisting of, or containing, calcium.

Caldera—a large crater produced by explosion or collapse at the summit of a volcano.

Caliche—a crust of calcium carbonate often formed in arid regions.

Cambrian—a period (the earliest) in the Paleozoic Era.

Carboniferous—a period in the Paleozoic Era, a term used principally in Europe for the Pennsylvanian and Mississippian periods as used in North America.

Carbonization—the retaining of carbon from organic material while most other elements are lost.

Carotenoid (Carotene)—a yellow pigment with a molecular structure similar to that of vitamin A.

Cast—a mass of sediment filling a cavity formerly occupied by an organism, and thus assuming the same form as the organism.

Caudal—referring to the tail.

Cenozoic—the most recent era of geological time.

Cephalothorax—a combined head and thorax, as illustrated by the body form of crabs.

Chaparral—shrubby brush in certain semiarid regions of the Southwest.

Chitin—a tough but flexible substance found in the exoskeletons of insects and other arthropods.

Chromatin—the hereditary material within the nucleus of a cell.

Chromosomes—rod-shaped or round objects located in the cells, carriers of hereditary characteristics.

Cirque—a rounded depression in the side of a mountain caused by the plucking action of a glacier as it moves away from the mountain.

Class—a unit of classification above the order and below the phylum.

Clastic—made up of fragments; fragmental detritus.

Coal balls—balls found in coal that contain a miscellaneous assemblage of vegetable structures.

Coccoliths—tiny calcareous plates produced by certain kinds of marine protozoans.

Coelenterates—a phylum of invertebrate animals (mostly marine) that develop from two germ layers and exhibit alternation of generation. Examples—jellyfish, corals, and anemones.

Colchicine—a chemical used to induce polyploidy in plants.

Comminuted—finely fragmented or ground up; reduced to powder.

Compression—that half of the split fossil which contains the compressed remains.

Chondrite—a stony meteorite.

Conglomerate—rock composed of rounded fragments of heterogeneous size and composition cemented together.

Connecting link—an organism considered to be a step in the supposed evolutionary history of its kind.

Continuum—continuous blending with no distinct demarcations.

Contractile vacuole—a small pumping organelle in protozoans involved in the regulation of water content and excretion of wastes.

Convergence—merging or coming closer together; in evolutionary terminology, becoming more similar in morphology.

Coprolite—fossilized excretory remains.

Cosmic rays—high-frequency rays originating outside the earth's atmosphere.

Cosmology—the study that deals with the organization of the universe.

Cranium—the brain case of vertebrates.

Cretaceous—a period in the Mesozoic Era.

Crinoids—echinoderms with a structure resembling a miniature palm tree. Buttonlike sections of the stem are often seen as fossils.

Crustacean—a large class of marine animals with articulated appendages belonging to the phylum Arthropoda. Examples—crabs and shrimp.

Crystalline—crystallike in nature.

Ctenophorans—a small phylum of marine invertebrates, usually transparent or translucent. Examples—sea walnuts or sea gooseberries.

Cystoids—an extinct group of echinoderms somewhat resembling crinoids or sea lilies.

DNA—an abbreviation for deoxyribonucleic acid. The actual hereditary material within the nucleus of the cell.

Delta—a deposit of sedimentary material laid down by a river or stream flowing into standing water.

Dermal plates—hard protecting scales or shields produced by the skin of an animal.

Desiccation—the process of becoming parched or dried up.

Devonian—a period in the Paleozoic Era.

Dew claws—hanging toes of ungulates that do not reach the ground or are not used for support.

Diastema—gap, or vacant space, between teeth in the jaw.

Diatom—a small single-celled plant with a surrounding silicious capsule; belongs to division Thallophyta or Chrysophyta.

Dike—a horizontal wall of igneous matter pushed up through overlying rocks and sediments.

Dinotheria—an extinct elephantlike mammal.

Dioecious—an organism that is either male or female but not both.

Dip—the angle of a stratum's deviation from horizontal.

Dolomite—calcareous rock with part of the calcium replaced by magnesium; usually harder than limestone.

Dominant—the stronger of two genes involving the same characteristic.

Dorsal—concerning the back, or sometimes the top.

Drumlin—an oval-shaped dome of sediment produced by a glacier and aligned in the direction of the movement of the glacier.

Durain—a dull, somewhat granular component of bituminous coals, consisting of very fine fragmented vegetable material.

Echinoderms—a phylum of marine animals usually having spiny skins. Examples—the starfish, sea urchins, et cetera.

Ecological niche—that limited area in which all ecological conditions are suited for the existence of an organism.

Ecological zonation—zones of different associations of living things controlled by the environmental factors prevailing in those areas.

Ecology—the study of the relationships of organisms to one another and to their environment.

Ectoparasite—a parasite living on the outside of an organism.

Elasmobranchs—fishes with cartilaginous skeletons. Examples—the sharks, skates, rays, et cetera.

Element—a substance that cannot be broken down into simpler substances.

Embryology—the study of the development of an organism from conception until birth.

Endemic—confined to, or native to, an area.

Endoparasite—a parasite that lives within an organism.

Eocene—an epoch in the Cenozoic Era.

Epoch—a small unit of geologic time into which the periods are divided.

Era—a major period of time (there are three—Paleozoic, Mesozoic, and Cenozoic), into which geologists have divided time since the origin of life on the earth.

Erratics—rocks and boulders transported from another source and deposited on the surface of the ground.

Esker—a long, serpentine mound of debris deposited by a stream beneath a glacier.

Evaporite—a product precipitated out of an evaporating solution.

Exoskeleton—an external skeleton such as that of insects.

Extraterrestrial—outside this earth; not of this earth.

Extrusive—igneous rock that has cooled and hardened on the surface of the ground.

Family—a unit of classification above the genus and below the order.

Fault—fracture zone between two masses of rock that have moved in relation to each other.

Fault block—a large block of rock that has moved in relation to the adjoining region.

Fecal droppings—solid waste or excretory droppings.

Fiord—a glacial valley invaded by the sea.

Flagellum—a hair or fiber often used in locomotion in certain types of protozoans.

Flint—a hard, fine-grained silicious rock containing much silica (SiO_2).

Formation—a clear-cut unit of rock with a uniform lithology, and usually mapable.

Fungi—a group of plants devoid of chlorophyll. Examples—molds and mushrooms.

Fusulinid—a type of marine fossil, in appearance somewhat like a grain of wheat; belongs to the Foraminifera.

Galactose—a type of sugar commonly found in plants.

Gastrolith—gizzard stones supposedly used by dinosaurs.

Gastrula—a stage of embryological development consisting of a ball of cells two or more layers thick.

Gene—a small portion of a chromosome concerned with the inheritance of a specific characteristic.

Genesis kind—a kind of organism originally created by God.

Genetics—the study of inheritance.

Genotype—the actual genetic formula of an organism in reference to particular characteristics.

Genus (plural, genera)—a unit of classification above the species but below the family.

Geologic column—the total vertical sequence of strata considered to have been laid down during geological time.

Geosyncline—a major basin or depression that has been filled with sediments and sometimes uplifted into mountains.

Germ plasm—the protoplasm of the reproductive cells; protoplasm directly involved in perpetuating the species.

Glucose—a very common six-carbon sugar sometimes referred to as grape-sugar.

Gneiss—coarse-grained metamorphic rock, usually indistinctly banded.

Gravid—pregnant with young or eggs.

Grazing—eating grass and low-growing herbs.

Guide fossils—fossils especially characteristic of sediments laid down at a certain position in the geologic column. See Index fossil.

Gumbotil—leached, oxidized clay or thoroughly weathered glacial drift or till.

Guyot—an isolated flat-topped mountain rising from the ocean floor but not reaching the surface.

Gymnosperms—a group of plants consisting mainly of evergreen trees with cones and needles.

489

Half-life—the time necessary for half of a substance to be lost by radioactive disintegration.

Herbivore—an animal that subsists on vegetable matter.

Heteroploid—an organism with a chromosome number different from that usually found in the species.

Heterozygous—two genes for any particular inherited characteristic, one each from father and mother, but not identical. One may be dominant and the other recessive.

Homozygous—the genes for any particular inherited characteristic, from both the father and mother, but identical.

Hybrid—the result of crossing two different kinds of organisms.

Hyperpituitarism—an overfunction of the pituitary gland that leads to gigantism.

Hypothesis—a theoretical idea as yet unproved but usually based on at least a few facts.

Hypotonic—a fluid less dense than another fluid to which it is compared.

Igneous—rock that has been molten, such as lava or granite.

Immunology—the branch of science that deals with immunity to invading foreign (often disease-producing) substances.

Impregnation—becoming saturated with a hardening substance.

In situ—in natural position; not transported or moved.

Index fossils—fossils with narrow stratigraphic ranges and wide geographic distributions that are useful for determining the position, within the geologic column, of the stratum in which the fossils are found.

Indigenous—native or endemic to a region.

Indurated—hardened.

Inorganic—matter not part of, or derived from, living organisms.

Insectivores—an order of mammals that includes the shrews and moles.

Intrusive—an igneous rock that has been pushed into, and hardened beneath, the surface of the earth; it has not flowed out onto the surface before hardening.

Invertebrates—animals that do not have backbones consisting of distinct bony vertebrae.

Isostasy—supposed balance of portions of the crust of the earth as though they were floating on denser material.

Isotonic—two fluids with the same density or the same osmotic pull.

Isotope—variant or different species of an element resulting from radioactive transformations and differing slightly in atomic weight.

Jurassic—a period in the Mesozoic Era.

Kames—hummocky terrain caused by glacial activity.

Kettles—round depressions in the ground caused by the melting of blocks of ice that were previously surrounded by sediments.

Kyphosis—a humpbacked condition; curvature of the spine.

Laccolith—an upward pushing magmatic mass that has domed the overlying rock.

Lamprey—a jawless fish with a sucking mouth by which it attaches to other vertebrates as a parasite.

Lapidary—of, or pertaining to, the art of cutting stones.

Lepidodendron—an ancient club moss that reached a foot or more in diameter and 100 ft. tall.

Lichen—a type of plant growth representing a symbiotic relationship between algae and fungi.

Lignite—a soft grade of coal, usually brown in color.

Lithification—consolidation of sediment into rock.

Liverwort—a plant that grows on wet ground, usually with a leaflike thallus but without true roots, stems, or leaves; belonging to the division Bryophyta or Hepatophyta.

Lycopods—see Lycopsids.

Lycopsids—a group of plants known commonly as club mosses and belonging to the Tracheophyta or the Pteridophyta divisions.

Macroevolution—the evolution that would be necessary to cause organisms to undergo major changes into other types of organisms.

Magma—molten matter within the depths of the earth from which igneous rocks are considered to have been derived.

Magnetometer—an instrument used for measuring the earth's magnetic field.

Mantle—the portion of the earth between the core and the crust. Top of mantle lies 6 to 12 miles below the surface of the earth.

Marine—of, or pertaining to, the oceans.

491

Marl—a clay rich in calcareous material or in shell fragments.

Mastodon—a prehistoric elephant.

Matter—any substance that occupies space.

Melanism—a dark-color phase in comparison with the usual color.

Mesozoic—the middle of the three eras of geological time.

Metamorphic rock—rock formed in the hard state by heat, pressure, and chemicals acting on sedimentary materials.

Microfossils—fossils too small to be seen well without the aid of magnification.

Mimicry—imitation of an animal or a plant by form or behavior.

Miocene—an epoch in the Cenozoic Era.

Missing link—a gap in the supposed evolutionary history of an organism.

Mississippian—a period in the Paleozoic Era.

Mold—a hole or cavity similar in shape to an organism that formerly occupied it.

Moraine—heterogeneous boulders and debris left along the sides and front of a glacier.

Morphology—the study of the form and major structure of living things.

Mutation—a sudden inheritable change not previously seen in any immediate ancestors.

Mutualism—two or more organisms that live together for mutual benefit.

Nautili—a group of mollusks belonging to the Cephalopoda. Example—the chambered nautilus.

Nekton—larger swimming marine organisms.

Neutron—an uncharged particle occurring in the nucleus of the atom.

Niche—see Ecological niche. The exact place where an organism lives.

Nuclear fission—the release of energy resulting from the splitting and reorganization of the nucleus of the atom.

Nuclear fusion—the reorganization of the nucleus of the atom resulting in release of energy as illustrated in the hydrogen bomb.

Nucleic acid—complex acids (DNA, RNA) found in the nucleus of the cell.

Nucleoplasm—the ground substance of a cell nucleus.

Oligocene—an epoch in the Cenozoic Era.

Ontogeny—the development of an organism from conception until death.

Ooze—ocean bottom mud composed mainly of the skeletons of microscopic marine organisms.

Order—a unit of classification above the family and below the class.

Ordovician—a period in the Paleozoic Era.

Oreodont—an extinct mammal about the size of a small sheep with characteristics of the pig and the deer.

Organic—any matter consisting of, or produced by, living organisms.

Orogeny—the process of forming mountains, usually by folding and thrusting.

Orthogenetic—pertaining to evolution in a straight line or in a single direction.

Osmosis—the movement of a fluid of less density through a membrane into a fluid of greater density.

Osteoarthritis—arthritis affecting the bones.

Ostracoderms—armored, jawless fish the remains of which are found in Paleozoic sediments.

Overthrust—a mass of rock pushed over on top of another.

Oviparous—organisms that lay eggs.

Ovoviviparous—organisms that produce eggs but keep them within the body until they are hatched.

Ozone—a form of oxygen—O_3.

Paleobotanist—one who studies plant fossils.

Paleocene—an epoch in the Cenozoic Era.

Paleoecology—the study of the ecology of organisms living in the past.

Paleozoic—the most ancient era of geological time.

Part and Counterpart—the two evidences (impression and compression) revealed when a rock is split on the plane of the fossil.

Pathology—the study of disease; the condition produced by disease.

Peat—partly decomposed plant materials that have accumulated in lakes, marshes, or bogs.

Peduncle—a flower stalk; the stem or stalk of certain sessile marine animals.

Pelagic—inhabiting the open water in contrast to the shore or the bottom of the sea.

Pennsylvanian—a period in the Paleozoic Era.

Period—a subdivision of time into which the major eras are divided.

Periostracum—dark outer covering or layer on the shell of a mollusk.

Permafrost—permanently frozen ground.

Permian—a period (the most recent) in the Paleozoic Era.

Petrification—the process of becoming hard like rock.

Petroglyph—a picture or design chiseled into rock.

Petrology—a study of the detailed structure of rock.

Phenotype—the visible appearance of an organism with reference to particular characteristics.

Phosphagen—a substance containing high energy phosphate useful as an energy source in living systems.

Photosynthesis—the process of manufacturing food from water and carbon dioxide in the presence of chlorophyll, in green plants.

Phylogeny—the supposed evolutionary history of an organism, or the lines of evolutionary descent of a group of organisms.

Phylum—a large unit of classification. The animal kingdom is divided into phyla.

Phytosaur—a crocodilelike prehistoric reptile.

Piedmont glacier—a large glacier that has become stagnant.

Pinnate—progressive divergence along a central axis, as with a feather.

Planetoids—bodies in the heavens resembling planets.

Plankton—small, floating marine organisms.

Pleistocene—the epoch of the Cenozoic Era in which glaciation occurred.

Pliocene—an epoch in the Cenozoic Era.

Polyploidy—an organism with more than two sets of chromosomes—triple or quadruple or more.

Porphyropsin—a pigment in the eyes of fresh-water fishes and other occupants of lakes and rivers.

Preadaptation—changes in an organism which later permit it to expand into a new habitat or environment.

Precambrian—all time or deposits before the Cambrian period.

Prehistoric—before written records.

Primordial—pertaining to the first, or primitive, or beginning.

Proton—a positively charged particle occurring in the nucleus of the atom.

Protozoa—one-celled animals usually microscopic in size.

Pteridosperms—an extinct group of seed plants resembling ferns.

Pterodactyl—a group of extinct flying reptiles.

Pteropod—an open-ocean snail with its foot modified into a swimming appendage.

Pyroclastic—formed of explosively produced fragments, as in some types of volcanoes.

Radioactivity—the release of radiant energy owing to the disintegration of the nuclei of atoms.

Radiolarian—single-celled marine protozoans with silicious tests.

Recapitulate—to go back over; to repeat. This word is used in the expression "ontogeny recapitulates phylogeny," which means that in its development an organism, from conception until death, repeats its alleged past evolutionary history.

Recent—time since the Pleistocene epoch.

Recessive—the weaker of two genes involving the same characteristic.

Recombination—new combinations of traits different from those exhibited by the parents.

Reef—a growth of coral and other marine organisms near the surface of the ocean.

Regeneration—the ability to grow back a missing part.

Replacement—substitution of the original organic material replaced by another substance, such as calcium or silicon.

Rhodopsin—a purple pigment in the retina of the eye necessary for vision.

Rhyolite—fine-grained, light-colored extrusive igneous rock, acid in nature; distinguished from basalt, which is basic.

Riparian—pertaining to, or living beside, water.

Rostrum—a pointed projection or beaklike extension; for example, the rostrum projecting forward between the eyes of a crab.

Salinity—the concentration of salts in a fluid.

Sauropod—a very large herbivorous dinosaur primarily belonging to the order Saurischia.

Schist—metamorphic rock that splits into irregular plates or layers.

Scoria—volcanic slag, often frothy or clinkerlike.

Scute—an external horny or bony plate, especially on a fish or reptile.

Seamount—an isolated mountain rising from the ocean floor but not reaching the surface.

Sedimentary—composed of particles; consisting of sediments.

Seismic—caused or produced by earthquakes or earth movements.

Serum—that fraction of the blood that remains after clotting.

Sessile—permanently attached; unable to move about.

Shale—fine-grained clastic sedimentary rock that breaks into sheets.

Shield—a great mass of continental rock (usually Precambrian) that is generally not greatly disturbed.

Sigillaria—a large extinct scale tree found abundantly associated with coal deposits in carboniferous sediments.

Silicious—consisting of, or containing, silicon.

Silicon—an abundant element in the earth usually combined with other elements, as in quartz (SiO_2).

Sill—horizontal sheet of igneous material intruded between strata while molten.

Silt—loose particles ranging in size between those of sand and clay.

Silurian—a period in the Paleozoic Era.

Simian—monkeylike or apelike.

Speciation—the process of producing new species or kinds of organisms.

Species—a unit of classification below the genus. Animals and plants able to interbreed are usually considered in the same species, while those unable to interbreed are not.

Splint bones—supposed vestigial remains of what were formerly additional toes.

Spontaneous generation—supposed spontaneous development of life from a nonliving source.

Sporophylls—scales or leaves that contain, or are attached to, the spore capsules or sporangia.

Stigmaria—rootlike structures associated with scale trees in carboniferous deposits.

Stratigraphy—the study of stratified rocks as they relate to the crust of the earth.

Stratum—a bed or layer of sedimentary rock; a portion or section of a formation.

Striation—mark made on rock by a moving solid such as ice or other rock.

Stromatolite—laminated calcareous structure thought to be produced by calcareous algae.

Suture—the line or crack where two bones or plates meet; as between the bones of the human braincase.

Symbiont—one of two or more organisms that live together.

Symbiosis—the living together of two organisms.

Syncline—concave or downward bending of strata.

System—the sediments laid down during a geologic period.

Taxonomy—the study of the relationships and the classification of organisms.

Tectonics—activity and results on rock accompanying mountain building.

Terrestrial—pertaining to land.

Tertiary—that portion of geologic time that includes the epochs of the Cenozoic other than Pleistocene and Recent.

Tests—the hard covering or exoskeleton of many invertebrates. Examples—protozoans, mollusks, echinoderms, and crustaceans.

Tetrapods—animals with four walking legs. Examples—the amphibians, reptiles, and mammals.

Thermal—of or pertaining to heat.

Thrustfault—a fault that has resulted from one mass of rock's being thrust onto another.

Thyroxin—a hormone produced by the thyroid gland.

Till—unsorted and unstratified sediment deposited by a glacier.

Tillite—rock resulting from cemented till.

Topography—the configurations and relief of a surface.

Triassic—a period in the Mesozoic Era.

Trilobite—an extinct arthropod resembling somewhat the present-day sow bug, or pill bug.

Tuff—rock consisting of small compacted fragments of volcanic rock; compacted ash (welded tuff).

Tundra—an arctic condition of wet ground covered with mosses, lichens, and liverworts, and interspersed with shallow lakes.

Ungulate—any hoofed animal.

Uniformitarianism—the doctrine that present geological processes are adequate to explain the past.

Uniformity—a concept of similar or uniform conditions or processes, usually applied to the geologic past.

Valvules—small valves or valvelike structures.

Varves—rhythmic deposits of coarse and fine or light and dark sediments in water resulting from seasonal, glacial, or other causes.

Vascular plants—plants with sap- and water-conducting tissues.

Vertebrates—animals with a backbone consisting of vertebrae.

Vestigial—rudimentary or undeveloped.

Virology—the branch of science dealing with viruses.

Viviparous—pertaining to organisms that give birth to their young.

Welded tuff—volcanic ash fused together into hard rock by heat.

INDEX

NOTE: Major consideration of a subject listed in the Index is indicated by boldface type, and a picture or other illustration by italics, as for example, under the entry "Alps."

501

509